To order or receive additional information on these or any other McGraw-Hill titles, in the United States please call 1-800-822-8158. In other countries, contact your local McGraw-Hill representative.

BC15XXA

Data Communications Using Object-Oriented Design and C++

Anil Ananthaswamy

TCSI Corporation
Berkeley, California

McGraw-Hill, Inc.

New York   San Francisco   Washington, D.C.   Auckland   Bogotá
Caracas   Lisbon   London   Madrid   Mexico City   Milan
Montreal   New Delhi   San Juan   Singapore
Sydney   Tokyo   Toronto

Library of Congress Cataloging-in-Publication Data

Ananthaswamy, Anil.
    Data communications using object-oriented design and C++ / Anil
Ananthaswamy.
        p.   cm.—(McGraw-Hill series on computer communications)
    Includes index.
    ISBN 0-07-911857-7
    1. Object-oriented programming (Computer science)   2. C++
(Computer program language)   3. Data transmission systems.
I. Title. II. Series.
QA76.64.A54   1995
005.7′11—dc20   95-10572
                                                      CIP

1 2 3 4 5 6 7 8 9 0   **DOC/DOC**   9 0 9 8 7 6 5

P/N 001609-7
PART OF
ISBN 0-07-911857-7

*The sponsoring editor for this book was Jerry Papke, the editing supervisor was
Stephen M. Smith, and the production supervisor was Donald F. Schmidt.*

McGraw-Hill books are available at special quantity discounts to use as premi-
ums and sales promotions, or for use in corporate training programs. For more
information, please write to the Director of Special Sales, McGraw-Hill, Inc., 11
West 19th Street, New York, NY 10011. Or contact your local bookstore.

This book is printed on acid-free paper.

To my family

ABOUT THE AUTHOR

Anil Ananthaswamy designs software for TCSI Corporation, Berkeley, California. His expertise includes network management systems, client-server architecture, object-oriented design and programming, telecommunications, and computer communications. He holds a M.S. in electrical engineering from the University of Washington and teaches communication systems implementation using object-oriented design and C^{++} at the University of California, Berkeley, Extension.

Contents

Given the large number of books already available on data communications, which include the excellent, the good and the forgettable, I feel obliged to provide a rationale for writing yet another book on the topic.

The impetus for this book came from my experiences as a fresh-out-of-school graduate attempting to write data communications software. In spite of some excellent texts that I had read, when it came down to implementing a protocol recommended by a well-known standards body, I found myself unable to understand and appreciate the intricacies of datacomm software development. There were a large number of issues that no text had addressed, and it stood to reason that I was ill-prepared to implement a soundly designed piece of software. Soon after that experience, an idea for a practical, nuts-and-bolts book on data communications was hatched, which addressed those issues that were given short shrift in most of the otherwise excellent books.

As it so often happens, there was no action on my part for a good time to come. In this case, it has proved fortuitous, since I learned object-oriented programming in the meantime, and in OOPS, I have found a new, exciting and topical vehicle for explaining and illustrating implementation-specific issues relating to protocols, layers and interfaces. So, what we have in this book now is a object-oriented case study of how to design and implement a protocol layer and its interface. The language of choice is C++, mainly because that is the language I know best.

The text is organized around the implementation of the ISO 7776 standard - an industry standard data link layer protocol. Implementing an entire layer also allows us to examine the concepts of layers and their interfaces. The example code attempts to conform to the specified protocol standards. The code is not claimed to be bug-free, and readers are welcome and encouraged to send in bug reports and/or fixes.

It is important to mention what this book does not attempt to accomplish. This book is not a comprehensive text on either data communications or object-oriented design and programming. It can be used to effectively supplement senior-level undergraduate or graduate courses in computer networks and data communication, providing a hands-on introduction to the topics. The reader is expected to have a good working knowledge of C++ and a familiarity with the Unix operating system.

A diskette accompanies this book which contains the entire source code used in the book. The diskette contains a unix tar file. Use "tar xvf <deviceName>" to extract the files. The nature of this book is such that the code is sometimes presented in fragments, necessitating some editing of the actual code. The source code in the diskette should be regarded as the correct version in case there is any ambiguity in the text. The source code can also be downloaded by anonymous ftp from ftp.uu.net. The file datacomm.tar.Z in /published/ mcgraw-hill/datacomm-ood/ contains the entire source code, tarred and compressed. (The programs and code fragments in this book may be used freely, without royalty or fee. Please acknowledge the source.)

I have done my best to make the book accurate, but it is inevitable that some mistakes have crept into print. I take full responsibility for any such mistakes and would appreciate being notified of any errors (conceptual, factual or programming) via McGraw-Hill. Any suggestions for improving the book are also welcome.

Anil Ananthaswamy

Acknowledgments

It's that page of a book
Where one loves to take a look
At all the friends, family and people
Who made this book feasible

Many people have encouraged, helped in and contributed toward the completion of this book. My sincere thanks go to all of the following people: Sriram Srinivasan, to whom I first broached the idea for this book about four years ago, has been a constant help all along by providing review comments and bright ideas, and by being a source of near unlimited knowledge. Sean Gavin, a chance internet acquaintance, has contributed enormously by reviewing the entire book, specially the data communication aspects. He withstood repeated e-mail enquiries from me without deciding to disappear into cyberspace. I have never met him, but his internet addresses tell me that he operated first from Santa Monica, CA and now from Berkshire, England. Ralph Saavedra provided valuable comments on the earlier chapters and got me thinking about my prose style. He's a proud father now (no causal relation to this book). My editors at McGraw-Hill - Gerry Papke and J. Ranade - received the proposal for this book enthusiastically, and have been supportive throughout the process, allowing me almost complete freedom in deciding on both the form and content of the book. Stephen Smith, senior editing supervisor at McGraw-Hill, provided invaluable editing support, and helped in putting the finishing touches on the book. I would especially like to thank Harish Rao (VP), who encouraged me and arranged for TCSI Corporation to partially fund the writing of this book by keeping me fully employed while letting me work half-time. Ranjit Ghate, my manager, worked around his schedules to allow for the time I needed and didn't mind it (at least he didn't show it). I would like to thank many of my colleagues at TCSI, who have had a definite influence on my abilities (technical and otherwise) and who make TCSI a special place to work and learn. I'm also obliged to TCSI for allowing me access to resources to write the book, resources which otherwise would have been difficult to obtain.

Rosu, a very special friend, believed that the book was a really worthwhile project right from the very start and kept pushing me to start. A host of friends - Alka, Banny, Rao, Malini, Ramki, Praveen and Sundar (who scared me into action by telling me stories about unsuccessful authors) - all helped in ways that I cannot put into words. Finally, my family helped by being awed that someone in the family was writing a book.

ABM	Asynchronous Balanced Mode
ARM	Asynchronous Response Mode
ARQ	Automatic Repeat Request
CA	California
DCE	Data Circuit-terminating Equipment
DISC	Disconnect
DM	Disconnected Mode
DMA	Direct Memory Access
DTE	Data Terminal Equipment
FCS	Frame Check Sequence
FDDI	Fiber Distributed Data Interface
FRMR	Frame Reject
FSM	Finite State Machine
HDLC	High-level Data Link Control
ICI	Interface Control Information
IDU	Interface Data Unit
Iframe	Information Frame
IPC	Inter-process Communication
ISO	International Organization for Standardization
ITU	International Telecommunication Union
IUT	Implementation Under Test
LAPB	Link Access Procedure-Balanced
NRM	Normal Response Mode
OOD	Object-Oriented Design
OOP	Object-Oriented Programming
OSI	Open System Interconnection
PCI	Protocol Control Information
PDU	Protocol Data Unit
PLP	Packet Layer Protocol
RNR	Receiver Not Ready
RR	Receiver Ready
SABM	Set Asynchronous Balanced Mode
SAP	Service Access Point
SDU	Service Data Unit
STDIN	Standard Input
TSAP	Transport Service Access Point
UA	Unnumbered Acknowledgment
UI	User Interface

1

THE CONCEPTS

The first five chapters in this book will lay the conceptual groundwork for the implementation of a protocol layer. Protocols, layers and interfaces will be examined in Chapter 2. Object-oriented design and programming will be introduced in Chapter 3. Chapter 4 will study in detail the elements of a protocol, and the rationale for various procedures that are used in the protocol to be implemented. Chapter 5 will provide a high-level design and overview of the entire implementation.

Introduction and Overview

1.1 The Objective

There are two main objectives to this book. First, to gain an insight into some of the important concepts and issues involved in the implementation of data communication protocols, layers and interfaces. Second, to develop an understanding of the process of object-oriented design and implementation. The book will address both objectives by studying in detail an object-oriented design and implementation of a data communication protocol, its layering, and its interfaces.

A protocol defines the manner in which two entities communicate. Computer communication involves a host of protocols at various levels of communications (from transferring bits and bytes to file transfers, for example). To deal with the complexity of these protocols, they are logically, and physically organized into entities called layers, where each layer provides some specific kind of service (again, for example, a layer to transfer bits versus a layer to perform file transfer). The interaction between these layers is via well-defined interfaces.

1.2 An Implementor's Perspective

The reason for the existence of this text is the belief that although a theoretical understanding of the core concepts of protocols, layers and interfaces is necessary, it is not sufficient in order to appreciate how these building blocks fall into place. In this text we will gain an implementor's perspective by working our way through an implementation of the data-link layer protocol specified by the ISO 7776 standard. In order to achieve data transfer, we will implement a physical layer using Unix IPC mechanisms. We will also implement a rudimentary driver layer which will interface with the data-link layer. The driver layer will also function as our user interface, allowing us access to the services of the data-link layer. It is important to emphasize that even though we are implementing a data-link layer, the concepts are universal and will be invaluable when working with other layers and protocols. Some of the fundamental concepts that we will tackle via the implementation are:

- Principle of layering.

- Interfaces between layers.

- Elements of protocols.

- Flow control mechanisms.

- Error detection and error recovery.

An implementation of the kind we are examining needs a significant amount of development of related tools and utilities. We will study in detail:

- A tracing and debugging utility

- Lists

- Principles of asynchronous programming

- Finite state machines

Finally, we will briefly introduce the concept of conformance testing of protocols. Our protocol can be tested using the user interface. Error conditions can be induced, and the protocol behavior can be monitored as we put it through its paces.

For those of you unfamiliar with datacomm jargon like OSI, ISO, data-link layers, physical layers etc., take heart - we will be explaining all of that as we go along.

1.3 Object-Oriented Design and Programming

Another important implementation aspect of this text is that we will be using object-oriented design and programming to accomplish our task. The field of OOD and OOP are areas of study in themselves. We will attempt to gain a general understanding and appreciation of OOP and OOD by tackling a specific problem which is to design an object-oriented solution to the problem of protocol implementation, layers and interfaces. We will not be advocating any formal design methodology. Instead, our focus will be to develop an intuitive understanding of the design process. The problem domain is quite formidable, and allows us ample opportunity to explore object-oriented design and implementation. The fundamental concepts of OOD that will be emphasized throughout this process are:

- Abstraction

- Encapsulation

- Modularity

- Inheritance

Finally, reusability of code is one of the promises of OOD. Methods for realizing this promise will be described and demonstrated.

1.4 The Approach

The philosophy underlying this text is that a technical topic such as data communications is best understood by getting your hands dirty (or your feet wet, depending on your preference!). We will tackle a specific problem in protocol implementation, and by understanding the specific in its entirety, we will gain an appreciation of the intricacies of the general.

The approach in this text will be to first state the objective, analyze it, design a solution, and then implement it. A design makes sense only when the problem is well defined. At each stage, we will clearly state the problem, and then proceed with the design. The design will then be implemented. We will be implementing our software using C++ on a Unix platform. The design of the system will be modular enough that it can be ported to other operating systems with relative ease.

1.5 Source Code

Source code in C++ will form an integral part of the text. Many of the best texts for software professionals and students have used source code to great advantage. Source code can be used very effectively to explain an implementation and demonstrate underlying concepts. There will be times in this text where source code rather than prose will be used to elucidate a point. Even though the entire source code is provided in the book, the logistics of presentation make it necessary, at times, to present fragments of source code at any given stage rather than a complete function, class or method. For readers who find this inconvenient, a diskette is provided with this book which contains the complete source code. A printout of the source code would be a worthwhile companion to the book, as it will provide a single point of reference.

1.6 The Organization of the Text

The text is organized around an implementation of a protocol layer. The presentation is divided into three parts. It is assumed that readers of this text will be interested in one or more parts, and, as such, the division allows the reader to go directly to the area of interest.

1.6.1 Part 1 - Concepts and High-Level Design

Part 1 deals with the necessary concepts.

- Chapter 1 is an introduction.

- Chapter 2 will address the principles of layering in data communication software, with an emphasis on the OSI stack, and provide an in-depth introduction to layering, services and interfaces. It will also introduce the elements of a protocol.

- Chapter 3 will provide an in-depth introduction to the principles of object-oriented design and implementation.

- Chapter 4 will analyze the ISO 7776 protocol in depth, providing a rationale for the behavior of the protocol. All protocol elements will be examined in detail.

- Chapter 5 will contain a detailed statement-of-problem, and a high-level design and solution will be proposed.

1.6.2 Part 2 - The Framework for Implementation

Part 2 will be devoted to developing a library of utilities which will form the framework for further development. The utilities and solutions will, in a true sense, be reusable in other similar projects. The main effort will be towards understanding the problem domain, and coming up with an appropriate solution. The chapter level break-up is as follows:

- Chapter 6 will develop a set of generic utilities for tracing/debugging, lists, queues and stacks, and a data packet class for inter-layer data exchange.

- Chapter 7 will analyze the behavior of asynchronous systems, and develop a set of classes for scheduling, event handling, and timers to facilitate asynchronous programming.

- Chapter 8 will introduce the concept of finite state machines (FSMs). The focus will be on using an object-oriented solution to the problem of FSMs. This approach will be contrasted with the traditional table driven FSM implementation. Using the FSM concepts, a physical layer on Unix IPC will be developed. And, to complete the framework, the primary elements of the driver layer will be implemented.

1.6.3 Part 3 - The Protocol Implementation

Part 3 concentrates on the actual protocol and layer implementation. The chapters are organized as follows:

- Chapter 9 will begin the design by identifying states and events for the data-link layer FSM, and by identifying the state machine classes necessary to implement the FSM. Other classes needed to complete the data-link layer will be identified.

- Chapter 10 will look at the implementation of connection management in the data-link layer.

- Chapter 11 will deal with the concepts and implementation of flow control and sliding window protocols.

- Chapter 12 will deal with the concepts and implementation of error detection and error recovery in protocols.

- Chapter 13 will tie together all the loose ends. The user interface, the issue of conformance testing of protocols, and how to test the implementation will be addressed.

- Appendix A develops the algorithm for frame check sequence calculations used in this book.

- Appendix B explains the conventions used to illustrate finite state machines in this book.

- Appendix C contains a listing of the useful header files (which contain constants and extern declarations) used in the implementation.

- Appendix D introduces the current trends in data communications. It briefly examines LAPD and Frame Relay technologies.

1.7 Summary

This text, though focused on a single implementation, will deal with several key concepts in both data communications and object-oriented design. The following are the main items on our agenda:

- Layers and interfaces

- The ISO 7776 data-link layer protocol

- Fundamentals of object-oriented design and implementation

- Flow control and sliding window protocols

- Error detection and error recovery

- Principles of asynchronous programming, scheduling and event handling

- Finite state machine implementation

- Physical layer-data-link layer and data-link layer-network layer interfaces
- Reusable object-oriented libraries for tracing/debugging, lists, stacks and queues

2

Protocols, Layers and Interfaces

2.1 Introduction

There was a time when you could get a job in the data communications industry by naming the seven layers in the OSI Reference model. Times have changed, and one needs to know considerably more in order to land a datacomm job, but believe it or not, one might still be asked to name all the seven layers before being interviewed any further. Even though this text is concerned with a specific protocol, its layering and its interfaces, we will examine the OSI Reference model for completeness, and for the sake of successful interviews. We begin by examining the concept of a protocol, the need for layering in datacomm systems, and the consequent emergence of interfaces and services due to layering. Finally, we will examine the specifics of the network - data-link layer interface, and the data-link-physical layer interface.

2.2 Protocols

Consider a telephone conversation between two individuals. For effective communication, certain rules and conventions need to be observed. For example, both individuals need to speak in a commonly understood language. A language implies the existence of a certain vocabulary, and grammar. Also, the individuals need to take turns speaking, so that each gets a chance to speak and be heard. Even before the actual conversation starts, certain procedures need to be followed to set up the telephone call. All these rules put together form the protocol necessary for a cordial telephone conversation.

Similarly, when any two entities in the computing world need to communicate they need to settle on a protocol, which defines the manner in which they exchange information.

Holzmann [1] identifies the following elements which form the basis for understanding a protocol:

- The service to be provided by the protocol

- The assumptions about the environment in which the protocol is executed

- The vocabulary of messages used to implement the protocol

- The encoding (format) of each message in the vocabulary

- The procedure rules guarding the consistency of message exchanges

When we examine the protocol to be implemented, we will revisit these elements, and study the protocol using these guidelines.

2.3 The Need for Layering

Given the proliferation of technologies used in computers and computer communications, and the varied services offered to users by this industry, the sheer number and types of protocols used can become unmanageable. Layering provides the solution to manage this complexity.

Figure 2.1 Monolithic implementation

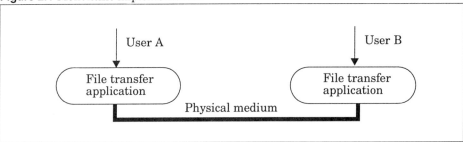

Figure 2.1 shows a monolithic implementation of a file transfer application. Consider two entities, A and B, which exchange information over a physical medium, allowing two users, A and B, to achieve file transfers from one system to another. The file transfer application provides the following features:

- A file transfer protocol implementation which provides ASCII data transfer.

- A user interface.

- Hardware-dependent software to interface with the physical medium (coaxial cables).

The entire application is implemented as one unit with no distinct separation between the functional modules. When examined from a programming standpoint (C/C++), this could imply:

- A single `main()` routine.

- Shared global variables.

- Code which is highly interdependent.

All this in itself poses no problems until the system has to be modified. Consider the following scenarios:

- If the underlying technology which achieves data transmission were to change from using coaxial cables to using fiber optic cables, the monolithic block would have to be changed in order to accommodate the new technology.

- If binary data transfer were required, the file transfer protocol, which allows only ASCII data transfer, would have to be modified to allow binary data transfer as well. This would again mean modifying the single unit of software/hardware to accommodate the new feature.

Given the rate at which technologies change, maintenance of such software/ hardware as one unit to accommodate all changes could become a nightmare.

Figure 2.2 Layering

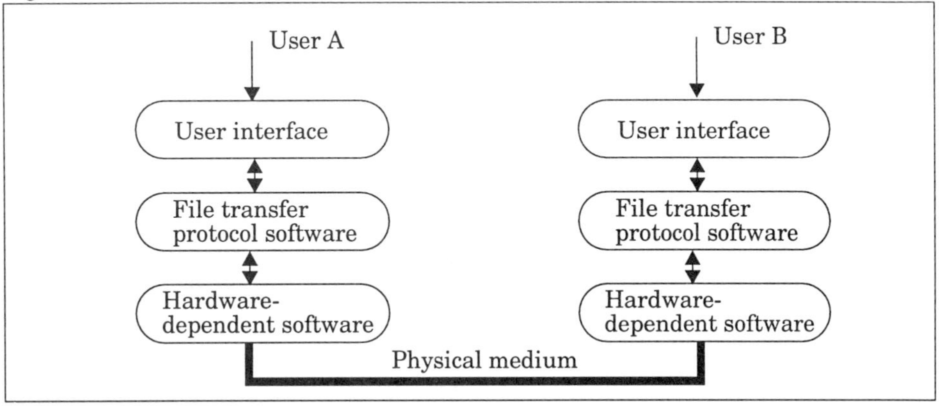

This is where layering enters the picture. Figure 2.2 shows how such a monolithic block could be organized so as to localize functionality, and break down the complexity into manageable portions. By organizing the communication system into a hardware dependent layer, a file transfer layer, and a user interface layer, we have now been able to isolate the functionality, so that changes in one layer do not affect the other layers.

For example, if the underlying physical medium technology were to be upgraded, only the hardware dependent layer would need to change, allowing us to use the top two layers without any changes. Also, if the file transfer protocol were to change, all changes could ideally be restricted to the layer implementing the protocol. From a programming standpoint, layering makes the maintenance, upgrade, and modification of software/hardware easier.

2.4 The Emergence of Interfaces and Services

Given that we have managed to organize a data communication system into layers, we now have the problem of defining how these layers exchange information between themselves.

First, let us address the concept of services. From Figure 2.2, it should be clear that the hardware-dependent layer provides certain facilities for data transmission that can be used by the file-transfer protocol layer to achieve data transfer. The sum total of all facilities offered by one layer to another layer are termed services.

Keeping in mind that layers are essentially software or hardware entities, services can be accessed through well defined entry points into these entities. For example, if one were to consider the Unix operating system as a layer, then the services it offers can be accessed through system calls. The complete set of entry points, which allow us access to the services offered by a layer, define the interface to a layer.

For layering to work it is obvious that the services and interfaces should be well defined, well publicized, and unchangeable over the lifetime of a certain layered data communications system. This is where the standards-making organizations enter the picture.

2.5 What Is OSI?

OSI stands for Open Systems Interconnection and is an attempt towards achieving standards for data communication which will allow computing entities from various manufacturers to communicate with each other. The standards provide a layered architecture for data communication systems, define protocols used in each layer, define the services offered by the layers, and their interfaces. The main standards-making organizations that participate in the development of the OSI standards are:

- ISO - The International Organization for Standardization

- ITU - International Telecommunication Union (previously CCITT).

- ECMA - European Computer Manufacturers' Association

- IEC - International Electrotechnical Commission

There is a wide body of literature devoted to analyzing the merits, demerits, the politics and frustrations of these standards, and standards-making organizations. We will avoid any such discussions, and proceed to look at the seven-layer architecture - the OSI Reference model (the ISO 7498 international standard document [2]).

Figure 2.3 Snow white and the seven layers

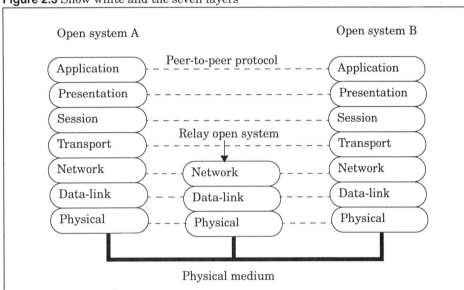

2.6 The ISO/OSI Basic Reference Model

Figure 2.3 depicts the OSI seven-layer architecture for a data communications system, also known as the Basic Reference Model. The figure, though visually simple, incorporates a fair number of important concepts. Each layer is named so as to provide an insight into its functionality. ISO has identified a number of principles to help determine the layers [2]. Before we discuss the rationale for each layer, let us examine Figure 2.3 in detail, and identify the conceptual elements.

2.6.1 Layer

As mentioned above, the task of communications is logically organized into different levels, with each level handling a certain specific functionality. The level is termed a layer in the reference model.

2.6.2 Services

A service is a facility provided by one layer to the layer above, in order to

accomplish some aspect of data communications. The totality of facilities provided by a layer comprises its services.

Figure 2.4 Service providers, users and SAPs

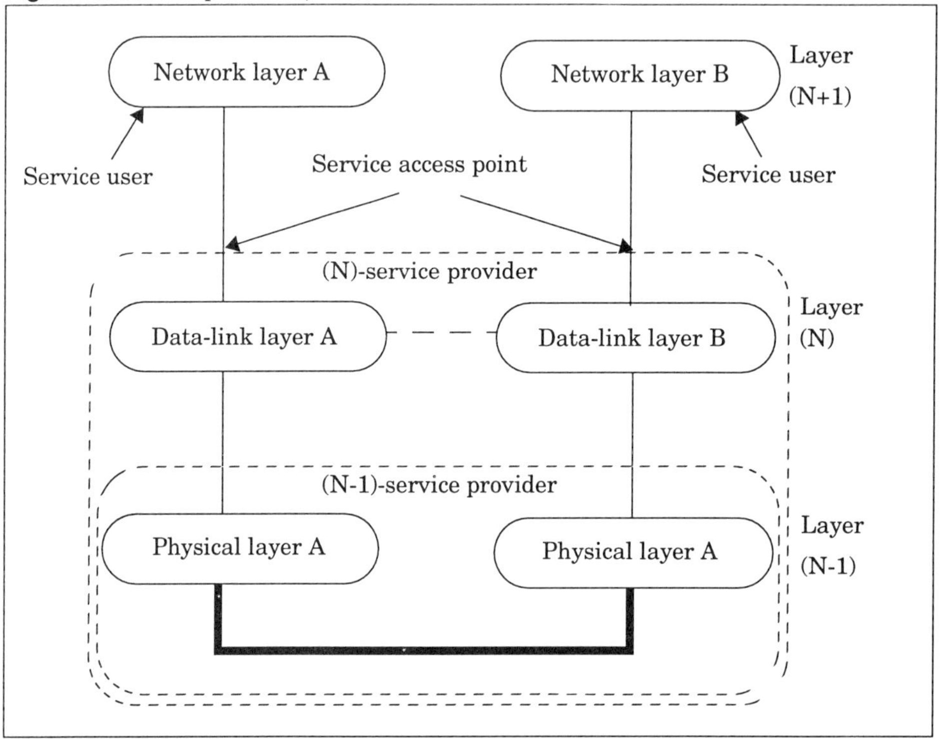

2.6.3 Service Providers, Users and SAPs

Figure 2.4 shows the relationship between service providers, service users,
and service access points. The figure uses specific layers as examples, but the
relationship is valid for any set of layers.

When a layer, such as the network layer, uses the services provided by the
data-link layer - the data-link layers on both ends of the communication channel combine to form a *service provider*. The network layer entities, in this case,
will be termed *service users*. Figure 2.4 identifies the relationship between a
service provider, and service users.

The service provider makes available its services to the layer above via *service access points (SAPs)*. A SAP is essentially the entry point into a layer.

2.6.4 Layer Numbering

Figure 2.4 also identifies the numbering scheme used in the OSI Reference
Model. "Layer-(N)" is used to identify any generic layer. In our case, the data-
link layer is the "Layer-(N)". A layer conceptually above is called "Layer-

(N+1)", and the layer below is called "layer-(N-1)".

In a parallel nomenclature, the data-link layer is the (N)-service-provider, the data-link layer entities are (N)-service entities, the network layer entities are (N)-service users. The data-link layer entities use the services of the physical layer which is called the (N-1)-service provider. Again, it is important to stress that these numbering schemes are generic and hold true for any set of layers.

The service offered by a service provider can also be described in terms of service primitives and time sequence diagrams. We shall defer a discussion of these till we are ready to look at our specific problem - the interface between the network-data-link layers and the interface between the data-link-physical layers.

2.6.5 Open Systems

Computer systems which provide a well publicized interface for other systems to communicate with are called open systems. Systems which adopt the seven layer model provide one example of such open systems - hence the name Open Systems Interconnection (OSI).

2.6.6 Relay Open System

Sometimes, two open systems are not physically connected with each other, and have to rely on intermediate open systems to provide connectivity. These intermediate open systems are called relay open systems. Note that relay open systems may not require the entire complement of layers in order to achieve their purpose.

2.6.7 Peer-to-Peer Communications

Each layer in an open system logically communicates with its peer layer in another open system. The protocol used to achieve such communication is called a peer-to-peer protocol, and the communications is referred to as peer-to-peer communications. The dotted lines in Figure 2.3 depict the peer-to-peer communications.

2.6.8 Inter-Layer Data Transfer

It is time we discussed what actually gets exchanged between two layers. Let us take a specific case of one network layer wanting to send data to its peer network layer. Figure 2.5 shows the relationship between the various units of data (or rather, the terminology).

Figure 2.5 Inter-layer data transfer

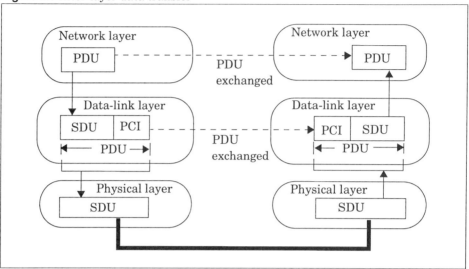

When a network layer wants to send data to its peer layer, the unit of data exchanged is called a protocol-data-unit (PDU). But the data cannot be sent directly to the peer network layer. Hence, the data is handed down to the layer below to be transmitted. This unit of data is called a service-data-unit (SDU). Thus, the network layer PDU and a data-link layer SDU are the same data. The data-link layer on receiving the SDU, adds protocol-control-information (PCI) to make it a data-link protocol-data-unit. This combination of a SDU and a PCI now forms a data-link PDU. Again, since the data-link layer cannot directly access the peer layer, it hands the PDU to the physical layer, which transmits the bits over the physical medium. Note that the data-link layer PDU is a SDU for the physical layer.

On the receiving side, the process is repeated in reverse, until the data makes it up to the network layer as a network layer PDU. Some things to note in this example:

- The physical layer is a special case. It merely transmits the bits received from the data-link layer, without adding protocol-control-information. Any other layer will always add a PCI.

- The example shows the simplest case of data exchange, where one SDU results in one PDU. This might not always be the case. The OSI Reference model (ISO standard 7498 [2]) mentions other possible types such as segmenting/reassembling, blocking/deblocking and concatenation/separation. We are only interested in the simple case.

- Not shown in the figure is any control information that might be required as part of the service definition of a layer. In case the data-link layer needs some additional information (specifically, to identify the type of service being requested), then the network layer will attach an interface-control-information unit (ICI) along with the SDU, giving rise to an interface-data-unit (IDU). The ICI is implementation dependent.

2.6.9 Physical Medium

The physical medium is the actual transmission medium which achieves the transfer of bits of data. The physical medium between Open System A and the Relay Open System can be different from the physical medium between the Relay Open System and Open System B.

2.7 The Seven Layers

It is time to examine each layer, its functionality, and purpose. Note that we are not looking at a rationale for the existence of seven layers (i.e. why seven and not eight). Seven is not sacrosanct, but given that ISO chose that number, we can look at each one briefly. It should be pointed out that these descriptions are not exhaustive, and there will be aspects of each layer that are too complex for discussion here. We will concentrate on connection-oriented services, since that is the nature of the implementation in this book. Also, it is important to note that the functionality for these layers has evolved over time, and sometimes it is obvious what services a layer needs to provide, whereas at times the services seem sensible only in retrospect.

2.7.1 Physical Layer

The existence of a physical layer is the easiest to explain. Given the rate at which hardware technologies for communication change, it is imperative that the rest of the data communication systems be made impervious to such changes. The physical layer provides an abstraction, which can be relied upon to provide a consistent interface, even if the underlying physical medium were to change. Two physical layer entities are connected by a physical medium, and they are concerned with transmitting raw bits over it. The physical layer provides the following services to the data-link layer:

- Activation of the physical connection
- Deactivation of the physical connection
- Transmission of raw bits over the physical connection
- Indications of the link status (up/down)

We have examined a point-to-point connection between physical layer entities. It is possible for a physical layer entity on one open system to establish connections with multiple physical layer entities on other open systems. In such a scenario, the physical layer would have to provide additional services to allow the data-link layer to differentiate between physical connections. Another interesting capability (that can be provided by the physical layer) is the ability to broadcast its transmission to all other physical layers in the network. In this book we'll concern ourselves with a point-to-point connection between two physical layer entities.

2.7.2 Data-link Layer

The data-link layer uses the services of the physical layer in order to achieve raw data transmission. But the physical medium can be error-prone, and it becomes the task of the data-link layer to convert it into as reliable a data transmission link as is possible. (This view of the data-link layer is changing with the advent of highly reliable optical fiber communications. See Appendix D.) Also, given that the physical layer transmits bits, and data transfer is usually in logical blocks of data, it is the task of the data-link layer to somehow turn this stream of bits into a link that recognizes blocks of data. There also needs to be some mechanism whereby the sender of data does not overload the receiver of data. This is achieved via flow control mechanisms in the data-link layer. Thus, the data-link layer can be said to perform the following tasks (with exceptions in certain protocols):

- Error detection and error recovery
- Framing of data into blocks
- Flow control

Viewed as a service provider, the data-link layer offers the following services to the network layer:

- Data-link connection establishment
- Data-link connection release
- Data-link data transfer
- Data-link connection reset

The PDU exchanged between data-link layer entities is also called a frame.

2.7.3 Network Layer

This is an appropriate stage to introduce the concept of subnetworks. In today's complex networks, when two open systems need to communicate, it is quite conceivable that they might have to go through one or many intermediate networks. Figure 2.6 shows such a scenario, where two open systems which we can call the end-open systems, use two intermediate networks to communicate. These intermediate networks, which are actually several systems with their own transmission medium, are called subnetworks. The figure also shows how two subnetworks could use an intermediate open system to communicate between themselves.

The stage is set for a layer to assume the responsibility of making the existence of such subnetworks transparent, so that higher layers can communicate end-to-end with impunity! Enter the network layer. The network layer provides a conceptual network connection between two communicating end open systems. Among the services provided to higher layers by the network layer are:

- Establish, maintain, and release network connections.

- Exchange higher layer data across network connections. This service includes the ability to perform flow control, error detection, and error recovery.

- Isolate the higher layers from the hassles of routing and relaying data when a network connection spans one or many subnetworks.

Figure 2.6 Routing/relaying through subnetworks

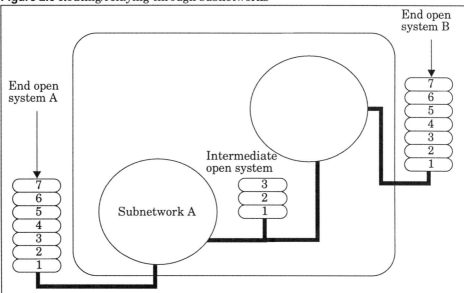

The PDU exchanged between network layer entities is also called a packet.

2.7.4 Transport Layer

With the network service, we now have the ability to open network connections and exchange data across these connections, as if we were directly talking to an end open system, irrespective of any subnetworks that exist between the two end open systems.

The next higher layer is called the transport layer. By now it should be apparent that in a connection-oriented scenario each layer establishes some sort of connection with its peer layer on the other end. The data-link layer had the data-link connection, the network layer had the network connection, the transport layer now has a transport connection, and so on.

The transport layer uses the services of the network layer in order to provide end-to-end connections. Again, the services provided by the transport layer fall into the well known categories of connection establishment, data transfer, and connection release. The transport layer enhances the network layer services by providing extra features. It should be noted that the transport layer services depend on the level of services provided by a network layer. If the network service is connection-less, then the transport layer needs to enhance the service to make it reliable. A transport layer which uses a connection-oriented network service can afford to be less complex, and provide a smaller subset of services.

2.7.4.1 Transport connection establishment

A transport layer connection is established by two transport service users. The transport service users are identified by the address at a transport service access point (TSAP). The address is composed of a transport selector and a network address.

In order to service more than one transport service user, each transport-entity might be associated with more than one transport address. Thus, it is possible for connections to exist between transport addresses which use the same underlying network connection. Figure 2.7 shows how the transport layer is responsible for multiplexing transmissions from multiple transport addresses on to a single network address, and, conversely, splitting messages received on a single network address to multiple transport addresses.

Figure 2.7 Multiplexing and splitting in the transport layer

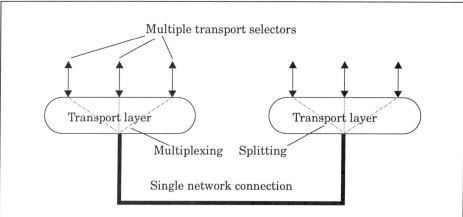

2.7.4.2 Transport data transfer

The transport layer exchanges data in units called transport-protocol-data-units. But the higher layers, which depend on the transport service, are now going to be in the realm of service users who will have data in sizes more suitable for user applications, like file transfers. Such data cannot be transferred in one packet over the network connection. Thus, the transport layer provides the service of breaking up large data into smaller, manageable sizes and sending them over the network connection. Of course, these data need to be reassembled on the receiving side, before being passed on to the higher layers. This process is known as segmentation and reassembly. Thus, depending on how good the network connection is, the transport service might provide some or all of the following services:

- end-to-end data transfer

- end-to-end error detection, and error recovery

- end-to-end flow control

- end-to-end segmentation and reassembly

2.7.4.3 Transport connection release

A transport connection release can be abrupt, i.e., any data being transferred when the connection is released is lost. This also has been the manner of connection release for data-link and network connections.

More robust transport layer protocols provide for an orderly release in which an attempt is made to not lose any data while disconnecting.

2.7.5 Session Layer

The session layer is the first layer in the so-called "upper layers" or "user-oriented layers". The first four layers so far have been concerned with raw data communication. The top three layers transform these services into a more application/user palatable form.

The session layer provides its users with the ability to have sessions (hence, the name) or "conversations". A session layer provides facilities which are somewhat similar to the services provided by a moderator in a debate between two people. Some of the services offered would be:

- Connection establishment (this should not be a surprise!).

- Normal data exchange (the moderator stays out of the way).

- Orderly connection release - This is where the session layer becomes useful. Until now connection releases have been abrupt (except for some transport services), but here, the release is orderly so as not to lose any data in transit. It's as if the moderator was making sure everything that was said was heard!

- Interaction management - Here's where the moderator really comes in handy. The conversation is managed by the session layer so that each service-user gets a chance to speak.

■ Connection synchronization - The session layer allows users of a session to be reset the session-connection to a known state. The known state is notified to the session layer by the service-user.

2.7.6 Presentation Layer

The presentation layer allows for open systems with different modes of data representation to converse with each other. But, first and foremost, the presentation layer allows users to access the session layer services (i.e., establish, release, and manage sessions). As far as data representation goes, the presentation layer provides for a common-syntax for communication between the service users, and also provides mechanisms to translate between the service-user syntax and the common-syntax. The service users can negotiate (during connection establishment), and renegotiate the syntax (after a connection is established). The need for a presentation layer is obvious, given the various data representations, data structures adopted by manufacturers, and applications.

The actual topic of data representation, syntax, and transformation requires a good deal more space. The reader is referred to Tanenbaum[3] for a sound treatment of the topic.

2.7.7 Application Layer

Finally, we come to the layer which allows us mere mortals to communicate with the OSI environment. The application layer provides services to applications or user programs/processes. Two peer applications use the services of the application layer, and establish an "association", which is synonymous with a connection. The application layer further provides services to manage this association, allowing the applications to communicate. The application layer, in turn, uses the services of the presentation layer in order to achieve its functionality.

The application layer provides the following services:

■ Association establishment

■ Association release

■ Service-user initiated abort of an association

■ Service-provider initiated abort of an association

Application processes use the application layer to interact with the OSI environment to establish any parameters necessary for their communication. See [2] for details.

2.8 Service Primitives

Before we focus on the details of a specific interface, we need to discuss the concepts of service primitives, time sequence diagrams, and service types.

It is clear to us that each layer offers certain services. Exactly how does a layer provide a service? We mentioned earlier that a Unix operating system provides services to its users (i.e. access to its resources) via system calls. A layer can also be said to provide services via function calls which are entry points into the layer. The term function call is used conceptually, since the actual method of communicating with a layer will depend on how the layer is implemented. Consider the following examples:

- A physical layer might be implemented completely in hardware, and the interaction with the physical layer might be via DMA (Direct Memory Access).

- The network layer might be implemented as a C/C++ library, providing actual functions which might be used to access the layer.

- The transport layer might be implemented as a distinct process in Unix. Thus, communicating with the layer would involve inter-process communication (IPC) mechanisms.

We have a term for the conceptual function call - a service primitive. OSI identifies the following service primitives:

- request primitive

- indication primitive

- response primitive

- confirmation primitive

A given service is implemented in a layer by using one or more service primitives. Each service primitive is associated with the following properties:

- Direction - A given service primitive can be invoked by a service-user on a service-provider (denoted as DOWN in the rest of the discussions), or by a service-provider on a service-user (denoted as UP).

- Parameter -A service primitive may be associated with one or more parameters. This is analogous to the parameters being passed in function calls.

Figure 2.8 shows an example of a data transfer service provided by the physical layer to the data-link layer. The service is implemented using two primitives - the Data-Request primitive and the Data-Indication primitive. The request primitive is directed from the service-user to the service-provider, and the indication primitive is directed from the service-provider to the service-user. Each primitive is associated with one parameter - the service-user data to be transferred.

Figure 2.8 Service primitive direction and parameters

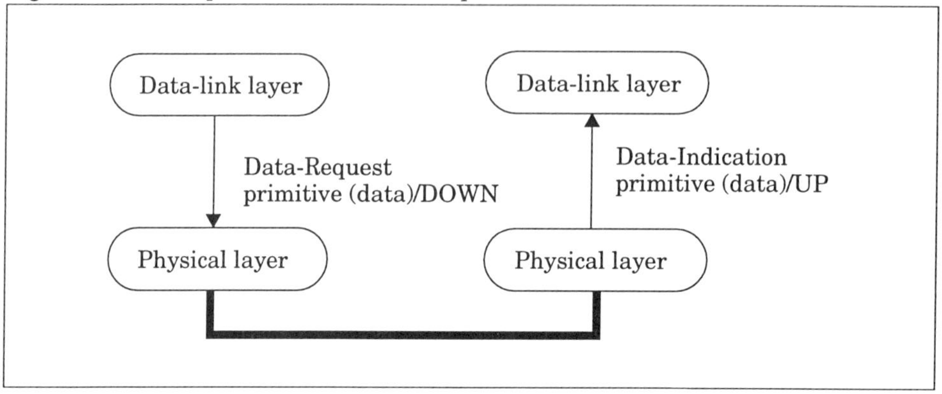

2.9 Service Types

Three kinds of services can be offered by a layer:

- Confirmed service, in which there is an acknowledgment of the success or failure of the requested service. A confirmed service will use all the four primitives.

- Unconfirmed service, in which there is no acknowledgment of the success or failure of the requested service. An unconfirmed service uses only the request and indication primitives.

- Provider-initiated service, in which the service-provider will initiate the service. This service uses only the indication primitive. Consider a physical connection which is disrupted because of a hardware failure. The physical layer entities on either end of the connection will notify their respective data-link layers of the disconnection using an indication primitive.

An orthogonal aspect of services is their mode - whether they are connection-oriented or connectionless. Connection-oriented services have three distinct phases of operation:

- Connection establishment

- Data transfer

- Connection release

Note that each of these phases can be implemented using confirmed or unconfirmed services.

The connectionless mode allows for peer entities to communicate without establishing connections. There are no specific phases involved during communication in the connectionless mode. We will restrict ourselves to the connection-oriented mode in this book.

Figure 2.9 Confirmed service

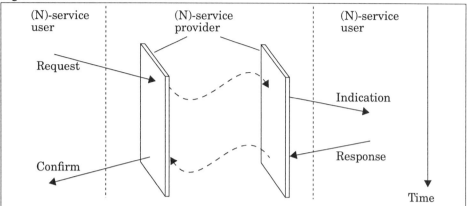

2.10 Time Sequence Diagrams

Time sequence diagrams are used to depict the sequence of service-primitive interactions necessary to implement a service. Figure 2.9 shows the sequence of primitives in time needed to implement a confirmed service. All four types of primitives are needed to provide a confirmed service.

Figure 2.10 Unconfirmed service

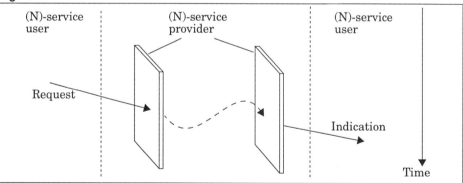

Figure 2.10 shows the sequence of primitives in time needed to implement an unconfirmed service. Notice that only two primitives, the request and indication, are needed. Figure 2.11 depicts the time-sequence diagram for a provider initiated service. In this, some internal event in the service-provider results in an indication to the service-users of the event.

Figure 2.11 Provider initiated service

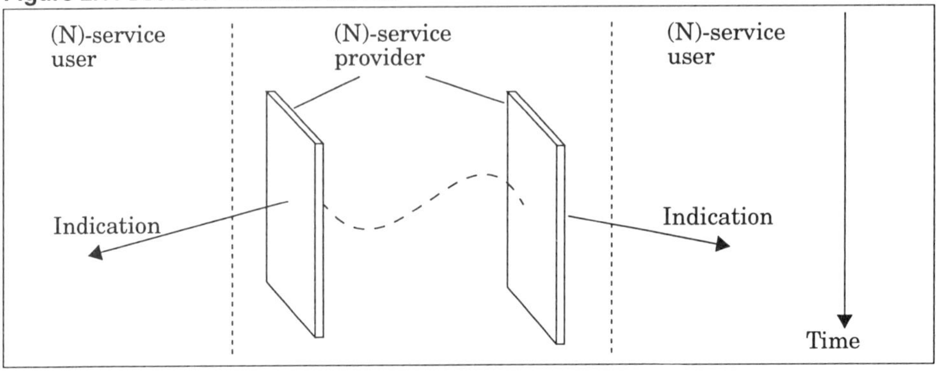

2.11 Data-link Layer - Physical Layer Interface

The physical-data-link layer interface can be completely specified in terms of the services offered by the physical layer to the data-link layer. The physical layer functions in three distinct phases, and we can examine the services offered by the layer within the context of each phase. Each service is completely described by identifying the following:

- The name and type of service

- The set of primitives needed to implement the service

- The direction of the primitives

- The parameters that each primitive needs

Table 2.1 Physical layer connection activation phase primitives

Service/Type	Primitive	Parameters/Direction
Physical channel activation (unconfirmed)	Ph-Activate request ---------------------------- Ph-Activate indication	None / Down -------------------------------- None / Up

Table 2.2 Physical layer data transfer phase primitives

Service/Type	Primitive	Parameters/Direction
Data transfer (unconfirmed)	Ph-Data request -------------------------- Ph-Data indication	Ph-user data/ Down -------------------------------- Ph-user data/ Up

Table 2.3 Physical layer connection deactivation phase primitives

Service/Type	Primitive	Parameters/Direction
Physical channel deactivation (unconfirmed)	Ph-Deactivate request ---------------------------- Ph-Deactivate indication	None / Down ------------------------------- None / Up

Table 2.1 shows the primitives needed to activate a physical layer connection. It is an unconfirmed service. Table 2.2 shows the primitives needed to transfer data across a physical layer connection. It is an unconfirmed service. Table 2.3 shows the primitives needed to deactivate a physical layer connection. It is an unconfirmed service.

2.12 Network Layer - Data-link Layer Interface

The following tables identify the different phases in which the data-link layer operates, and the primitives it provides to the network layer. The primitives given below are tailored to work with the ISO 7776 data-link layer protocol. Apart from those shown, each of the primitives can take additional parameters which are not of significance to the protocol we are going to implement. The ISO standard for the primitives identifies a number of other parameters which can be used with other data-link layer protocols (e.g., LAPD which is used in ISDN).

Table 2.4 Data-link connection establishment phase primitives

Service/Type	Primitive	Parameters/Direction
Data-link connection establishment (confirmed)	Dl-Connect request ---------------------------- Dl-Connect indication ---------------------------- Dl-Connect response ---------------------------- Dl-Connect confirm	None / Down ------------------------------- None / Up ------------------------------- None / Down ------------------------------- None / Up

Table 2.5 Data-link data transfer phase primitives

Service/Type	Primitive	Parameters/Direction
Data Transfer (unconfirmed)	Dl-Data request ------------------------- Dl-Data indication	Dl-user data/ Down ------------------------------ Dl-user data/ Up
Data-link reset (confirmed)	Dl-Reset request ------------------------- Dl-Reset indication ------------------------- Dl-Reset response ------------------------- Dl-Reset confirm	None / Down ------------------------------ Reason / Up ------------------------------ None / Down ------------------------------ None / Up

Table 2.4 shows the primitives needed to establish a data-link connection. It is a confirmed service.

Table 2.5 shows the primitives that can be used during the data-transfer phase. Notice that in this phase we have two different services - normal data transfer and data-link reset. One important aspect of the reset service is that it can be initiated by either the service-user, or the service-provider. When the reset is initiated by the service-user it is a confirmed service, and when it is initiated by the service-provider it behaves like the provider-initiated service mentioned earlier (i.e., only the indication primitive is used). The "reason" parameter provides the service-user with information about why the connection was reset.

Table 2.6 Data-link connection release phase primitives

Service/Type	Primitive	Parameters/Direction
Data-link connection release (unconfirmed)	Dl-Disconnect request --------------------------- Dl-Disconnect indication	None / Down ------------------------------ Reason / Up

Table 2.6 shows the primitives needed to release a data-link connection. The data-link connection release service is an unconfirmed service when it is initiated by the service-user. The connection can also be released by the service provider, in which case only the indication primitive is used. The "reason" parameter provides the service-user with information about why the connection was released.

2.13 Summary

A protocol can be studied by examining the service it provides, the environment in which it functions, the vocabulary of messages, the encoding(format) of the messages and the procedures rules of the protocol.

The various protocols used in data-communications systems have been organized into layers. These layers provide standardized interfaces and services. The services can be described in terms of service-users, service-providers and service-access-points (SAPs). Each service, in turn, is made up of service primitives. Services can be confirmed or unconfirmed. The ISO seven-layer model (also known as the Basic Reference Model) proposes one such standard, conceptual framework to interconnect systems.

Time sequence diagrams provide an important insight into the manner in which services are implemented. The sequence of primitives which are used to implement any given service can be shown using these diagrams.

Connection-oriented services, which are of interest to us, have three distinct phases - connection establishment, data transfer, and connection release.

The physical layer functions in three phases - physical channel activation, data transfer, and physical channel deactivation. The physical layer service is connectionless. The data-link layer functions in three phases outlined above for connection-oriented services.

2.14 Exercises

1. In this chapter we only looked at how two physical layer entities or two data-link layer entities provide connection-oriented services in a point-to-point link. Examine how the services offered by these layers would change if point-to-multipoint connections were possible. What kind of issues would you need to be concerned about?

2. Examine the ISDN protocol stack. How does it relate to the Basic Reference Model?

3. Draw time sequence diagrams for the physical-data-link layer interface, and the data-link-network layer interface.

4. In Section 2.6.8 we mentioned that the interface-control-information (ICI) is implementation dependent. What kind of information would you need in the ICI in order to implement the network layer-data-link layer interface?

5. What issues would be of concern in a service which allows a connectionless mode of operation?

Object-Oriented Design and Programming

3.1 Introduction

For those of us who are conversant in the art of procedural programming and new to object-oriented design and programming, learning about OOD and OOP means bringing about a change in the manner in which we approach a problem, and arrive at the solution. To facilitate our transition from procedural to object-oriented design and programming, we will examine the differences in the two approaches. The following aspects of programming will be examined in order to highlight the differences:

- Abstraction

- Encapsulation

- Modularity

- Hierarchy

Once we have identified the major elements of object-oriented programming, we will turn our attention to the actual process of object-oriented design. We will not be examining any formal methods for design. Instead, our approach will be to develop an intuitive understanding of the design approach. Booch [8] and Rumbaugh [9] provide substantial and in-depth treatment of the design process and methodology.

3.2 Statement of Problem

Let us first examine the problem we are going to address in this chapter. Chapter 2 introduced the interface definitions for the physical layer, and the data-link layer. We also studied the set of primitives that are necessary for each layer to provide services to the layer above. In this chapter we will design C++ class declarations for the physical layer, the data-link layer, and the network layer. At a minimum, the layers should:

- Implement the complete set of service primitives, which provide the relevant services to the layer above.

- Implement a mechanism to allow us to simulate error conditions in a layer. This can be done by making the layer disregard a message it receives from another layer, or by preventing a layer from transmitting a message to another layer at the very last moment (i.e., after all the processing has been done). This will simulate loss of data. Note that this functionality in a layer is not something that would be implemented in a real-world implementation. We need it for our purposes of testing and learning about protocols.

First, we will try to understand the issues of abstraction, encapsulation, modularity and hierarchy by examining how an interface to an OSI layer might be implemented.

Figure 3.1 A street-parking sign in Berkeley, CA

3.3 Abstraction

Parking on most of the streets of Berkeley, CA, is a problem. Not only are you restricted to two hours of parking at a time, you also have to watch out for signs similar to the one shown in Figure 3.1, which prohibit parking during street sweeping. To complicate matters, every street has different times for being swept, which means you really have to pay attention to the signs.

After having lived in Berkeley for a while, I realized I had developed a method for processing the information on these signs while parking. First, I would look at only the time. If I was in no danger of violating the time, I would not read the sign any further. If I was parking during the times mentioned in the sign, then I would automatically look at the day of the week. For instance, if I was looking at the sign, and it was not Tuesday, I would not worry any further and go ahead and park. Only as a last resort would I calculate if it was the 4th Tuesday of the month.

The point here is that the human mind has a tendency to process information by ignoring the unnecessary details and zooming in on the essential characteristics. At each stage of reading the sign, I was looking at only what was essential in order to figure out whether I could park my car on the street or not. This process is what is known as abstraction.

High-level languages provide support for two important types of abstraction: data abstraction and procedural abstraction.

3.3.1 Data Abstraction

Data abstraction is something we commonly encounter in high-level programming languages. The basic data types like int, float, double, and char that are available in C and C++ are the perfect examples of data abstraction. As programmers, we are isolated from the internal representation of these data types, and we can concentrate on their essential properties while programming.

C/C++ also provide support for creating user-defined data types. For example, consider an OSI layer that we would like to implement. A minimal representation of a layer would be:

```
#define PHYSICAL_LAYER 1
#define DATALINK_LAYER 2

typedef enum { FALSE = 0, TRUE } Boolean;

typedef struct _layer {

int type;               /* 1 = physical layer, 2 = data-link etc*/
struct _layer *nPlus1; /* Pointer to layer above */
struct _layer *nMinus1;/* Pointer to layer below */

Boolean _blockXmit; /* if TRUE,transmission is blocked */
Boolean _blockRecv; /*if TRUE,recd. message is dropped */

} layer;
```

What we have is an abstraction for a layer, i.e., a layer data-type. Just like C/

C++ provide support for adding, subtracting, dividing and multiplying integers, we need procedures or functions which will hide the details of this data structure, and allow us to view it and use it as a single unit. This leads us to the next type of abstraction - procedural abstraction.

3.3.2 Procedural Abstraction

Procedural abstraction is another abstraction familiar to most programmers. A procedural language like C provides us with a construct - the *function*, which allows us to write code that provides a certain functionality. Functions hide the details about a certain implementation, and allow programmers to build their programs in a modular fashion.

To understand procedural abstraction further, let us consider the physical layer - which needs to implement the following primitives in order to provide the necessary services to the data-link layer:

- Ph-Activate request

- Ph-Data request (parameter-user data)

- Ph-Deactivate request

Note that the rest of the physical layer primitives - the *indication* primitives - have a direction of service-provider to service-user, and, hence, they will actually be invoked on the data-link layer, and we will not concern ourselves with them just yet. Consider the implementation of a function Command().

```
/*
 * Constants for primitives. The constants used in the
 * implementation are not sacrosanct. They could be any
 * value except for the constant values identified by ISO 7776.
 */

#define PH_ActivateReq      100
#define PH_ActivateInd      101
#define PH_DeactivateReq    102
#define PH_DeactivateInd    103
#define PH_DataReq          104
#define PH_DataInd          105


#define PHYSICAL_LAYER 1
#define DATALINK_LAYER 2

/*
 * Function : Command() - implements the layer primitives.
 * Input :
 *   l - pointer to a layer.
 *   cmd - identifies the primitive to execute.
 *   data - pointer to a dataPacket structure.
 *       contains data to be transmitted/received.
 *
```

```
 *
 * Output:
 *   returns an error code.
 */

/*
 * Note : Ignore the dataPacket structure for now. It
 * will be dealt with in due course.
 */

int
Command(l, cmd, data)
layer *l;
int cmd;
dataPacket *data;
{
if ( l->type == PHYSICAL_LAYER ) {
    switch (cmd ) {
        case PH_ActivateReq:
            /* Code to implement primitive */
            break;

        case PH_DeactivateReq:
            /* Code to implement primitive */
            break;

        case PH_DataReq:
            /* Code to implement primitive */
            break;
        }
    }
    else {
            /* Handle DATA-LINK primitives here */
    }
}
```

This function provides us with an example of procedural abstraction, wherein the actual implementation of the primitives is hidden from the user of these services. The service-user only needs to know the interface. Of course, the function `Command()` might call many other functions, in turn, to realize its functionality.

3.3.3 Abstraction in Object-Oriented Programming

Nothing we have seen so far distinguishes between procedural languages like C and object-oriented languages like C++. An object-oriented language provides us with powerful mechanisms to integrate the two types of abstractions. Study the `layer` class shown below:

```
class layer {
 public:

    layer(int aType); // Constructor
    ~layer();         // Destructor

    // Method to implement primitives

    void Command(int cmd, dataPacket *data, int &errorCode);

    int type;        // Type of layer
    layer *nPlus1;   // Pointer to layer above
    layer *nMinus1;  // Pointer to layer below
    Boolean blockXmit;// Block transmission if TRUE
    Boolean blockRecv;// Block reception if TRUE
};

layer::layer(int aType) :
    nPlus1(0), nMinus1(0),
    blockXmit(FALSE), blockRecv(FALSE),
    type(aType)
{
}

void
layer::Command(int cmd, dataPacket *data, int &errorCode)
{
    // Code identical to what was in the
    // previous Command() function.
}
```

The class layer is a single entity which provides both procedural and data abstraction.

Notice however, that we still need to access the other data members of the both the layer structure, and the layer class, in order to really use it (data members like blockXmit, blockRecv, nPlus1 etc.). We can increase the level of procedural abstraction by providing more functions (or member functions for the C++ class) to hide the use of the rest of the data, but the fact remains that the data is still visible to the programmer, and errant programmers can violate the principle of abstraction by directly accessing and modifying data members. The following segment of code illustrates the problem:

```
SomeFunction()
{
    int errorCode;
    dataPacket *data;

    layer *l = new layer(PHYSICAL_LAYER);
    layer *d = new layer(DATALINK_LAYER);
```

```
    l->nPlus1 = d;
    d->nMinus1 = l;

    /*
     * So far so good..
     */

    l->Command(PH_ActivateReq,data,errorCode);
    l->type = 0; /* A mistake! */

    /* This will create problems! */
    l->Command(PH_DataReq,data,errorCode);

}
```

We need the next step - encapsulation - to enforce abstraction.

3.4 Encapsulation

Encapsulation is the process of hiding the internal workings of a module in order to support or enforce abstraction. Examine the following `main` function.

```
#include "layer.h"
#include "consts.h"

main(argc,argv)
int argc;
char *argv[];
{
    dataPacket data; /* ignore for now */

    InitializePhysicalLayer();

    /* Activate Physical layer */
    Command(PH_ActivateReq,0);

     /* Data transfer */
    Command(PH_DataReq, &data);

    /* Now, block transmission to simulate error */
    PhBlockXmit();

    /* Data transfer again */
    Command(PH_DataReq, &data);

    /* Unblock */
    PhUnblockXmit();
```

```
        /* Deactivate the physical layer */
        Command(PH_DeactivateReq, 0);
}
```

The above fragment of code illustrates what we want to achieve - encapsulation. Functions are provided which allow us to initialize a physical layer, and invoke primitives on it, as well as block and unblock transmission. Nowhere in the above code do we have access to a layer's internal data. We don't even have access to the layer structure itself. How can we achieve this encapsulation in a language like C? The following code, which is now split into a header file (`layer.h`), and the source file (`layer.c`) shows us how it can be done.

```
/*
 * File layer.h
 */

typedef enum { FALSE = 0, TRUE } Boolean;

typedef struct {
    char *data;
} dataPacket;

void InitializePhysicalLayer();
int Command(/* int cmd, dataPacket *data */);

void PhBlockXmit();     /* Block ph. layer from transmitting */
void PhUnblockXmit();   /* Allow ph. layer to transmit */
void PhBlockRecv();     /* Block ph. layer from receiving */
void PhUnblockRecv();   /* Allow ph. layer to receive */
```

Notice that the header file does not provide any idea of what a layer data-structure looks like. The source file described below provides the implementation.

```
/*
 * File layer.c
 */

#include "consts.h" // Constant definitions - see Appendix C
#include "layer.h"

typedef struct _layer {
    int type;
    struct _layer *nPlus1;  /* Pointer to layer above */
    struct _layer *nMinus1; /* Pointer to layer below */

    Boolean _blockXmit; /*if TRUE,transmission is blocked */
    Boolean _blockRecv; /*if TRUE,recd. message is dropped*/
```

```
} layer;

/*
 * Static layer instance - invisible outside this file
 */

static layer phlayer; /* The physical layer */
static layer dllayer; /* The datalink layer */

/*
 * Function : InitializePhysicalLayer() - performs
 *   any necessary initializations.
 */

void
InitializePhysicalLayer()
{
    /* Initialize layer pointers */

    phlayer.type = PHYSICAL_LAYER;
    phlayer.nPlus1 = &dllayer;
    phlayer.nMinus1 = 0;

    /* Unblock recv. and xmit */

    phlayer._blockXmit = FALSE;
    phlayer._blockRecv = FALSE;
}

/*
 * Function : Command() - implements the layer primitives.
 * Input :
 *   cmd - identifies the primitive to execute.
 *   data - pointer to a dataPacket structure.
 *       contains data to be transmitted/received.
 *
 * Output:
 *   returns an error code.
 */

int
Command(cmd, data)
    int cmd;
    dataPacket *data;
{
    switch (cmd ) {
        case PH_ActivateReq:
            /* Code to implement primitive */
            /* Access phlayer data structure*/
        break;
```

```
                    case PH_DeactivateReq:
                        /* Code to implement primitive */
                        /* Access phlayer data structure*/
                    break;

                    case PH_DataReq:
                        /* Code to implement primitive */
                        /* Access phlayer data structure*/
                    break;
                    }
        }

        /*
         * Functions to Block and Unblock the physical layer.
         * One example should suffice.
         */

        void
        PhBlockXmit()
        {
            phlayer._blockXmit = TRUE;
        }
```

Let's revisit the salient features of the above example:

- The layer structure is not visible to the user, and thus provides complete data-abstraction.

- The service-user is provided with functions which access a layer, providing complete procedural abstraction.

- The internal data-representation and function implementation can change (in layer.c). As long as the interface to the module (layer.h) remains constant, the service-users are not affected. This means the physical layer is completely encapsulated.

The current implementation restricts us to one physical layer module. What if some system that we were building required more than one physical layer? This would involve changing both the interface, and the implementation. If the above code were provided to us in the form of a C-library, then it would be impossible for the users of the library to create multiple physical layers, since they would have no access to the source code. Thus the designer of the C-library should design an interface which allows for multiple physical layers to be created, if such a need is anticipated.

3.4.1 Encapsulation in Object-Oriented Programming

You might have guessed that all this is leading up to something. Yes, C++ and object-oriented programming provide an elegant solution to the above prob-

lem. Let's examine how encapsulation can be achieved in C++.
Consider the following class declaration of the `layer` class.

```
/*
 * File layer.h
 */

/*
 * Class - layer
 */

enum Boolean { FALSE = 0, TRUE };

class dataPacket;// Just a forward declaration

class layer {
 public:

    layer(int type); // Constructor

    ~layer();        // Destructor

    // Method to implement primitives

    void Command(int cmd, dataPacket *data, int &errorCode);

    void SetNPlus1Layer(layer *l) { _nPlus1 = 1; }
    void SetNMinus1Layer(layer *l){ _nMinus1 = 1; }

    void UnblockXmit() { _blockXmit = FALSE; }
    void UnblockRecv() { _blockRecv = FALSE; }
    void BlockXmit()   { _blockXmit = TRUE; }
    void BlockRecv()   { _blockRecv = TRUE; }

  private:

    int type;         // Type of layer
    layer *nPlus1;    // Pointer to layer above
    layer *nMinus1;   // Pointer to layer below
    Boolean blockXmit; // Block transmission if TRUE
    Boolean blockRecv; // Block reception if TRUE

  };

 /*
  * File layer.C
  */

 /*
  * Constructor
```

```
    */

    layer::layer(int type) :
        _nPlus1(0), _nMinus1(0),
        _blockXmit(FALSE), _blockRecv(FALSE),
        _type(type)
    {
    }

    /*
     * Function : Command()
     */

    void
    layer::Command(int cmd, dataPacket *data, int &errorCode)
    {
        switch ( _type ) {
            case PHYSICAL_LAYER:
                // Process physical layer primitives
                break;
            case DATALINK_LAYER:
                // Process datalink layer primitives
                break;
            default:
                break;

        }
    }
```

The data is now private and we have methods to access and modify the data. Thus the encapsulation is complete, in that the programmer can both ignore the inner workings of the data structure, and also prevent unsafe tampering with the data. Also, future changes can be made to the data representation as long as the interface to the data is not modified.

How does the layer class allow us to create multiple physical layers? Consider the following fragment of code which creates two physical layer objects, and one data-link layer object (not of much use at this stage, but it illustrates the point!).

```
    #include "consts.h"
    #include "layer.h"

    main(int argc, char *argv[])
    {
        // Instantiate two physical layers
        layer *ph1 = new layer(PHYSICAL_LAYER);
        layer *ph2 = new layer(PHYSICAL_LAYER);

        layer *dl = new layer(DATALINK_LAYER);
        ph1->SetNPlus1Layer(dl);
```

```
        ph1->SetNMinus1Layer(0);

        ph2->SetNPlus1Layer(dl);
        ph2->SetNMinus1Layer(0);
}
```

It is clear the encapsulation is enforced with relative ease in C++ compared to C.

3.5 Modularity

Modularity, or the process of breaking up a system into modules, allows us to better manage the complexity of large systems. And large systems seem to be the order of the day.

In procedural languages, we have two main types of modularity:

- Procedure or function level modularity

- File level modularity

Object-oriented languages provide a more useful level of modularity:

- Class level modularity

- File level modularity

Class level modularity, brings with it the inherent advantages of data abstraction and encapsulation. Also, in large software systems, development of individual classes with well-defined interfaces provides a convenient module for development, wherein the development can proceed on a class-by-class basis to a large extent.

Figure 3.2 A hierarchy of user-defined types

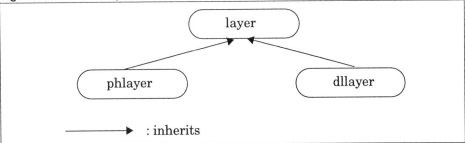

3.6 Inheritance

Finally, object-oriented languages provide support for defining a hierarchy of user-defined types, which truly set them apart from procedural languages.

What is a hierarchy of user-defined types? Figure 3.2 shows one such hierarchy. We have an abstract class `layer`, from which we derive two concrete classes - `phlayer` and `dllayer`. The process of creating this hierarchy of use defined types is called inheritance.

Why do we need inheritance?

Consider the class `layer` defined earlier. It has a `_type` data member which identifies what kind of layer it is. The `Command()` method examines this `_type` field before processing the command. If we were writing code for all the seven layers in this one method, we would have an extremely complicated method. Something that looks like the following:

```
void
layer::Command(int cmd, dataPacket *data, int &errorCode)
{

    switch ( _type ) {
        case PHYSICAL_LAYER:
            // Process physical layer primitives
            break;
        case DATALINK_LAYER:
            // Process datalink layer primitives
            break;
        case NETWORK_LAYER:
            // Process network layer primitives
            break;
        case TRANSPORT_LAYER:
            // Process transport layer primitives
            break;
        case SESSION_LAYER:
            // Process session layer primitives
            break;
        case PRESENTATION_LAYER:
            // Process presentation layer primitives
            break;
        case APPLICATION_LAYER:
            // Process application layer primitives
            break;
        default:
            break;
        }
}
```

This is not to mention all the other information we would need to maintain in the class `layer` in order to implement all the seven layers. It makes sense to create a separate class for each layer and write the `Command()` method specifically for each layer. By defining an abstract class we can implement a generic and consistent interface to a layer. All layers are guaranteed to have this interface if they inherit it from the abstract class. Also, any common functionality like blocking/unblocking, setting and getting pointers for (N+1) and (N-1) layers can be implemented in the abstract class. All other layers automatically inherit this functionality.

From the above discussion it becomes clear that inheritance can be used to:

- Inherit an interface.

- Inherit an implementation. (This is where an object-oriented language provides real value over a procedural language.)

The process of identifying abstractions, identifying a hierarchy of user-defined types, and identifying the actions that can be invoked on these datatypes is the focus of object-oriented design.

3.7 Object-Oriented Design

Procedural languages lend themselves to a *top-down* approach of programming, where the problem is tackled at the highest level first, by identifying the function the program needs to perform. Then this function is repeatedly broken down into smaller and smaller functions, until we have manageable and easily implementable functions.

Object-oriented design differs from such an approach in that it is neither *top-down* nor *bottom-up*. The emphasis shifts to thinking of the solution in terms of classes and objects. The C++ Tutorial [4] identifies the following as necessary steps in object-oriented design:

- Identify the classes

- Assign attributes and behavior

- Find relationships between the classes

- Arrange the classes into hierarchies

Given a certain problem, the above steps can be applied iteratively in order to arrive at a satisfactory solution. This intuitive approach to design has been followed throughout the text. In the rest of this chapter, we will design the classes for the physical, data-link, and network(driver) layers. This one piece of design is not going to provide a complete overview of the design process. Chapter 5 will address the problem as a whole and will identify the major modules that need to be implemented. The subsequent chapters will deal with the design and implementation of these major modules. Given the various concepts that need to be covered, and the amount of code that we need to discuss, it is not possible to discuss the design process in very fine detail. But the reader should rest assured that the above-mentioned steps have led to the solution presented in the text, and the design will be presented such that the explanation and other material are optimally mixed.

3.8 Layer Interface

We are finally ready to design the interface to the first 3 layers. Let us proceed with the design steps enumerated above.

3.8.1 Identify the Classes

From our earlier discussion about having a class for each layer we arrive at the following classes:

- phlayer

- dllayer

- nwlayer (we'll refer to the driver layer as the network layer in this chapter)

Also we need a `dataPacket` class which encapsulates the data being exchanged between layers.

3.8.2 Assign Attributes and Behavior

We have already identified that each layer needs the following attributes:

- Attributes which point to the (N+1) and (N-1) layers.

- Attributes which hold the transmit/receive blocking states.

If we examine the physical layer service definition and the data-link layer service definition, it is clear that there are three different sets of service-primitives, and that each one requires the same number and type of arguments.

Primitives with no parameters

The primitives which take no parameters can be implemented by the following member function:

```
Command(int cmd, int &errorCode);
// cmd - identifies the service-primitive
// errorCode - holds any return error code
```

Note that the arguments to the function make up the interface-control-information (ICI).

Primitives with user-data

Primitives which require user-data as a parameter can be implemented by the following member function:

```
Command(int cmd, int &errorCode, dataPacket *data);
```

```
// data - contains user-data
```

The data argument is the service-data-unit (SDU).

Primitives with "reason"

Primitives which require a "reason" can be implemented by the following member function:

```
Command(int cmd, int &errorCode, int reason);
// reason - the reason for invoking the primitive
// originator - the originator of the primitive
```

We have already identified the member functions that modify and access the private attributes. The following is a first attempt at the class declarations:

```
/*
 * Forward declarations
 */

class dataPacket;
class dllayer;
class phlayer;
class nwlayer;

/*
 * Class phlayer
 */

class phlayer {
 public:
    phlayer();
    ~phlayer();

    // Method to implement primitives
    void Command(int cmd, int &errorCode);
    void Command(int cmd, int &errorCode, dataPacket *data);

    // Modifier methods to set private data
    void SetNPlus1Layer(dllayer *l) { _nPlus1 = l; }

    // methods to access private data
    dllayer *GetNPlus1Layer() { return _nPlus1; }

    // Methods for blocking and unblocking
    void UnblockXmit() { _blockXmit = FALSE; }
    void UnblockRecv() { _blockRecv = FALSE; }
    void BlockXmit() { _blockXmit = TRUE; }
    void BlockRecv() { _blockRecv = TRUE; }
```

```
   private:
      dllayer *_nPlus1;
      Boolean _blockXmit;
      Boolean _blockRecv;
};

/*
 * Class dllayer
 */

class dllayer {

 public:

    dllayer();
    ~dllayer();

    // Method to implement primitives
    // Note that we need all three Command() methods.

    void Command(int cmd, int &errorCode);
    void Command(int cmd, int &errorCode, dataPacket *data);
    void Command(int cmd, int &errorCode, int reason);

    // Modifier methods to set private data
    void SetNPlus1Layer(nwlayer *l) { _nPlus1 = l; }
    void SetNMinus1Layer(phlayer *l) { _nMinus1 = l; }

    // methods to access private data
    nwlayer *GetNPlus1Layer() { return _nPlus1; }
    phlayer *GetNMinus1Layer() { return _nMinus1; }

    // Methods for blocking and unblocking
    void UnblockXmit() { _blockXmit = FALSE; }
    void UnblockRecv() { _blockRecv = FALSE; }
    void BlockXmit() { _blockXmit = TRUE; }
    void BlockRecv() { _blockRecv = TRUE; }

 private:
    nwlayer *_nPlus1;
    phlayer *_nMinus1;
    Boolean _blockXmit;
    Boolean _blockRecv;
};

/*
 * Class nwlayer
 */
```

```
class nwlayer {
 public:
    nwlayer();
    ~nwlayer();

    // Method to implement primitives
    void Command(int cmd, int &errorCode);
    void Command(int cmd, int &errorCode, dataPacket *data);
    void Command(int cmd, int &errorCode, int reason);

    // Modifier methods to set private data
    void SetNMinus1Layer(dllayer *l) { _nMinus1 = l; }

    // methods to access private data
    dllayer *GetNMinus1Layer() { return _nMinus1; }

    // Methods for blocking and unblocking
    void UnblockXmit() { _blockXmit = FALSE; }
    void UnblockRecv() { _blockRecv = FALSE; }
    void BlockXmit() { _blockXmit = TRUE; }
    void BlockRecv() { _blockRecv = TRUE; }

  private:
    dllayer *_nMinus1;
    Boolean _blockXmit;
    Boolean _blockRecv;
};
```

Note that the physical layer and network layer maintain a pointer only to the data-link layer, while the data-link layer keeps pointers to both the physical and network layers. If we were implementing a transport layer, the network layer would have to maintain pointers to both the layer above and the layer below.

3.8.3 Find Relationships between Classes

As we proceed with our design and implementation of classes, it will become obvious that each class has some relationship to other classes. Very few of our classes will be isolated such that the objects of that class can exist and function without other objects.

This is a good place to introduce certain types of relationships that can exist.

Composition

When one class contains data members which are objects of another class, then the relationship between the classes is a *composition* relationship.

Uses

One class uses another class to realize its own functionality. Sometimes the dependency can be restricted to knowing the interface to the classes, sometimes it might be necessary to know about the internal details about a class. When one class has to know the internal details about another class, the C++ friend mechanism can be used.

Inheritance

When one class inherits from another class, the relationship is one of *inheritance.* As mentioned earlier, a class can inherit an interface and/or an implementation.

Figure 3.3 identifies the initial relationships that exist between the classes. Note that at this stage we only have the *uses* relationship.

Figure 3.3 Initial relationships

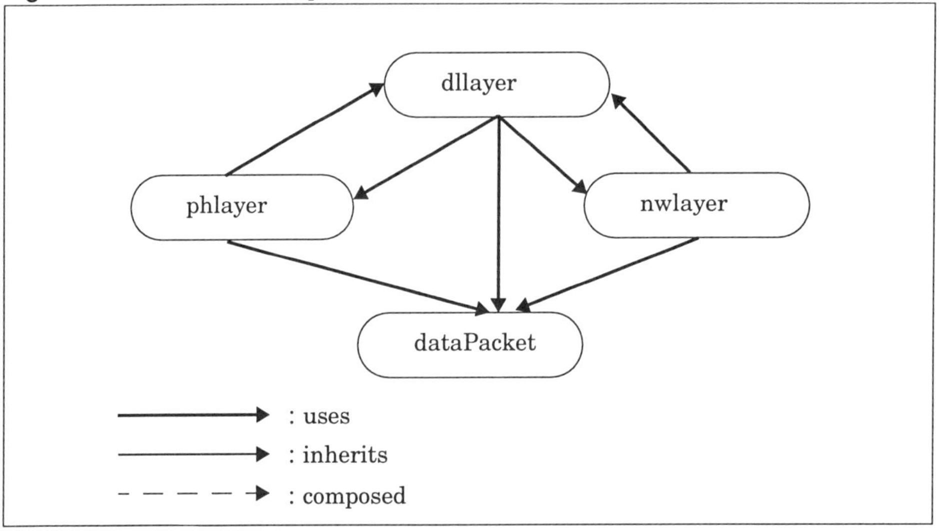

3.8.4 Arrange the Classes into Hierarchies

Hierarchies among classes can be developed by examining whether there is any common implementation or a common interface that can inherited. In our case, both are valid. There is behavior related to blocking/unblocking that can be moved to an abstract base class. Also, the design would be consistent if all the layers shared an identical interface (this might not be feasible if we were trying to design an abstract class for all the seven layers. For the three layers we are interested in we can achieve this to illustrate the point). Thus, methods for implementing the primitives could also be moved to an abstract base class to provide the common interface. We arrive at the following abstract base class - `layer`.

```
class layer {
 public:
    layer();
    virtual ~layer() {};

    virtual void Command(int cmd, int &errorCode);
    virtual void Command(int cmd, int &errorCode,
                         int reason);
    virtual void Command(int cmd, int &errorCode,
                         dataPacket *data);

    // Modifier functions to set private data
    void SetNPlus1Layer(layer *l)  { _nPlus1 = l; }
    void SetNMinus1Layer(layer *l) { _nMinus1 = l; }

    // functions to access private data
    layer *GetNPlus1Layer()    { return _nPlus1; }
    layer *GetNMinus1Layer()   { return _nMinus1; }

    void BlockXmit()    { _blockXmit = TRUE; }
    void UnblockXmit()  { _blockXmit = FALSE; }
    void BlockRecv()    { _blockRecv = TRUE; }
    void UnblockRecv()  { _blockRecv = FALSE; }

 protected:

    Boolean  _blockXmit;
    Boolean  _blockRecv;
    layer *  _nPlus1;
    layer *  _nMinus1;

};
```

Classes `phlayer`, `dllayer` and `nwlayer` can now inherit from the class `layer`, and redefine the methods needed to implement the primitives.

```
class phlayer : public layer {

 public:
    phlayer();
    ~phlayer();

    virtual void Command(int cmd, int & errorCode);
    virtual void Command(int cmd, int &errorCode,
                         dataPacket *data);
};

class dllayer : public layer {

 public:
```

```
      dllayer();
      ~dllayer();

      virtual void Command(int cmd, int & errorCode);
      virtual void Command(int cmd, int & errorCode,
                           dataPacket *data);

};

class nwlayer : public layer {

  public:
      nwlayer();
      ~nwlayer();

      virtual void Command(int cmd, int & errorCode);
      virtual void Command(int cmd, int & errorCode,
                           int reason);
      virtual void Command(int cmd, int & errorCode,
                           dataPacket *data);
};
```

Note that the physical layer needs to redefine only two of the Command()
methods.

Figure 3.4 Hierarchy of types

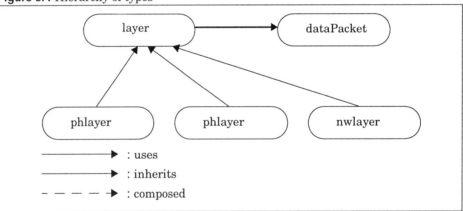

Figure 3.4 depicts the new relationships between the classes. A new type of
relationship - *inherits* - is introduced into the picture.

We have gone through one iteration of the design steps in order to arrive at
a solution for the layer interface. Most problems will require more than one
iteration before a satisfactory solution can be obtained.

3.9 Summary

The major elements of object-oriented programming are:

- Abstraction - The process of highlighting the main features and hiding the unnecessary details. Two types of abstraction are commonly used - data abstraction and procedural abstraction. Object-oriented languages provide powerful mechanisms to combine the two types (for e.g., a class in C++).

- Encapsulation - The process of hiding the internal workings of a module in order to support or enforce abstraction. In C++, declaring data members or functions private or protected is a way of enforcing abstraction.

- Modularity -The process of programming in modules, which allows for better manageability of software. C++ provides class and file level modularity.

- Inheritance - The process of creating a hierarchy of user-defined types in order to derive the benefit of a common interface or a common implementation. Object-oriented languages provide powerful mechanisms to design and implement inheritance.

The following intuitive steps are useful in object-oriented design [4]:

- Identify the classes

- Assign attributes and behavior

- Find relationships between the classes

- Arrange the classes into hierarchies

The `layer` class provides an abstraction for an OSI layer. It has overloaded `Command()` methods for implementing primitives in sub-classes. The `layer` class also provides for mechanisms to block/unblock the transmitting and receiving of data (so that error conditions can be introduced while we are testing the implementation).

The `phlayer`, `dllayer`, and `nwlayer` classes inherit from the `layer` class, and redefine the appropriate `Command()` methods to provide their services.

3.10 Exercises

1. Provide a solution for encapsulation in C which will allow us to create multiple physical layers.

2. We used #defines instead of enums for primitive types. We could have defined primitives as an enum as follows:

```
enum Primitive { PH_ActivateReq, PH_ActivateInd,
            PH_DataReq, PH_DataInd,
            PH_DeactivateReq, PH_DeactivateInd };
```

What would we have gained and/or lost by using enums?

3. In the constructor for the layer class, why can't we initialize the _nPlus1 and _nMinus1 data members in the constructor?

4

The Anatomy of a Protocol

4.1 Introduction

The thesaurus that is available with my word processor provides the following synonyms for the word anatomy: dissection, enquiry, examination, investigation, and study. Any of these words can adequately describe the purpose of this chapter - which is to study in-depth how the ISO-7776 standard data-link protocol functions, and, more importantly, why the protocol is designed the way it is. The standards document [5] is not particularly easy to read. This chapter will clarify the fundamental concepts, and also provide insights into the functioning of the protocol. This should help make the standards document as close to bed-time reading material as is humanly possible. A copy of the standard would be a worthwhile companion to this book, since the exact description is not duplicated in this book. The source code used in this book does, however, describe the protocol exhaustively.

Before we embark on studying the protocol, there are a few general concepts that need to be examined.

4.2 X.25, DTEs and DCEs

The title on the standards document reads "...*High-level data link control procedures - Description of the X.25 LAPB-compatible DTE data link procedures*". Decidedly cryptic, until we understand the acronyms used in the title.

Private companies and even governments in various countries have developed networks (also known as public networks) which allow subscribers to use their services for data communication. To provide a standard interface to communicate with these public networks, International Telecommunication Union (ITU) developed a standard for the physical, data-link, and network layers for communication between subscribers and the public networks. This standard is collectively known as X.25. Figure 4.1 shows an example of a network, consisting of a public network and subscribers (only the three X.25 layers are shown). Also shown are elements called DTE and DCE. DTE stands for Data Terminal Equipment, and it is basically the subscriber equipment. DCE stands for Data Circuit-terminating Equipment and it is the equipment in the public network with which the DTE interfaces.

Figure 4.1 An example of a public network

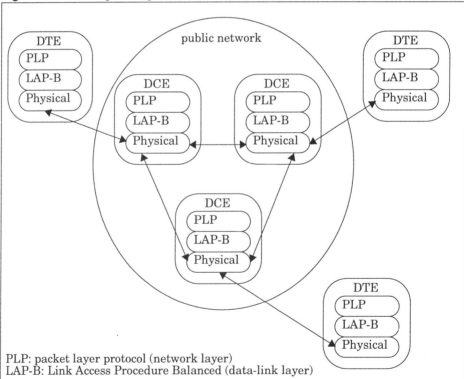

PLP: packet layer protocol (network layer)
LAP-B: Link Access Procedure Balanced (data-link layer)

Our concern is with the data-link layer protocol used in X.25. X.25 layer 2 defines a data-link protocol standard for communication between a DTE and a

DCE. The ISO 7776 standard that we are interested in is adopted from (and is almost identical to) the X.25 standard, and it provides a description of the protocol as viewed by the DTE (The ITU standards document is on-line. The URL is gopher://info.itu.ch). The document also describes how two DTEs can communicate at the data-link level without an intervening public network. Because we will restrict ourselves to DTE-DTE communications in this book, we will not have to worry about public networks.

4.3 Data-link Operation Modes

A protocol is used to communicate between two entities and contains procedures for managing the communication. ISO defines three types of entities which can communicate based on their data-link management capabilities [13]:

- Primary station - This is the entity on one side of a data-link that is responsible for link management, i.e., connection establishment, connection reset and connection release.

- Secondary station - This is an entity which can receive commands from a primary station, send responses, and, in some cases, initiate data-link error recovery.

- Combined station - This entity, as the name suggests, combines the functions of a primary and secondary station.

Figure 4.2 Data-link configuration

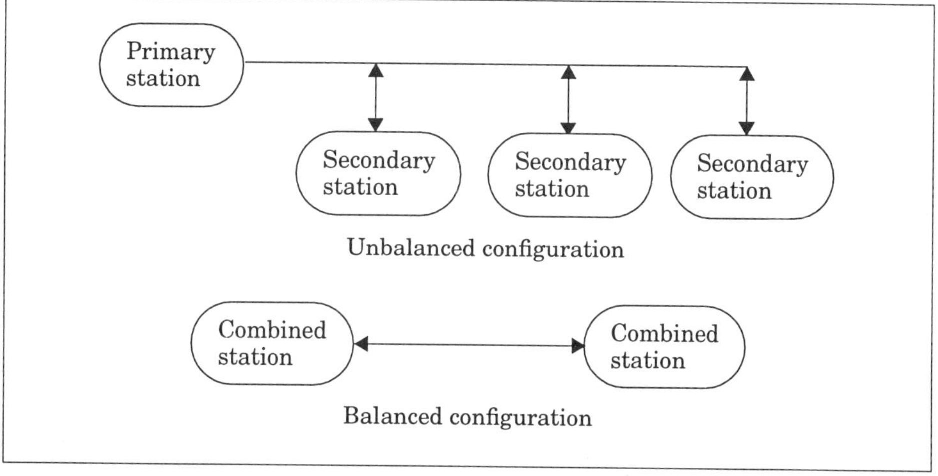

In the figure: Primary station connects to three Secondary stations — "Unbalanced configuration". Two Combined stations connect to each other — "Balanced configuration".

Given the three types of stations, Figure 4.2 shows the different possible configurations for a data-link as defined by ISO. In the unbalanced configuration, the data-link can operate in two modes - the *Normal Response Mode* (NRM), or the *Asynchronous Response Mode* (ARM). We will not be dealing with these modes in this book.

Our interest lies in the balanced configuration - where two data-link entities, each acting as a combined station, can communicate. The data-link is said to operate in the *Asynchronous Balanced Mode* (ABM). Thus, the set of procedures defined by ISO-7776 for such a data-link is called the *Link Access Procedure Balanced* (LAPB).

4.4 Review of Data-link Functionality

Chapter 2 identified the major functional areas of a data-link layer as framing, error detection, error recovery, and flow control. Also, in terms of services offered to the network layer the data-link layer needs to provide services for connection establishment, connection release, data transfer, and connection reset. Let us discuss these major functional areas, and develop a rationale for the data-link layer procedures detailed in the document.

4.5 Framing

The physical layer is capable of transmitting bits. When the physical layer passes on the received bits to the data-link layer it is the responsibility of the data-link layer to convert this bit-stream into logical units of data. This involves recognizing the beginning and end of a logical block of data in a bit-stream, and the process by which this is achieved is called framing. Hence, a unit of data-link data is called a frame. ISO 7776 uses starting and ending flags to clearly identify the boundaries of a frame in a given bit-stream. The flags are identical and have the following bit pattern:

```
01111110 - an 8-bit sequence (0x7E in hex)
```

4.5.1 Bit-Stuffing

Framing data-link data with flags gives rise to another problem. A bit pattern identical to the flag can very well occur in the data that is contained between the flags. This can cause errors when it comes to recognizing the frame boundaries. A procedure called bit-stuffing is used to overcome this problem. When the transmitting DTE notices five consecutive "1" bits in the bit-stream, it inserts a "0" bit after the five "1" bits to ensure that the flag sequence is not repeated. On the receiving side the receiver will strip off any "0" bit that follows five contiguous "1" bits. Note that the bit-stuffing is done only for the data between the flags, and not the flags. This allows the receiver to recognize frame boundaries.

Since our implementation is not over a real physical channel, but over Unix IPC, we really don't have to worry about bit-stuffing and bit-stripping. In any case, real-life implementations typically rely on hardware to accomplish this task.

4.6 Error Control

If we had a perfect physical channel, then framing would be sufficient to exchange error-free data between two DTEs. But we know that is never the case. It becomes the data-link layer's responsibility to convert an error prone physical channel into an error-free one. Before we come up with solutions for error control, let us examine the kind of errors we can expect.

- Errors during transmission can introduce bit-errors, where some bits in the data have been corrupted.

- Errors during transmission can result in entire frames being lost.

The first type of error requires that the data-link layer be capable of detecting bit errors in a received frame. The data-link achieves this by adding error detecting codes to the frame. A common example of such a mechanism is the parity bit. The amount of information that is added on to the data being transmitted determines the extent of error detection that can be carried out (in terms of the number of bit-errors that can be detected). ISO 7776 uses a more elaborate scheme - the cyclic redundancy check. We will deal with this scheme in greater detail in a later section.

The second type of error, where a transmitted frame might not make it to the receiving data-link layer, requires more elaborate procedures to recover from. How does the transmitter know whether the frame it sent has been received or not? It is clear that the transmitter should be notified in some manner by the receiver when a frame has been received. One common procedure is for the receiver to send an acknowledgment for every frame that it receives. This is called a positive acknowledgment or "ack". Another variant of this is a negative acknowledgment or "Nack", where a receiver receives a garbled frame (detected by the earlier mechanism) and it asks for the frame to be retransmitted.

What happens if the ack or Nack gets lost? It stands to reason that even acks/nacks can be lost, since they are just another type of frame. The transmitter has no way of knowing whether the frame it sent was received or not. The transmitter can retransmit the frame, but it should ensure that the receiver is given enough time to respond. This can be achieved by using timers. The transmitter can start a timer as soon as it transmits a frame, and if it doesn't receive a positive acknowledgment before the timer expires, the frame can be retransmitted. Of course, a negative acknowledgment will also result in a retransmission.

Retransmissions introduce another problem when it comes to data transfer frames (those containing service-user, i.e., network layer data). Suppose the receiver sent a positive acknowledgment for a frame, but the acknowledgment got lost. The transmitter would retransmit the frame in due time and the receiver would process the received frame. How is the receiver to know whether it is receiving a new frame, or a retransmission? Obviously, there needs to be some kind of distinction between consecutively transmitted

frames. This distinction is brought about by using sequence numbers to identify each frame. We will be dealing with sequence numbers in detail later in
this chapter.

Thus, a significant portion of the procedures in ISO 7776 are devoted to
managing the error detection and recovery mechanisms, which involves ini-
tializing and possibly re-initializing sequence numbers, sending acknowledgments, and notifying the transmitter of corrupted frames and retransmissions. All this implies exchanging control information (in the form of control frames) between the DTEs.

4.7 Flow Control

Consider the case when the transmitting DTE is a sending a steady stream of
frames (with different sequence numbers) and the receiving DTE happens to
be a slower processor, and is unable to process the frames as fast as they are
coming in. The receiver will end up losing frames, either because internal
buffers are going to get overwritten by newly arriving frames, or the new
frames will be discarded because there is no buffer space available. We need
some mechanism where the receiver can indicate to the transmitter whether
it's capable of receiving frames or not. Also, a limit can be set on the maximum
number of frames that can be transmitted without receiving an acknowledgment. These mechanisms come under the purview of flow control. Some more
control frames will be needed to coordinate flow control. The ISO 7776 implementation will provide us with a good insight into its fairly elaborate flow control mechanism.

4.8 Connection Management

Flow control and error control mechanisms are provided by ISO 7776 to realize the data transfer services. The service-user merely requests data transfer,
and the data-link layer has to ensure that the transfer is error free. The other
major set of services that the data-link layer has to provide have to do with
link connection set-up, reset, and release. Again, control frames will need to
be exchanged in order to implement these services.

4.9 Elements of a Protocol

Chapter 2 identified five elements that form the basis for understanding a
protocol. Its time to examine ISO 7776 in terms of those elements.

4.9.1 Service Specification

This element defines the services provided by the protocol. In previous chapters we have studied in detail the services a data-link layer needs to provide.
ISO 7776 provides the same set of services to the network layer.

4.9.2 Assumptions About the Environment

The "environment" of ISO 7776 can be described in terms of the physical layer, whose services are used, and the network layer, which uses the services of the data-link layer.

In a real-world implementation, the physical layer provides a transmission channel. This channel can distort transmissions, as well as lose messages, or deliver them out-of-sequence. Our example of the implementation of the physical layer uses Unix IPC, and, hence, will not be as error-prone as a hardware transmission channel.

The network layer is expected to use the services of the data-link layer for setting, resetting, releasing connections, and data transfer. The network layer cannot be relied upon to execute the service primitives in any particular order. Hence, the data-link layer should be designed to function in such an environment.

4.9.3 Vocabulary

We now know that apart from data frames being transferred between two DTEs, we also need many other types of frames for managing connections, flow control, error detection, and error recovery. ISO 7776 defines the following frame types:

- SABM - Set Asynchronous Balanced Mode

- DISC - Disconnect

- UA - Unnumbered Acknowledgment

- DM - Disconnected Mode

- FRMR - Frame Reject

- RR - Receive Ready

- RNR - Receive Not Ready

- REJ - Reject

- Iframe - Information

We are going to look at the necessity for each of these frame types in detail. Can you determine what each of these frame types might be used for?

4.9.4 Encoding

Another element of a protocol is the encoding or format of the messages. Figure 4.3 shows the various frame formats defined by ISO 7776. Note that the format is different for frames carrying information.

Figure 4.3 Frame format

Flag	Address	Control	FCS	Flag
F 0111110	A 8-bits	C 8-bits	FCS 16-bits	F 01111110

Flag	Address	Control	Info	FCS	Flag
F 0111110	A 8-bits	C 8-bits	I N-bits	FCS 16-bits	F 01111110

The flag bytes have been discussed earlier. Let us examine the other fields in detail.

4.9.4.1 Control field

The 8-bit control field encodes the frame type. The frame types mentioned earlier are grouped into three categories:

- Unnumbered format (U) - These frames do not have a sequence number associated with them, and are used for link initialization, reset and disconnection.

- Supervisory format (S) - As the name suggests, these frames are used for supervising the link after it has been initialized.

- Information transfer format (I) - These frames are used for data transfer. The information field in these frames carry service-user data.

Figure 4.4 shows the encoding of the control byte. The control byte format is fixed for each type of unnumbered frame, except for the value of the p/f bit. The control byte format is fixed for each type of supervisory frame except for the p/f and n(r) bits. The information frame control byte has a bit 1 equal to zero, and the other values of n(s), p, and n(r) can vary.

We will defer the discussion of the fields p/f-the poll/final bit, n(s)-the send sequence number and n(r)-receive sequence number until we examine a need for these parameters.

Figure 4.4 Control field encoding

Unnumbered format (U)

control field bits:	1	2	3	4	5	6	7	8
	1	1	M	M	p/f	M	M	M
SABM	1	1	1	1	p	1	0	0
DISC	1	1	0	0	p	0	1	0
UA	1	1	0	0	f	1	1	0
DM	1	1	1	1	f	0	0	0
FRMR	1	1	1	0	f	0	0	1

Supervisory format (S)

control field bits:	1	2	3	4	5	6	7	8
	1	0	S	S	p/f	---- n(r) ----		
RR	1	0	0	0	p/f	---- n(r) ----		
RNR	1	0	1	0	p/f	---- n(r) ----		
REJ	1	0	0	1	p/f	---- n(r) ----		

Information transfer format (I)

control field bits:	1	2	3	4	5	6	7	8
	0	---- n(s) ----			p	---- n(r) ----		

4.9.4.2 Commands and responses

Frames can either be commands or responses. Commands are used to initiate procedures such as link setup, reset, disconnection, data transfer, etc. Frames which are transmitted as a reply to these command frames are, obviously, response frames. The use of commands and responses will become clear as we study the protocol procedures.

4.9.4.3 Addressing

The ISO 7776 standard describes the addressing mechanism to be used when communicating between a DTE and a DCE. Two addresses are used in any frame:

- Address A, hex value 0x03

- Address B, hex value 0x01

A command frame transmitted from a DCE to DTE has an address A.

A command frame transmitted from a DTE to DCE has an address B.

A response frame transmitted from a DCE to a DTE has an address B.

A response frame transmitted from a DTE to a DCE has an address A.

ISO 7776 does not specify the address allocation for DTE-DTE communications. For addressing purposes, we will view one of the DTEs as a DCE.

4.9.4.4 Frame Check Sequence (FCS)

The FCS field (16-bits) in every frame is the frame check sequence that is computed for all bits before the FCS, including the starting flag. The FCS is used to detect bit-errors in the frame at the receiving DTE. We will defer a discussion of the algorithm for generating the FCS, and detecting errors until later. (See Chapter 9.)

4.9.4.5 Information bits

Information bits are sent in I frames, and FRMR frames. The information bits in an I-frame are service-user data that has to be transferred to the peer service-user. The information bits in a FRMR frame contain information about link operation. We will be discussing this in Chapter 12.

4.9.5 Procedure Rules

We have now identified the type and format of the various messages that can be exchanged between two DTEs. We now have to study the final element of a protocol - the procedure rules that specify the manner in which these messages can be exchanged. The ISO 7776 is mostly devoted to these procedure rules. We will not repeat that information here. Instead, we will examine these procedures in light of the services the data-link layer needs to provide. We will also emphasize why these rules are needed. Instead of merely explaining the ISO 7776 we will start at a basic level and work our way up to the complex procedures.

4.10 Connection Establishment

There are four primitives that combine to provide services for data-link connection establishment. The data-link is said to be setup when the connection has been established.

Figure 4.5 Link setup - connection accepted

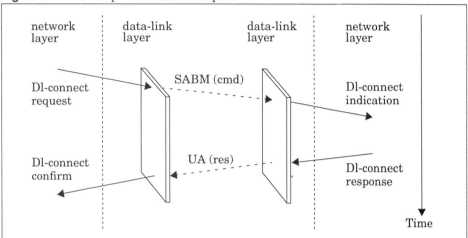

If we look at the frame types available, the SABM (set asynchronous balanced mode) is the obvious choice for a link-set up command. Figure 4.5 shows the relationship between the primitives invoked on the data-link layer and the frames exchanged between the peer data-link layers.

The UA (unnumbered acknowledgment) response frame is used as a positive acknowledgment to accept the connection request.

Figure 4.6 Link setup - connection refused

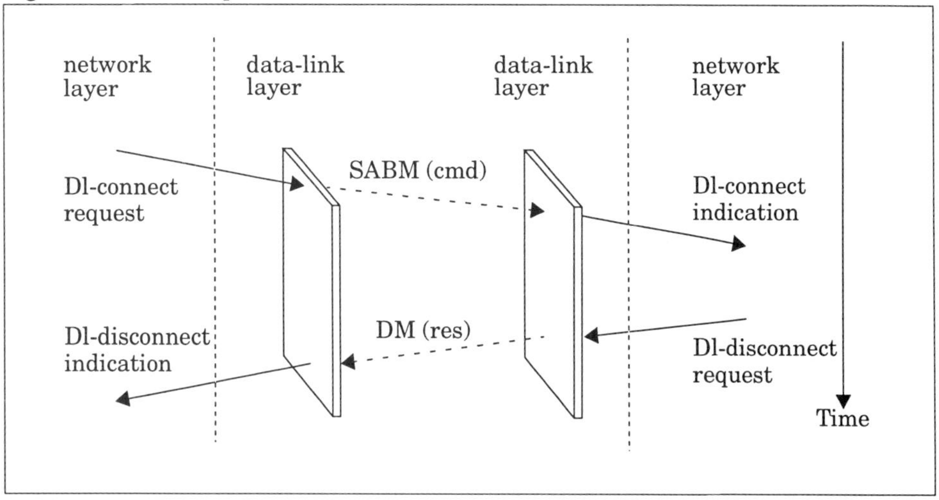

Figure 4.6 shows the case when a connection request is refused by the peer network layer. The peer data-link layer transmits a DM (disconnected mode) response to indicate that the link setup command is being refused.

Figure 4.7 DTE internal states while using timers

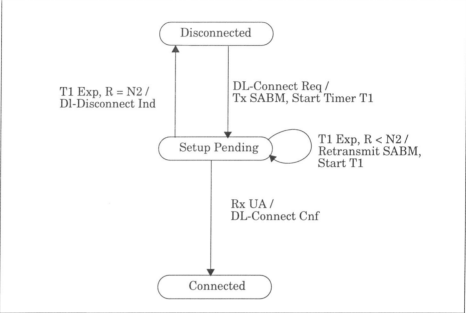

4.10.1 Why Do We Need Timers?

The scenario we have seen for link setup is valid in an error-free situation. Consider what would happen if the SABM command got lost, garbled, etc., in effect, never making it to the peer data-link layer. There would be no response, and the transmitting end would wait indefinitely. Obviously, that is not permissible. After some amount of elapsed time, the layer which transmitted the SABM should initiate some recovery procedure. ISO 7776 defines a timer T1 to keep track of elapsed time. The timer is started when a SABM is transmitted. If timer T1 expires before a response is received, the SABM command is retransmitted. Given that the command can get lost again, this leads us to another question. How many times should the command be re-transmitted? The standard prescribes a system parameter N2 for the maximum number of retransmissions. Both T1 and N2 should be made known to both DTEs and agreed to for a designated period of time (in reality, T1 and N2 don't have to be the same for both sides). In our implementation these parameters can be changed from the user interface, allowing us to examine how the protocol functions with different values of T1 and N2.

Figure 4.7 shows the internal states a DTE might go through in the course of transmitting and retransmitting a SABM command. (See Appendix B for a description of conventions used for describing state machines.) Note that the timer functioning is also valid for other commands transmitted by a DTE for which responses are expected but none are received.

4.10.2 The Poll/Final (P/F) Bit

So far, the DTE transmitting a SABM command assumes that the command or response got lost if does not receive a reply within time T1. What if the receiving DTE did in fact receive the SABM, but for some reason did not reply? Then the transmitter (which is waiting for an ack) will not know if the SABM never reached, or the ack got lost, or the receiver never replied. There should be some mechanism in the protocol which forces the receiver of a command to send a response. Only then can the lack of a response to a command (e.g., SABM) be attributed to failure.

Here's where the P/F bit comes in handy. In a command frame, the bit is known as the Poll (P) bit, in a response frame, the bit is known as the Final (F) bit. When a DTE wants to solicit a response, it sets the P-bit to 1 in the command frame. The receiving DTE is required to send a response, with the F-bit set to 1.

If a command was sent with P=0, and the receiving DTE responds, it must set the F-bit to 0. This is to distinguish between responses that were solicited, and those that were not.

Figure 4.8 Link disconnection

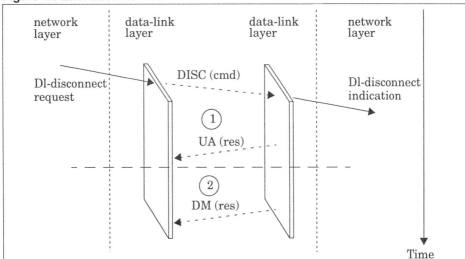

4.11 Connection Release

Once a data-link has been set up, the connection can be disconnected during the connection release phase. Two primitives are used to provide this service. The DISC command frame is used to initiate the disconnection. Figure 4.8

shows the time-sequence diagrams for this service. Note that the receiving DTE can respond with a UA frame if it is disconnecting, or with a DM frame if it was already in a disconnected state. Also, note that the connection release service is an unconfirmed service.

4.12 Link Reset

After the data-link connection has been established it can perform data transfer. During data transfer the link might detect error conditions from which it cannot recover.

Figure 4.9 Service-user link reset - accepted

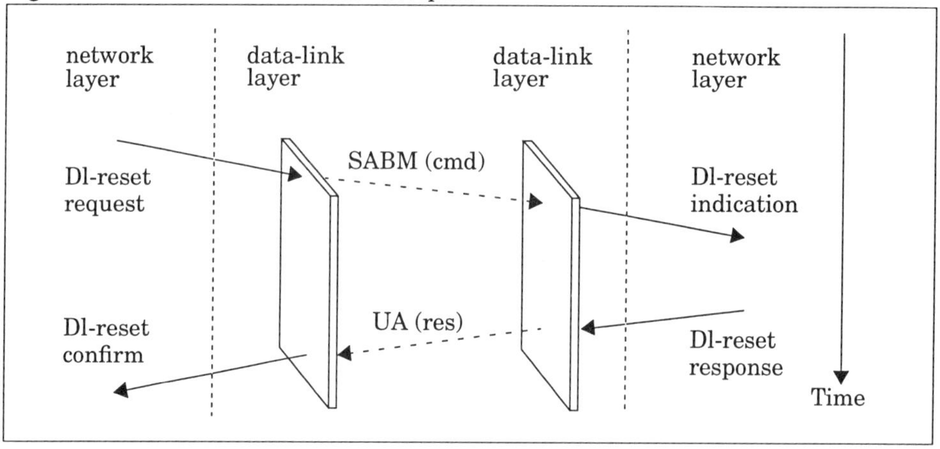

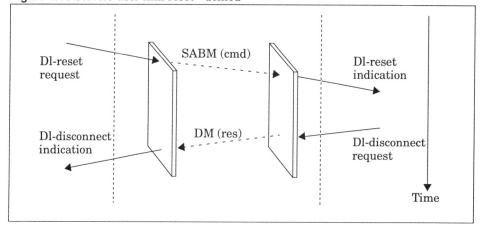

Figure 4.10 Service-user link reset - denied

For such situations, the data-link layer also provides a connection reset service, where the service-user can invoke primitives to reset the connection. The link can also be reset by the service-provider (the data-link layer) because of some internal error condition. The SABM frame is used to reset a link.

- Figure 4.9 shows a service-user initiated reset, accepted by the peer

- Figure 4.10 shows a service-user initiated reset, denied by the peer

- Figure 4.11 shows a service-provider initiated reset

A DTE can also send a DM response with the f-bit set to 0, to request the peer DTE to initiate link reset procedures.

Figure 4.11 Service-provider link reset

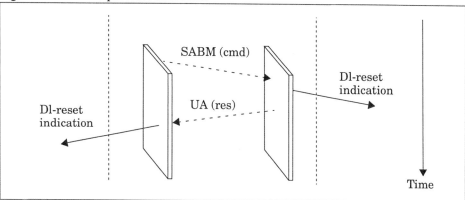

4.13 Collision of Unnumbered Commands

Time-outs and retransmissions can help detect and correct errors caused due to lost frames. Error situations can also arise due to race conditions. Consider the case when service-users (on both sides of the data-link layer) issue a connection request primitive. SABM commands will be issued simultaneously, and the protocol should be designed to handle a contingency like this. The ISO 7776 is designed to handle collision of unnumbered commands (SABM, DISC). The standard prescribes a choice of procedures to handle collisions between SABMs issued simultaneously, DISCs issued simultaneously, or, a SABM and a DISC issued simultaneously. We will implement the procedures depicted in Figure 4.12 and Figure 4.13. Note that the network layer does not get a DL-connect indication when the Dl-connect requests collide. Also note that no Dl-disconnect indications are issued to the network layer when the Dl-disconnect requests collide.

Figure 4.12 Collision of similar unnumbered commands

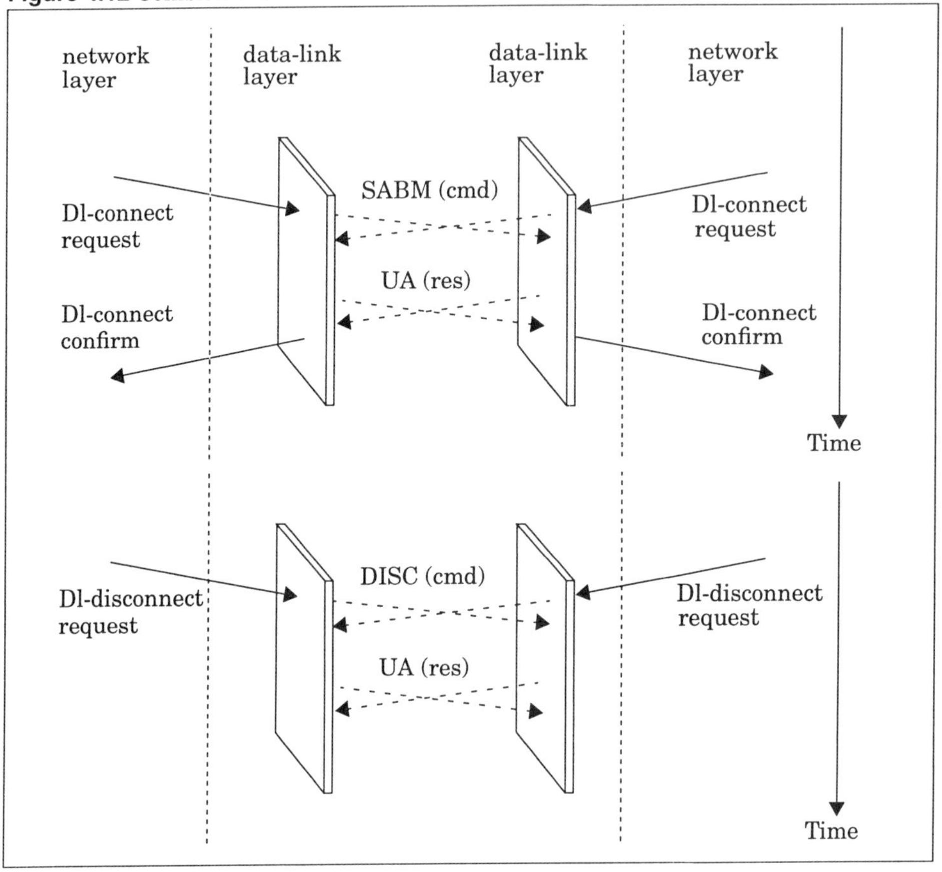

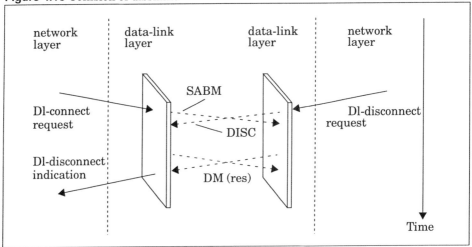

Figure 4.13 Collision of dissimilar unnumbered commands

4.14 Data Transfer

Finally, we come to the service for which we have gone to all this trouble so far: data transfer. The I-frame is used for data transfer. The information field in an I-frame is set to whatever data the service-user has provided in order to transfer it to the peer service-user. Once the data-link has been set up, the service-user can invoke any number of Dl-data request primitives to transfer data. Figure 4.14 shows a simple, unrestricted scenario for data transfer.

Figure 4.14 A simple, unrestricted data transfer

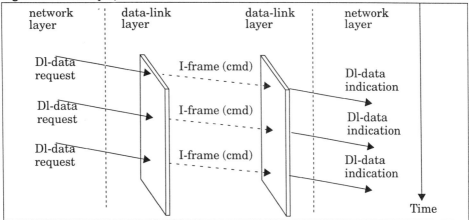

A number of potential error conditions can arise in this simple scenario. For instance, how does the sender of I-frames know whether the frames have been received and processed by the peer data-link layer. We talked about acks as a way of notifying the sender that frames have been received. Suppose we were to use the RR (Receive Ready) frame as an ack. The sender would wait for an ack for every I-frame before it transmits the next frame. Figure 4.15 shows what is called a stop-and-wait protocol.

Figure 4.15 A stop-and-wait protocol

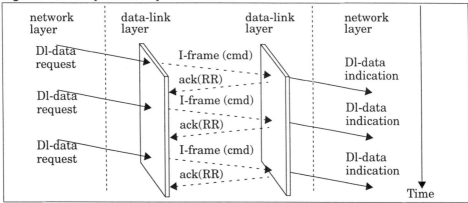

What if the acknowledgments were to be lost? Well, we know what to do about that. We start timer T1 when an I-frame is transmitted, and if an ack is not received before T1 expires, then the I-frame is retransmitted. Figure 4.16 shows such a scenario. Can you identify another potential problem with this scenario?

Figure 4.16 Retransmissions

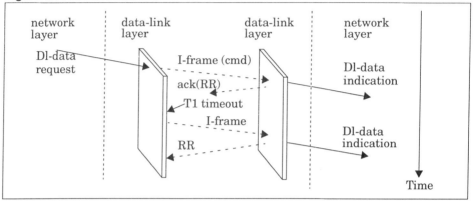

4.14.1 Sequence Numbers and State Variables

In the previous scenario, the receiver has no way of determining whether a received I-frame is a retransmission. It passes on the data contained in the I-frame to the service-user, which can be duplicate data if the I-frame is a retransmission. Obviously, we need some mechanism to uniquely identify an I-frame. What if we were to assign sequence numbers 0 and 1 to the I-frames? The transmitter starts with an I-frame with sequence number 0. Until I-frame(0) is successfully acknowledged, it keeps retransmitting it. If I-frame(0) is acknowledged, it transmits I-frame(1). The receiver keeps track of the sequence number of the I-frame to expect, and can discard duplicate I-frames. The RR frame now needs to contain the sequence number of the I-frame being acknowledged. A common method is to indicate the sequence number of the I-frame expected next. This is an implicit acknowledgment of the previous I-frame.

What we have accomplished is a one-bit sliding window protocol for data transfer. The window here refers to the set of sequence numbers that can be used to transmit I-frames without waiting for an acknowledgment. In our case, we have only one sequence number at our disposal at any given time (0 or 1), hence its called a one-bit window. The concept of sliding will become clear as we address larger windows. Figure 4.17 depicts the scenario.

Figure 4.17 A one-bit sliding window protocol

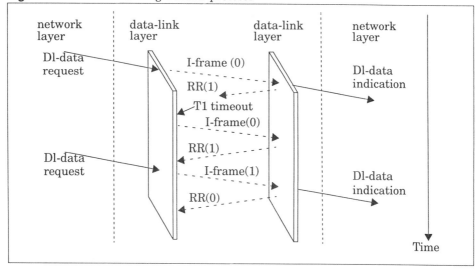

It is obvious that the data-link layer needs to maintain some information about what sequence numbers to send, or receive. ISO 7776 defines the following state variables for this purpose:

- v(s) - The send state variable. This is set to the sequence number of the next I-frame to be transmitted. This is incremented every time an I-frame is acknowledged.

- v(r) - The receive state variable. This is set to the sequence number of the next I-frame that the receiver is expecting. Whenever an I-frame is received successfully, V(r) is incremented.

Also, each I-frame that is transmitted should have a field which encodes the sequence number. Examine the control byte for an I-frame. A field n(s) is provided for the send sequence number. At the time of the transmission, it is set equal to the send state variable v(s).

The RR frame that acknowledges the I-frame should have a field which encodes information about the sequence number(s) being acknowledged. Again, examining the control byte for the RR frame, we can see that a field n(r) has been provided for the receive sequence number. At the time a RR frame is being transmitted, n(r) is set equal to v(r).

4.14.2 Flow Control Frames

Until now the receiver has always been ready to receive at least one I-frame. What if the receiver receives an I-frame, acknowledges it, but is not ready to receive another I-frame because of internal buffering constraints? Transmitting a RR would not help, since its significance (apart from acknowledgment) is that the receiver is ready to receive more I-frames. Our candidate is the

RNR (receive not ready) frame. The RNR frame indicates that the receiver is unable to receive I-frames until further notice. It also has a n(r) field to acknowledge I-frames received. Figure 4.18 depicts the scenario. Note that the receiver busy condition is cleared by transmitting a RR frame.

Figure 4.18 Receiver busy

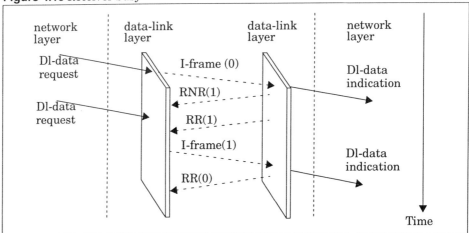

Figure 4.19 Full duplex data transfer

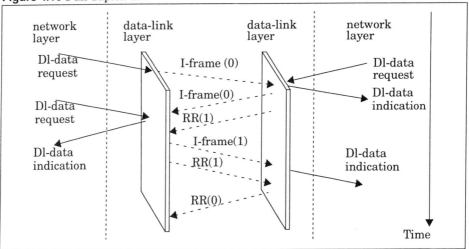

4.14.3 Full Duplex Connection

With I-frames, RR and RNR frames, sequence numbers, acknowledgments, and time-outs we have identified a fairly robust protocol for data transfer. What other issues are of concern to us now?

One issue we mentioned earlier is that both DTEs are combined stations (see Section 4.3), and hence should be capable of full duplex data transfer. Figure 4.19 shows a scenario where both DTEs are involved in transmitting Iframes. Note that sequence numbers are being used independently in each direction, and also acks are being sent in both directions.

Unfortunately, since RR frames are being used only for acknowledgment, this is a very inefficient use of the data-link bandwidth. It is possible to use Iframes themselves for acknowledgment.

4.14.4 Piggyback Acknowledgment

What if each I-frame also had a n(r) field, which could be used to acknowledgment I-frames! The control byte of the I-frame provides just that - a n(r) field. So I-frames in one direction can be used to acknowledge I-frames in the other direction. This is called piggybacking. Figure 4.20 identifies one such scenario. Each I-frame is now identified by a pair of sequence numbers - n(s), n(r). Notice the decrease in the number of frames exchanged between two DTEs to accomplish the same task as before.

Figure 4.20 Piggybacking

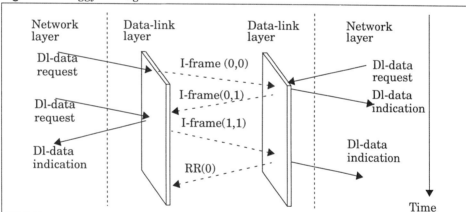

4.14.5 Sliding Window Protocols

Efficiency is still not what it can be. For every I-frame transmitted, there is one acknowledgment frame - either a RR, RNR or I-frame. It would be useful to be able to ack more than one I-frame at a time. Sliding window protocols let us transmit more I-frames before waiting for acknowledgments, thus allowing for multiple I-frames to be acknowledged with a single ack.

The one-bit sliding window protocol that we have seen is a special case of a family of protocols called sliding window protocols. With a modulo-2 window, or a window size of 1, we could have only one outstanding unacknowledged I-frame at any time. With a modulo-8 window, or a window size of 7, we can transmit up to 7 I-frames without waiting for an acknowledgment. Let us examine the modulo-8 window in detail (ISO 7776 allows for modulo-8 and modulo 128 windows; we will be using the modulo-8 window in this book).

Figure 4.21 Sliding windows

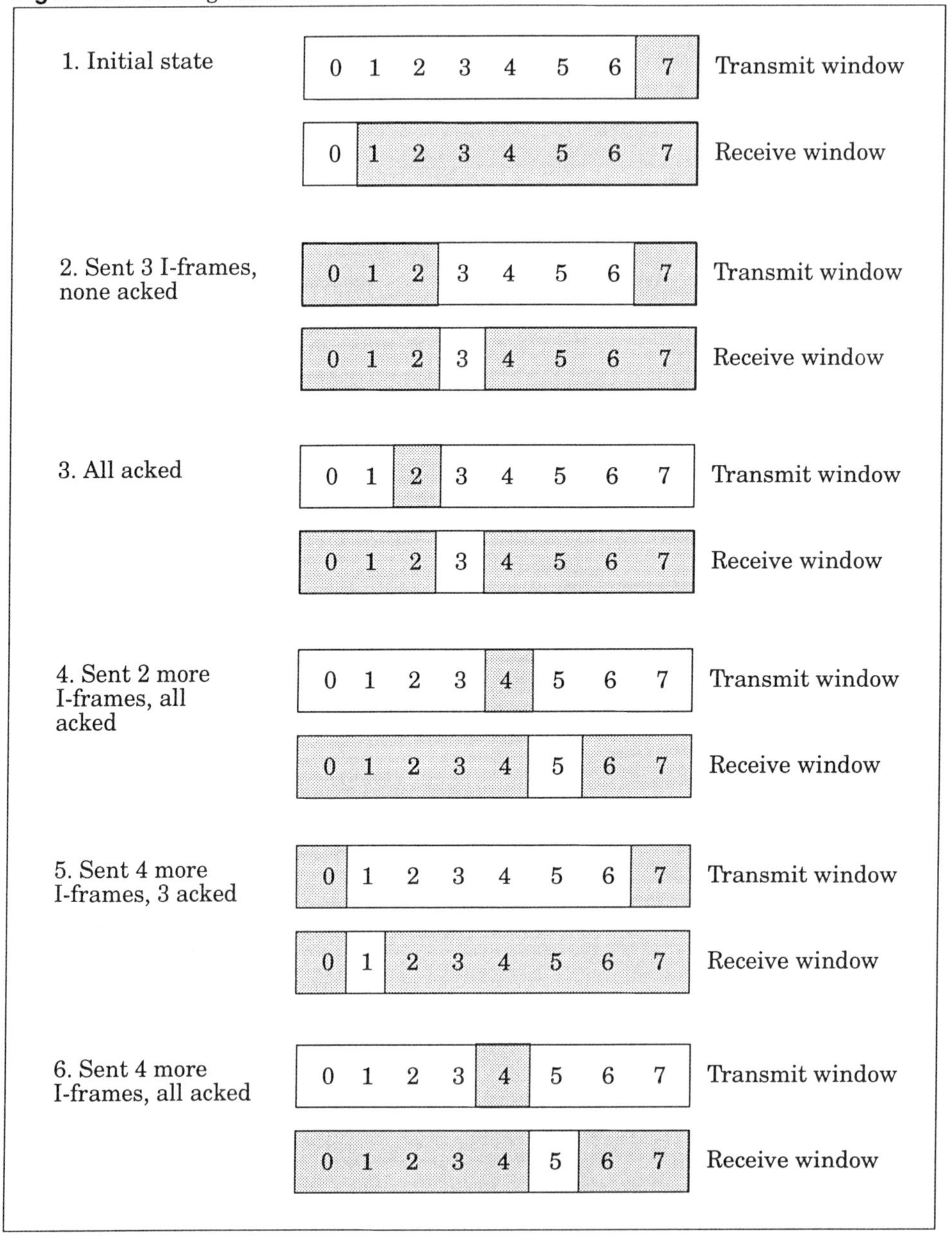

In a modulo-8 sliding window protocol Iframes can be assigned sequence numbers from 0 through 7. For the sender, the window refers to the set of sequence numbers that can be used for I-frame transmission at any given instant. This set can vary from a size of seven numbers to zero. For the receiver the window refers to the sequence number of the next I-frame to be received.

Figure 4.21 shows an example of an operation of such a protocol. The windows are organized in (transmitter, receiver) pairs. The non-grey numbers in the transmit window show the set of sequence numbers that can be used for transmission at any given instant. A full transmit window (i.e., all grey) means that the transmitter cannot transmit any more I-frames until the earlier I-frames are acknowledged.

The non-grey number in the receive window shows the expected sequence number of the next I-frame. In contrast to the transmit window, the receive window can have only one non-grey number (in ISO 7776).

Let's examine each of the states shown in the figure:

- State 1 - Initial state: Both windows are in their initial states. The transmitter can use up to 7 numbers (0,1,2,3,4,5,6) for transmitting I-frames. The receiver is expecting the first I-frame to have a sequence number of 0.

- State 2: The transmitter has transmitted 3 I-frames, and has received no acknowledgments. Its window now shows that only 4 more I-frames can be transmitted before the window is full. The receiver's window shows that the next expected I-frame should have a sequence number of 3.

- State 3: The receiver has acked all the I-frames. The receive window remains unchanged. The transmit window now shows the updated set of sequence numbers that can be used for transmitting I-frames before the window if full (3,4,5,6,7,0,1).

- State 4: The transmitter sends 2 more I-frames (3,4) and the receiver acknowledges them. The set of sequence numbers that can be used for transmission is now (5,6,7,0,1,2,3) and the receiver is expecting sequence number 5.

- State 5: The transmitter sends 4 more I-frames (5,6,7,0) and the receiver has acknowledged three (5,6,7). Even though the receiver has one un-acked frame (sequence no. 0), the sequence number for the next expected I-frame is 1. The transmitter is allowed only six numbers (1,2,3,4,5,6) since one I-frame is still un-acked.

- State 6: The transmitter sends 4 more I-frames (1,2,3,4) and all are acknowledged. The transmit window now allows the sequence numbers 5,6,7,0,1,2,3 and the receiver is expecting 5.

Note that even though the window is modulo-8, the transmitter is allowed only 7 frames that can be unacknowledged at any given time (see Exercise 1).

Since our concern has been efficiency, it is not enough to have a large window size. We have to remove the restriction that each I-frame should be acknowledged by a RR, RNR or I-frame. One such frame should be able to acknowledge multiple I-frames. Well, we already have the ability to do so. Since the $n(r)$ field informs the sender of the next sequence number expected by the receiver, it forms an implicit acknowledgment of all I-frames with sequence numbers up to $n(r)$ minus one. Thus, the receiver can wait for seven

I-frames, and then, with a single RR, acknowledge all of them. The n(r) field is three bits long.

4.14.6 Automatic Repeat Request (ARQ)

Now that we can have multiple outstanding I-frames which have not been acknowledged, we have introduced yet another problem. Consider the following sequence of I-frames that are received at one end of a data-link:

```
0,1,2,4,5,6,7
```

I-frame number 3 is missing. How do we get the transmitter to only retransmit I-frame 3? Two strategies seem possible:

- Selective Repeat ARQ: where the receiver transmits a message asking the transmitter to send I-frame 3 again.

- Go-back-N ARQ: where the receiver transmits a message acknowledging all I-frames from 0 to 2, and requests retransmissions of all I-frames from sequence number 3 onwards. The receiver discards any out-of-sequence I-frames. In our example, it discards I-frames 4,5,6 and 7.

Both schemes have their advantages and disadvantages. Selective Repeat ARQ results in lesser retransmissions, but requires that the receiver buffer out-of-sequence I-frames while it waits for the lost ones. Go-back-N ARQ results in potentially more retransmissions, but the receiver is simpler to implement. ISO 7776 uses Go-back-N ARQ.

Which brings us to the next question: which frame do we use to implement Go-back-N ARQ? The answer is the REJ (reject) frame. The n(r) field in a REJ frame implicitly acknowledges all I-frames up to n(r) minus one, and requests retransmissions of all I-frames from n(r) onwards.

4.15 Note About Supervisory Frames

Supervisory frames (RR, RNR, REJ) can be both responses and commands. The encoding of the address field determines whether a frame is a command or a response. In a command frame the p/f bit is interpreted as p (poll) bit, and in a response frame the p/f bit is treated as final (f) bit. All supervisory frames contain a n(r) field which acknowledges I-frames.

When a supervisory frame is transmitted as a response, it is used to indicate the status of the receiver. Thus, a receiver can be in a ready condition (RR), a busy condition (RNR), or ready to receive a very specific I-frame after having detected an out-of-sequence I-frame (REJ).

When a supervisory frame is transmitted as a command, it implicitly indicates the DTE's status for receiving I-frames (i.e., ready, busy, or waiting for a specific I-frame). But, since the frame is sent as a command it can be used to solicit a supervisory frame response from the peer.

4.16 Frame Reject Condition

One aspect of the protocol must be getting obvious now - most of the protocol is geared towards detecting and recovering from error conditions. What happens if error conditions are detected, but there is no way of recovering except resetting the link? In that case, a FRMR (frame reject) is used to initiate service-provider link reset when one of the following conditions occur after a valid frame is received:

■ The control field is encoded with a command or response type that is undefined, or not implemented.

■ The I-frame received has an information field that exceeds the maximum established length.

■ The n(r) value is invalid.

■ The frame received has an information field which is not permitted, or the frame received is a supervisory frame of incorrect length.

In all the above cases a FRMR is sent by the receiver which detected the error condition. When a FRMR is received by a DTE, it immediately starts a link reset procedure. The FRMR contains a three byte information field which identifies one of the above conditions. We'll be dealing with the specifics in Chapter 12.

4.17 Note About Time-Outs and Retransmissions

In Section 4.10.1, we saw the functioning of the timer T1 in the context of a link setup. The timer T1 is also used to effectively manage other procedures, even though we didn't mention it explicitly in the other scenarios we examined. Here's a list of other procedures where the timer is used (as explained in section 4.10.1):

■ Frame reject condition (while waiting for a response to a FRMR)

■ Link reset (while waiting for a response to a SABM)

■ Link disconnect (while waiting for a response to a DISC)

■ Data transfer (while waiting for a response to an I-frame)

■ Soliciting receiver status (waiting for a response to a supervisory command frame)

■ Request for retransmission (waiting for the I-frame with the correct sequence number after transmitting a REJ frame)

Once the number of retransmissions reaches the system specified limit (N2), then the data-link layer should initiate a higher level recovery according to the standard.

The higher level recovery is specific to the higher layer or service-user and we will address it in detail during the implementation.

4.18 Summary

ISO identifies data-link operation configurations as being unbalanced and balanced. In the unbalanced configuration, the data-link can operate in the *Normal Response Mode* (NRM) or the *Asynchronous Response Mode* (ARM). In the balanced configuration, the data-link is said to operate in the *Asynchronous Balanced Mode* (ABM). This book deals with the ABM mode. The set of procedures used for data-link operation in such a mode is called the *Link Access Procedure Balanced* (LAPB).

Some of the major functional areas of data-link functionality are:

- Framing

- Error-control

- Flow-control

- Connection Management

The ISO 7776 specifies the following set of messages to realize its functionality:

- SABM - Set Asynchronous Balanced Mode

- DISC - Disconnect

- UA - Unnumbered Acknowledgment

- DM - Disconnected Mode

- FRMR - Frame Reject

- RR - Receive Ready

- RNR - Receive Not Ready

- REJ - Reject

- Iframe - Information

The frames are categorized into three types:

- Unnumbered format (U) - frames without a sequence number, used for link initialization, reset, and disconnection.

- Supervisory format (S) - frames used for supervising a link during information transfer. They can be used for acknowledgments.

- Information transfer format (I) - frames used for data transfer. These frames contain sequence numbers and implicit acknowledgments.

A data-link entity requests a connection setup by transmitting a SABM frame. The peer entity transmits a UA frame to accept the connection, or a DISC frame to deny it.

The connection can be released by transmitting a DISC frame. The connection can be reset by either transmitting a SABM frame or a DM frame with the f bit set to 0.

Once the connection is setup, I-frames can be used to transmit service-user data. Acknowledgments of I-frames is performed by using the n(r) field in I-frames, or the n(r) field in supervisory frames.

The supervisory frames are used to indicate and solicit receiver status. A response supervisory frame indicates receiver status. A command supervisory frame indicates receiver status, and solicits the remote receiver status. A RR frame is used to indicate receiver ready status, a RNR frame is used to indicate a receiver busy status and a REJ frame is used to indicate that the receiver is trying to recover from an I-frame sequence error. ISO 7776 uses a modulo-8 sliding window protocol with Go-back-N ARQ for data transfer.

An error condition that cannot be recovered from results in a FRMR frame being transmitted, which eventually causes a link reset.

4.19 Exercises

1. In sliding window protocols, even though the modulo or window size is N, why is the maximum number of frames that can be outstanding (i.e., pending acknowledgment) equal to N-1? Study the problem for a modulo-8 window.

2. Is there a correlation between the retransmission strategy (i.e. selective repeat ARQ or Go-back-N ARQ) and the window size? For example, a small window size (say 8) is better suited for Go-back-N ARQ. Why?

3. In what kind of situations would a large window size (say 128) be of use? Hint - think about earth-to-satellite communications.

5

Architectural and
High-Level Design Overview

5.1 Introduction

The previous chapters examined concepts relevant to this book, and gave us a general idea of the system we are going to implement. In this chapter we will study the architecture of the system, i.e., the way in which parts or constituents are related in an organized whole, and we will also get an overview of the high-level design for the implementation. Issues of concern would be identifying the objectives of the system, major functional blocks, and the platform and trade-offs of the implementation.

5.2 Objectives

First and foremost, our objective is to learn about protocols, layers and interfaces. The approach will be to implement an entire layer. We know by now that we are going to implement the ISO 7776 data link layer protocol [5]. This particular protocol has been chosen for the following reasons:

- The ISO 7776 is a popular standard and it (or related protocols like LAPB or HDLC) is used extensively in the data communications industry.

- The protocol is small enough to be implemented as an exercise, but is sophisticated enough to explain some of the major concepts in protocols.

Any layer(N) we implement will need the services of a layer(N-1). By choosing to implement a data-link layer, we only need the services of an underlying physical layer. A physical layer is easily simulated, since it has the simplest interface of any of the layers.

Also, in order to use the data-link layer we need a data-link layer user (layer(N+1)) which will invoke the data-link layer primitives. We also need to provide a simple user-interface which will enable us to use the data-link layer.

Given the above elements, here's what we need to accomplish with our implementation:

- Understand how a layer is implemented, i.e., how does a layer provide services, how is a service primitive implemented.

- Understand how layers communicate with each other, i.e., how are service primitives invoked, and how data is exchanged between layers.

- Understand how a protocol is implemented.

- Understand how the service definition of a layer translates to the services provided by a protocol.

- Understand how system parameters of a protocol (e.g., the value of timer T1) affect the functioning of the protocol.

Figure 5.1 Example system architecture

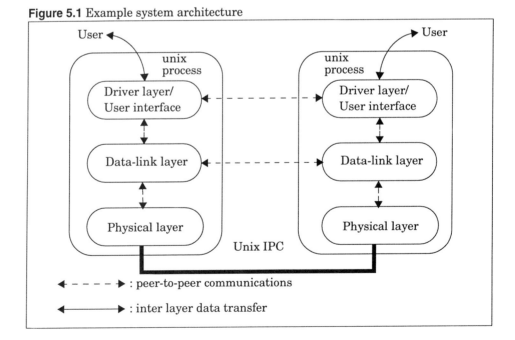

5.3 Architecture

Figure 5.1 identifies the major functional blocks in our implementation. The solid lines show the path of actual data transfer-inter-layer, and between the two physical layers. The dotted lines represent logical peer-to-peer communications.

5.3.1 Unix Processes

One of the first questions that comes to mind when we attempt to implement layers is - how do layers relate to the operating system environment in which they are executing? To bring the question closer to home, what is a layer in the context of a Unix Operating System?

When we execute programs in Unix, they run as Unix processes. Each process has the ability to communicate with other processes via various mechanisms grouped under the acronym IPC (inter-process communications). One way in which a layer could be implemented is as a stand-alone program, i.e., each layer executes as a separate process. This means that all inter-layer data transfer would use IPC.

Another approach would be to write a layer as a set of functions (a library in C), or as a C++ class library. A few such layers could be used in a single program to realize a part of, or, the entire, OSI stack. In such a case, the layers would be compiled into a single program, and would run as one process. Inter layer data transfer in such cases would translate to function calls, or invoking member functions on layer objects.

We will adopt the latter approach for our implementation. Since we are dealing with a point-to-point link between two DTEs, each DTE will be represented by a single Unix process. Each such process will contain three layers - the driver layer/user interface, the data-link layer, and the physical layer. Each of these layers will be a single C++ object, but more on that later. All inter-layer data transfer will be accomplished by invoking member functions on the layer objects. The processes will communicate via IPC.

5.3.2 Physical Layer

In a real-world implementation, the physical layer would use the services of communications hardware to accomplish data transfer. In our environment, the physical layer will use IPC to simulate a physical channel. The only data transfer between processes occurs when the physical layer in one process exchanges data with the physical layer in another process.

5.3.3 Data-link Layer

The data-link layer uses the services of the underlying physical layer to exchange data with the peer data-link layer in another process.

5.3.4 Driver Layer/User Interface

In order to use the services provided by the data-link layer, we need a data-link layer user. We will implement a driver layer which will act as a data-link service user. Our driver layer will also function as a menu-driven user interface allowing the user to invoke data-link layer primitives and initiate communication between the two processes. The driver will provide a layer interface to allow the data-link layer to invoke primitives like Dl connect-indication, Dl-data transfer, etc. These are actually data-link service primitives, but have a direction of service-provider to service-user. The terms driver layer and user interface will be used interchangeably for this functional block, depending upon the context of the discussion.

Figure 5.2 Message flow among layers

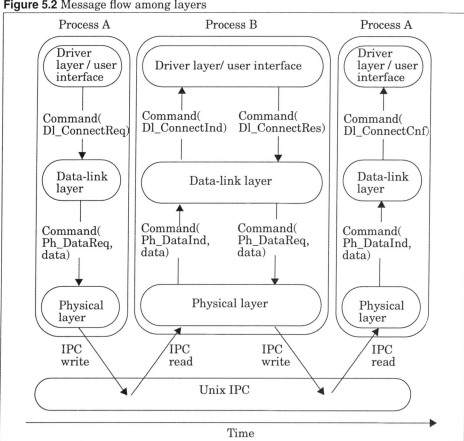

5.3.5 Message Flow Scenarios

Figure 5.2 shows an example of how layers and processes communicate when a data-link connection is being set up. The driver layer invokes the

Dl_ConnectReq primitive on the data-link layer using the `Command()` member function. The data-link layer, in turn, formats a message to be sent to the peer data-link layer, and invokes the Ph_DataReq primitive on the physical layer. In this case the `Command()` member function is also passed the data to be transferred (the data contains a SABM frame). The physical layer performs a `write()` on IPC to transfer data to the physical layer in the other process.

The peer physical layer is notified of data waiting to be read from IPC (we will discuss the notification in later chapters). It performs an IPC `read()`, figures out that the message is for the data-link layer, and invokes the Ph_DataInd primitive on the data-link layer, passing it the received data. The data-link layer examines the data, and invokes a Dl_ConnectInd primitive on the driver layer.

The driver layer accepts the connection request by invoking a Dl_ConnectRes primitive on the data-link layer, which in turn translates to a Ph_DataReq, as the data-link layer communicates with its peer. The flow of primitives is completed on the other side of the physical channel starting with an IPC `read()`, a Ph_DataInd, and a Dl_ConnectCnf.

Figure 5.2 shows two processes communicating. Note that Process A is split into two parts just for illustration.

5.4 Verifying Protocol Operation

One of our most important objectives is to verify the operation of the protocol that we will implement. Since most of the procedures in a protocol are designed to handle error conditions, our implementation should be capable of inducing errors if we are to successfully test our protocol.

Figure 5.3 Points of interception of messages

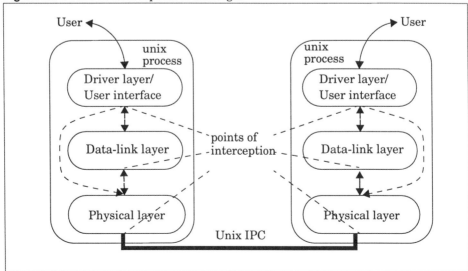

Chapter 3 introduced the interface to a layer, in which the layer could be blocked from transmitting (i.e., a message would be discarded just prior to transmission), or from receiving (i.e., a received message would be discarded). Figure 5.3 shows the multiple points of interception in our implementation, which will allow us to discard messages. We can use this mechanism to effectively induce error conditions, which will cause the protocol to initiate recovery mechanisms.

Discarding messages is not sufficient to simulate other error conditions. We also need the ability to send messages to each data-link layer independent of the peer layer. This can be accomplished by having mechanisms in each user interface which will directly access the physical layer interface to send invalid (or valid) data-link messages to its peer. We can use this mechanism to set a given DTE in a certain state, and then test the protocol operation by sending all possible data-link messages from the user interface in the peer DTE. It should be pointed out very emphatically that such mechanisms would not be available in real implementations. Specifically, a layer(N+1) would never have access to the interface of layer(N-1). This would violate the integrity of layers. We are doing this only because our implementation is a learning tool.

5.5 Implementation Trade-offs

The main objective being learning, the implementation is focused on simplicity. Sophisticated solutions, whether in the design or implementation, have been avoided in favor of keeping the code simple to understand. We will be trading off performance, small code size, etc., in order to achieve our objective. As such we will not be doing any performance analysis to calculate the throughput of our system.

Another aspect of implementation trade-offs concerns the data-link protocol procedures which have not been implemented mainly because the value they add towards learning is not worth the effort. Here's a list (Refer to the ISO 7776 standard [5]).

■ Transparency - Since we are not really working with a bit-oriented physical channel there is no need to perform bit-stuffing and bit-stripping in order to achieve transparency. (See Chapter 4.) In any case, the real world mostly utilizes hardware solutions to achieve transparency.

■ Hardware-related procedures like frame abortion, interframe time fill, and monitoring of data-link channel states will not be implemented.

■ Timers T2 and T3 will not be implemented. T3 is related to data-link channel states, and T2 is the amount of time available at the DTE/DCE before acknowledgment must be initiated. T2 is not a widely implemented timer even in real-world implementations.

5.6 High-Level Design Overview

This section provides an overview of the various modules which will be implemented. The details are left to the chapters dealing with the individual modules. We present a brief analysis of the modules, for the most part in the order in which they will be implemented.

5.6.1 Debugging and Tracing

For protocol verification we will need some kind of tool which will allow us to print information about messages being received and transmitted, the state of the data-link, the trace of the function calls being made, and other diagnostic messages. A debugging and tracing module will accomplish this task.

5.6.2 Lists

When the driver layer is requesting the data-link layer to transmit data, the data-link might have to queue up the data in its buffers, while it tries to accomplish error-free data transfer. We will need a list module which will support creation, deletion and manipulation of lists of data.

5.7 Asynchronous Programming

We have two independent processes acting as DTEs and communicating with each other, and users interacting with each DTE. Each process has to be ready to receive input either from the IPC mechanism, or the user, and ideally it should not be blocking on either. A common framework can be developed to deal with the asynchronous programming in such an environment. Chapter 7 will be devoted to developing such a module.

5.7.1 Physical Layer

The physical layer module will contain the implementation to interact with the Unix IPC. It should be capable of receiving asynchronous notification from the operating system when any messages are waiting for it on the IPC channel, and it should be capable of sending messages on the IPC channel.

5.7.2 Data-link Layer

The data-link layer will contain the implementation of the protocol, as well as the functionality to provide services to the network layer. The data-link layer will have modules for implementing the data-link protocol state machine, sliding window protocols, and data framing.

5.7.3 Driver Layer / User Interface

The driver layer provides an interface so that the data-link layer primitives which have direction from service-provider to service-user can be invoked. These primitives include:

- Dl_ConnectInd

- Dl_ConnectCnf

- Dl_DataInd

- Dl_ResetInd

- Dl_ResetCnf

- Dl_DisconnectInd

The user interface provides a simple menu driven interface. The following functions need to be accomplished by the user interface in order to fully test the implementation.

- Control printing of diagnostic information

- Directly access the physical layer primitives

- Block and unblock the transmitting and receiving in layers

- Modify data-link layer system parameters (N2 and T1)

- Invoke data-link service primitives

- Bypass the data-link layer and send data-link layer messages directly to the physical layer

5.8 Platform/Compatibility

The source code used in this book was written on a Sun Sparcstation 1+, running SunOS Release 4.1.2. The compiler used was the standard C++ compiler provided with the SunOS. The software was also tested on a 486 PC, running Linux. The compiler used was the GNU C++ complier - g++. This code should work on most Unix offerings, since the system calls used are amongst the most widely available. Any C++ compiler should suffice, since the code avoids using any compiler specific features, and particularly avoids new features of C++ which might not be widely available.

5.9 Summary

The system's main objective is to serve as a learning tool, and hence the architecture is geared towards making this possible. The system consists of two processes, each of which represents a DTE, communicating with each other over Unix IPC. Each process consists of a physical layer, a data-link layer, and a driver layer/user interface.

The high-level design overview identified the following modules:

- Debugging and tracing
- List module
- Asynchronous programming module
- Physical layer
- Data-link layer
- Driver layer / user interface

Subsequent chapters will deal with each of these modules in detail.

5.10 Exercises

1. Design some exercises for this chapter.

2. Solve the exercises designed above.

2

THE FRAMEWORK

Have you ever wondered why being called "spineless" is such an affront to human beings? My theory is that it implies the lack of a backbone, which, to us vertebrates, is a slap on our evolutionary pedigree. Just to preempt such slander, we will go about our task by first developing a backbone. And the backbone, in our case, is a set of classes which will form the framework for further development.

The framework is developed over the next three chapters. In Chapter 6 we will develop a trace utility to facilitate debugging, a list class which allows us to implement stacks and queues, and a generic data packet class useful for inter-layer exchange of information.

Chapter 7 addresses the issue of asynchronous programming, input sources, timers and scheduling. Chapter 8 is devoted to explaining the role of finite state machines (FSMs) in data communication systems, and provides an in-depth look at traditional and object-oriented methods of implementing FSMs.

6

Generic Utilities

6.1 Debugging and Tracing

A stitch in time saves nine. This old adage could not be more relevant than in software development. For those of us who have been working in a reasonably well-structured software development environment, it is familiar news that the cost of fixing a bug during development is approximately one-tenth the cost of fixing it once the software is in the field. Managers love to use this analogy to coerce software engineers to be more careful. Unfortunately, it's not just a managerial gimmick (though God knows there are many!). To aid us in developing robust software, the first utility we'll develop in this chapter will address the issue of debugging and tracing program flow. Tracing will enable us to print diagnostic information for protocol verification.

6.1.1 On/Off Tracing

A lot of debugging is traditionally done by inserting print statements to monitor program flow, and to print values of variables that are being affected by the program. One problem with using traditional *printf* statements is that they are compiled into the program. Once a certain section of code has been debugged it does not need those print statements. Unfortunately, in order to stop the printing they have to be edited out of the program, resulting in a recompile.

Ideally, we would like to insert print statements in our program which can be dynamically turned on or off. The statements would put forth the required information only if the printing is turned on. Once the code has been debugged, we should be able to turn the printing off, which would have the same effect as removing the print statements, i.e., no information is printed out.

```
For example:

printf("Testing Trace Utility\n");

Could be replaced by:

TRACE("Testing Trace Utility\n");
```

The output of the TRACE statement would be identical to that of the printf statement if tracing was turned on, otherwise there would be no output. The task of keeping track of the tracing status (on or off) could be entrusted to an object (think objects!). A preliminary examination of the object, or its class, leads us to the interface shown in Figure 6.1. The arrows indicate the various methods that can be invoked on the object. We can invoke methods on the trace object to turn the tracing on or off, and printing the debugging (or tracing) information. We will examine the exact nature of the TRACE statement later in the chapter.

Figure 6.1 A preliminary trace object

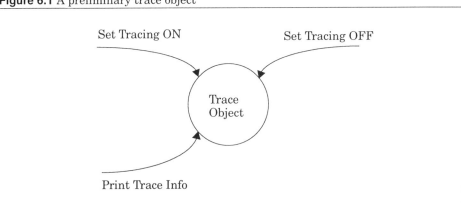

6.1.2 Tracing Levels

Another feature of debugging is that it usually proceeds in stages. Consider a function that has been written and debugged. After debugging, we would want to turn off the tracing for that function. Now, if a new piece of code is added to the same function, we might like to turn on the tracing for the new code, without turning it on for the already debugged code. To support this, a notion of levels in tracing is needed.

For example, consider the following TRACE statements:

```
void TestFunction() {

    TRACE(1,("Entering TestFunction\n"));
    TRACE(2,("Added new code here!\n"));
    TRACE(1,("Exiting TestFunction\n"));
}
```

If the tracing level was set to 1, all statements would print out their respective information. If the tracing level was set to 2, only the second TRACE statement would print out information. If the tracing level was set to 3, or any value greater that 2, no output would be generated by either statement.

Notice we have introduced an additional argument to the TRACE statement - the level of the TRACE statement. Now, the printing of debugging information is controlled both by the level at which the tracing is desired, and the status (on/off) of the tracing. Figure 6.2 now shows the necessary interface for a *trace* object. Of course, the SetTracingON and SetTraceLevel methods could be combined into a single method.

Figure 6.2 The trace object with tracing levels

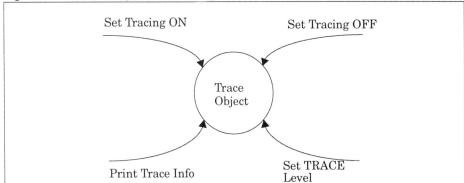

6.1.3 Module-Specific Tracing

Let us throw in another requirement - we need to be able to perform tracing on modules of our program independently of each other. Modules can be thought of as code in different source files. Consider the following statements:

```
// File test.C
void TestFunction()
{
```

```
        TRACE(testModule,1,("Entering TestFunction\n"));
        TRACE(testModule,1,("Exiting TestFunction\n"));
}

// File example.C

void ExampleFunction()
{
    TRACE(exampleModule,1,("Entering ExampleFunction\n"));
    TRACE(exampleModule,1,("Exiting ExampleFunction\n"));
}
```

By assigning each TRACE statement a module name (*testModule*, or *exampleModule* in this case), we have, presumably, provided the flexibility of manipulating the tracing status (on/off) and tracing level of each module independent of the other.

Again, the tracing status of each module can now be maintained by a unique instance of the TRACE object.

The need for such flexibility arises because software is usually developed in modules, and debugging of modules proceeds independently. For example, we might be writing software for a state machine module and a list service module. This approach allows us to trace the execution of the state machine module independent of the list service module, and vice versa.

Note that a third argument has been added to the TRACE statement - the module identifier.

6.1.4 Formatted Trace Statements

Earlier in our discussion we remarked that during debugging it is useful to be able to print out values of variables being used in the program. So, as a final requirement to our trace utility, we need to be able to print variable values much in the same manner that a `printf` statement prints out information depending upon a format string.

For example, consider the following code fragment:

```
int i = 5;
char *test = "Testing".

TRACE(testModule,1,("i = %d, test = %s\n",i,test));
```

The trace statement should be able to print out the following, provided the trace for *testModule* is turned on at a level less than or equal to 1:

```
testModule:: i = 5, test = Testing
```

Note that the name of the module is now printed before the statement in order to identify the module.

What is the *trace* class? How is a module defined? What does the TRACE statement do? The following sections discuss these issues.

6.1.5 Module Design

From our requirements analysis so far it is certain that we need a `trace` class - instances of which will control tracing for different modules. Since these `trace` objects need to be accessed at run-time, and their attributes modified, we need another class - `traceManager`. An instance of the `traceManager` class would keep track of all `trace` objects and provide access to them.

The attributes and behavior for the `trace` class can be derived from the following requirements:

- Attributes to store the name of a module, the tracing level and the tracing status (on/off)

- Methods to modify the attribute values, and access the attribute values

- Method to print tracing information

The attributes and behavior for the `traceManager` class would be:

- Attribute to keep track of all `trace` objects

- Method to add a new `trace` object

- Method to access any given `trace` object

The relationship between these classes is simple - they "use" each other, and there are no hierarchies in this design.

6.1.6 Class trace

Here's a declaration for the `trace` class.

```
class trace {

public:

    trace(const char *name);
    ~trace(void);
    Boolean IsModuleOn(void);
    int    Level(void);
    const char *Name(void);
    void SetTrace(int level);
    void ResetTrace(void);
    static void PrintTraceInfo(const char *,...);
    void PrintModuleName(void);

private:
```

```
int   _level;
Boolean _on;
char * _name;

};
```

The constructor initializes the private data members. The tracing is turned off (_on = FALSE) and the level is set to zero. Ignore the call to `traceManager::AddModule()` for now. We'll deal with it soon.

```
trace::trace(const char *name):
    _on(FALSE),
    _level(0),
    _name(0)
{
    _name = new char[strlen(name)+1];
    strcpy(_name,(char *)name);
    traceManager::AddModule(this);
}
```

The accessor methods `IsModuleOn()`, `Level()`, and `Name()` allow us to access the internal state variables of the trace object.

```
void
trace::PrintModuleName(void)
{
    fprintf(stderr,"%s::",_name);
}

Boolean
trace::IsModuleOn(void)
{
    return _on;
}

int
trace::Level(void)
{
    return _level;
}
```

`SetTrace()` turns the tracing on at a given level. `ResetTrace()` turns the trace off, and resets the level to 0. `PrintModuleName()` prints out the module name. `PrintTraceInfo()` takes a format string, and a variable number of arguments, and prints out a string in the same manner a printf statement does. Notice that `PrintTraceInfo()` is declared to be static. It does not pertain to any one instance of the trace class.

```
void
trace::SetTrace(int level)
{
    _on = TRUE;
    _level = level;
}

void
trace::ResetTrace(void)
{
    _level = 0;
    _on = FALSE;
}

void
trace::PrintTraceInfo(const char * format, ...)
{
#ifndef NTRACE

    char  buf[500];

    va_list pvar;
    va_start(pvar, format);
    vsprintf(buf,(char *)format,pvar);
    fprintf(stderr,"%s",buf);
    va_end(pvar);

    cerr << flush;

#endif
}
```

6.1.7 Declaring and Defining "trace" Objects

We have a *trace* class and we now need to instantiate a *trace* object for every module. Also, if a module is distributed over more than one source file, we need to be able to access the *trace* object for that module in all the source files. The macros DECLARE_TRACE_MODULE and DEFINE_TRACE_MODULE provide convenient ways of achieving the objectives.

```
#define DECLARE_TRACE_MODULE(module) \
    extern trace module;

#define DEFINE_TRACE_MODULE(module,name) \
    trace module(name);
```

If a module is restricted to only one source (.C) file, then only the macro DEFINE_TRACE_MODULE needs to be used to create a trace object for that module. If a module spans many source files, then the DECLARE_TRACE_MODULE

macro should be used in all the source files except one, in which the
DEFINE_TRACE_MODULE macro should be used.

6.1.8 Macro TRACE

Finally, we come to a definition of the TRACE statement. We analyzed earlier
that it should take a module identifier, a level, and a formatted string followed
by a variable number of arguments. The module identifier is obviously the
module we defined using the DEFINE_TRACE_MODULE macro, which also happens to be an instance of the trace class. Here's a definition of the TRACE
macro.

```
#ifdef NTRACE
#define TRACE(module,level,args)
#else

#define TRACE(module,level,args)              \
    if (module.IsModuleOn() == TRUE &&        \
        level >= module.Level())              \
    {                                         \
        module.PrintModuleName();             \
        (module.PrintTraceInfo args);         \
    }
#endif
```

Thus, the TRACE macro checks to see if the tracing for the module is on or off,
checks to see if the level of the TRACE statement is greater than or equal to the
trace level of the module, and, if all the conditions are met, it invokes methods
on the trace object to print the name, and the formatted string with its variable number of arguments.

What could be the use of the #ifdef NTRACE condition? A #ifndef also
appeared earlier in the PrintTraceInfo() method of the trace class. One
of the irritants about using printf() statements in our code for debugging
was that the source code would have to be edited to remove them after the
debugging was finished. We can edit out our debugging/tracing statements by
using -DNTRACE flag at compile time.

Well, now we can proceed to pepper our code with TRACE statements, knowing very well that they can always be turned off or even compiled out of existence! Here's an example of a TRACE statements for a module spread over two
source files.

```
// Header file test.h

#include "trace.h"// Contains trace module classes
DECLARE_TRACE_MODULE(testModule); // Defines testModule as extern
// Source file test.C
#include "test.h"
```

```
// Define a TRACE module called testModule. This is done
// in only one source file.

DEFINE_TRACE_MODULE(testModule,"testModule");

void test()
{
    TRACE(testModule,1,("Entering test()\n"));
    TRACE(testModule,2,("I love tracing \n"));
    TRACE(testModule,1,("Exiting test() \n"));
}

// Source file - newTest.C

// We will use the testModule trace object defined in test.h

#include "test.h"

// Note that we don't have to define the trace module again.
// We just use the extern declaration in test.h

void newTest()
{
    TRACE(testModule,1,("Entering newTest()\n"));
    TRACE(testModule,2,("Trace away! \n"));
    TRACE(testModule,1,("Exiting newTest() \n"));

}
```

6.1.9 Class traceManager

We have one more item to design - remember we have to be able to turn on/off and set levels on trace objects at run-time. That means we need some kind of storage from where all the trace objects can be accessed, and their attributes modified.

```
// File trace.h

const int MaxModules = 64;

class traceManager {

 public:

    static void AddModule(trace *module);
    static void PrintModules();
    static trace *GetModule(int index);

 private:
```

```
        static int _index;
        static trace *_modules[MaxModules];
};


// File trace.C

#include "trace.h"

int traceManager::_index  = 0;
trace *traceManager::_modules[MaxModules]  = {0};

/*
 * Function : AddModule
 *
 * Description : Adds a new trace object to the array
 * of pointers in the traceManager
 */

void
traceManager::AddModule(trace *module)
{

    if ( _index < MaxModules )
        _modules[_index++] = module;
}

/*
 * Function : PrintModules
 *
 * Description : For each module registered with the
 * traceManager, this function prints out the name
 * of the module, followed by the index of the module
 * into the array of trace object pointers.
 */

void
traceManager::PrintModules()
{
    for(int i = 0; i < _index; i++ )
        cout << _modules[i]->Name() << "(" << i << ")\n";

    cout << flush;
}

/*
 * Function : GetModule
 *
 * Description : Given an index, the function returns
 * a pointer to the trace object.
 */
```

```
trace *
traceManager::GetModule(int index)
{
    if ( index >= 0 && index < _index )
        return _modules[index];
    else
        return 0;
}

/*
 * Function : trace::trace
 *
 * Description : Constructor- initializes private data, adds
 * itself to the traceManager
 */

trace::trace(const char *name):
    _on(FALSE),
    _level(0),
    _name(0)
{
    _name = new char[strlen(name)+1];
    strcpy(_name,(char *)name);
    traceManager::AddModule(this);
}
```

Notice that all the member functions and data members of the traceManager are static. They might as well have been global functions and data. Enclosing them within a class gives them a home, and respectability. And, of course, no one can directly access the data members.

The private variable _modules is an array of pointers to trace objects, and is initialized to zero. Variable _index is also initialized to zero. Revisiting the constructor for the trace class, we note that the object adds itself to the traceManager by calling traceManager::AddModule(). Thus, whenever the macro DEFINE_TRACE_MODULE is encountered, a trace object is created, and it is added to the list maintained by the traceManager.

PrintModules() will print out information about all the modules, and their indices into the _modules array. For example, calling PrintModules() could generate this output:

```
phlayerModule::(0)
dllayerModule::(1)
nwlayerModule::(2)
phlayerModule::(3)
layerModule::(4)
```

If we wanted to get a handle on the trace object for the phlayerModule, we can invoke traceManager::GetModule() with the index of the module.

Here's an example of how the `traceManager` can be used to modify trace objects at run-time:

```
int moduleNumber, level;

// Print out information about all the modules
traceManager::PrintModules();

// Ask the user what unit needs to be modified.
// PrintModules provided an index value for each unit.
// Select one.

cout << "Type Module Number:";
cin >> moduleNumber;

// Get the trace object associated with
// the user inputted index

trace *module = traceManager::GetModule(moduleNumber);
if ( module == 0 ) return;

// Get user input on what level to set the tracing to.

cout << "Type Level :";
cin >> level;

// Set the tracing to ON at the user defined level.
module->SetTrace(level);
```

The above code fragment could be used in a user-interface, allowing us to set the tracing to any desired level, for any module that has a `trace` object associated with it. Of course, we should modify the above code to allow us to turn the tracing off (remember, that is why we started on this rigmarole in the first place!). Files `trace.h` and `trace.C` contain the entire source for the tracing and debugging utility.

6.2 Lists, Stacks and Queues

Lists, stacks and queues are probably among the most often used data structures in any data communications program. It is worthwhile to investigate them, and develop a class for representing them.[*]

The design of the list class in this section is based on the design and code by Shapiro [6] and is discussed in this chapter in a manner consistent with the presentation in this book.

*Portions of Section 6.2 are derived from J.S. Shapiro, *A C++ Toolkit*, (c) 1991.
Reprinted by permission of Prentice-Hall, Englewood Cliffs, NJ 07632.

Figure 6.3 Lists, list members and data

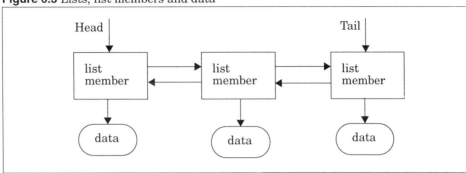

Figure 6.3 provides a pictorial representation of a list data structure. The list shown is a data structure which maintains a pointer to the first element in the list, the Head, and a pointer to the last element in the list, the Tail. Each element in the list is a list member. Each list member maintains a pointer to the next list member in the list, and a pointer to the previous list member in the list.

Also, each list member has a pointer to some data, which is why we need the list in the first place - to have a list of some data. The list is a doubly-linked list, which allows us to traverse the list in either direction, i.e., from Head to Tail, or vice-versa.

Note that the data is distinct from the list member. The list member has the pointers necessary to traverse the list, and to access the data. The data, on the other hand, has no knowledge of the list. This will allow us to manipulate the list without regard to what data is being stored. Implementing a list member in this fashion would mean an extra indirection would be necessary to access the data. Ideally, we would like the data to be a list member, with the next and previous pointers being an integral part of the data. In an object-oriented design, we can combine the two approaches by making the list member a base class. Any class which needs to be part of a list would have to inherit from the base class `listMember`.

6.2.1 List Module Design

We need two classes to implement the list module:

■ The `list` class - which models the data structure discussed above.

■ The `listMember` class - instances of which will be members of a list. Any class whose instances need to be part of a list will need to inherit from the `listMember` class.

The `listMember` class needs the following attributes and behavior:

■ A pointer to the next member

■ A pointer to the previous member

- Methods to access the pointers

The `list` class needs the following attributes and behavior:

- A pointer to the head of the list, which is a `listMember`

- A pointer to the tail of the list, which is also a `listMember`

- Methods to Append, Prepend, and Remove `listMember` objects from the list

- Methods to access the head and tail of the list

The design is simple enough that we don't need to worry about inheritance.

6.2.2 Class listMember

Here's a look at the `listMember` class.

```
class listMember {
    friend class list;
    int    _marked;

 protected:

    listMember *_next;
    listMember *_prev;

 public:
    listMember()
        { _next = _prev = 0; _marked = 0; }

    virtual ~listMember();
    listMember *Next()
        { return _next; }

    listMember *Prev()
        { return _prev; }

    int IsMarked()
        { return _marked; }

    void SetMarked()
        { _marked = 1; }
};
```

Notice that the `listMember` class provides no functionality to manipulate the list, i.e., it cannot insert, remove or rearrange itself in a list. This will enable us to implement a generic list class which can manipulate `listMember` objects as a list, stack or queue. Ignore the `_marked` attribute and the `SetMarked()` method for now. We'll see the use for them soon.

6.2.3 Class list

```
class list {
 protected:
    listMember *_head;
    listMember *_tail;

 public:

    list()
        { _head = _tail = 0; }

    virtual ~list() {};

    listMember *Head()
        { return _head; }
    listMember *Tail()
    { return _tail; }

    list& Append(listMember *);
    list& Prepend(listMember *);
    list& Remove(listMember *);
    list& CleanUpMarked();
    int     Length();

    listMember *GetNthMember(int n);

    list& Push(listMember *l)
        { return Append(l); }

    listMember *Pop()
        {   listMember *l = _tail;
            Remove(_tail);
            return l;
        }

    listMember *Top()
        { return _tail; }
};
```

Now, an instance of the list class will allow us to `Append()` a `listMember` object to the list, `Prepend()` a `listMember` object to the list, and `Remove()` a `listMember` object from the list.

```
/*
 * Function : Append
 *
 * Description : Appends a listMember object to the list.
 */
```

```
list&
list::Append(listMember *l)
{
    if (_tail) {
        _tail->_next = l;
        l->_prev = _tail;
    }
    else
        _head = l;

    _tail = l;

    return *this;
}

/*
 * Function : Prepend
 *
 * Description : Prepends a listMember object to the list.
 */

list&
list::Prepend(listMember *l)
{
    if (_head) {
        _head->_prev = l;
        l->_next = _head;
    }
    else
        _tail = l;

    _head = l;

    return *this;
}


/*
 * Function : Remove
 *
 * Description : Removes a listMember object from the list.
 * Rearranges pointers.
 */

list&
list::Remove(listMember *l)
{
    if (l == _head)
        _head = _head->_next;
```

```
      if ( l == _tail)
         _tail = _tail->_prev;

      if (l->_next)
         l->_next->_prev = l->_prev;

      if (l->_prev )
         l->_prev->_next = l->_next;

      l->_next =0;
      l->_prev = 0;

      return *this;
}
```

The Head() and Tail() methods access the head and tail of the list. Given a number n, method GetNthMember() returns a pointer to the nth listMember object in the list. The destructor, in this case, does not have to do anything, because the list does not create listMember objects, it merely manipulates them.

There are some mysterious methods and data in the listMember class - _marked, IsMarked(), SetMarked(), along with a seemingly related CleanUpMarked() method in the list class. Marked explanations are in order. Consider the following scenario:

```
list *testList;
listMember *lm = testList->Head();

int i = 0;
while (lm != 0 ) {

    if ( i%2 == 0 ) { // look for an even number
       testList->Remove(lm);
       delete lm; // Delete the list member
    }

    lm = lm->Next(); // Get the next item in the list
    i++;
}
```

The above fragment of code deletes even numbered items from the list. Can you see a fatal bug?

After deleting an even-numbered listMember, we are trying to access the next listMember. But the pointer to the next (odd) listMember could possibly be mangled because we are accessing a deleted listMember. This could possibly result in a crash! Unfortunately, we will be required to do such operations in our implementation. One solution is to mark the item to be deleted, and clean up after the entire list has been traversed.

```
// First traverse the list, and mark items to be deleted

while ( lm != 0 ) {
    if ( i%2 == 0 ) {
        lm->SetMarked();
    }
    lm = lm->Next();
    i++;
}


// Now remove the marked listMember objects from the list,
// and delete them.

testList->CleanUpMarked();
```

The method CleanUpMarked() traverses the list again, and removes the marked listMember objects, and also deletes them. The above example is a simplistic one. Usually some operations would be performed on each list-Member object during the first traversal.

```
/*
 * Function : CleanUpMarked
 *
 * Description : This function runs through the list
 * and removes any listMember objects which have been
 * marked for removal.
 */

list&
list::CleanUpMarked()
{
    listMember *lm;

    lm = _head;

    while ( lm != 0 ) {

        if ( lm->IsMarked() == 0 ) {
            lm = lm->_next;
            continue;
        }
        if ( lm == _head )
            _head = lm->_next;

        if ( lm == _tail )
            _tail = lm->_prev;

        if ( lm->_prev )
            lm->_prev->_next = lm->_next;
```

```
              if ( lm->_next )
                  lm->_next->_prev = lm->_prev;

              listMember *tmp = lm->_next;
              delete lm;
              lm = tmp;
          }
          return *this;
      }
```

6.2.4 Queues and Stacks

Both queues and stacks are lists. The queue is a first-in first-out list (FIFO), and the stack is a first-in last-out list (FILO). Shapiro [6] suggests ways of looking at the list, in order to turn it into a stack, or a queue.

- When you add an object to a stack, you want it to be the next object returned from the stack.

- When you add an object to a queue, you want it to be the last object returned from the queue.

Gavin[15] suggested the following down-to-earth analogies:

- A queue is like a supermarket line - obviously the first in line is first served, and hence first out.

- A stack is like a hay stack - the last piece of hay put on to the stack will be the first piece taken off.

Let's examine a stack first. We know a stack traditionally provides Push() and Pop() methods. Pushing an object onto a stack is identical to appending the object to the list. Popping an object from the stack is identical to removing and returning the head of the list.

The list class can be used as a queue by providing a way of accessing the top most element of the queue. Here's an enhanced list class (only the additional interface is shown):

```
class list {
// ...
public:
    list& Push(listMember *l)
        { return Append(l); }

    listMember *Pop()
        {   listMember *l = _tail;
            Remove(_tail);
            return l;
        }
```

```
listMember *Top()
    { return _tail; }

};
```

6.2.5 Storing Data

Now that we have the basic classes we need, it's time to examine how we can store data. We mentioned earlier that ideally the data should also be a list member. In OOP we can accomplish this by having the data class inherit from the listMember class.

Here's an example of a coordinate class, which is used in a list:

```
.class coordinate : public listMember {
    int x;
    int y;
};
```

Now instances of the coordinate class can be manipulated by the list class, thus allowing us to have a list of coordinates.

6.2.6 Inheritance and Type Safety

Suppose we have a class called dataPacket and we have to manipulate lists of dataPacket objects. According to our previous discussion, we will have to make dataPacket inherit from listMember. The following code illustrates how the list module can be used to manipulate lists of dataPacket objects.

```
// file main.C

#include <stream.h>
#include <list.h>
class dataPacket : public listMember {
 public:
    dataPacket(int len) : _len(len) {}
    int Length() { return _len; }
 private:
    int _len;
};

main(int argc, char *argv[])
{
    list dataPacketList;    // This is the list object.
    dataPacket *dp1, *dp2; // Pointers to dataPacket objects.

    dp1 = new dataPacket(20);// Data packet instance
    dp2 = new dataPacket(25);// Data packet instance
```

```
        cout << "Length of list :" <<
            dataPacketList.Length() << "\n";

        dataPacketList.Push(dp1);
        dataPacketList.Push(dp2);

        cout << "Length of list :" <<
            dataPacketList.Length() << "\n";
    }
```

The output of the above code would be:

```
Length of list: 0
Length of list: 2
```

So far, so good. What if we have to pop items off the list and perform operations on the dataPacket objects?

Pop() returns a pointer to a listMember object. We will have to cast a listMember object to a dataPacket object. This, at best, is a dangerous activity.

Here's an example piece of code that will work:

```
dataPacket *dp1 = new dataPacket(35);
dataPacketList.Push(dp1);

listMember *obj = dataPacketList.Pop();
dataPacket *dp = (dataPacket *) obj;

cout << "Length of data packet : " <<
        dp->Length() << "\n";
```

The following code, though it compiles and links, will, at best, have undefined behavior; at worst, it will cause a crash!

```
// First create a dataPacket object, and push it on
// to the list.

dataPacket *dp1 = new dataPacket(43);
dataPacketList.Push(dp1);

// Next, create a listMember object, and push it on
// to the list. This will work since Push accepts a
// listMember pointer.

listMember *lm = new listMember;
dataPacketList.Push(lm); // pushing a listMember

// Now, if we assume all items in the list are dataPacket
// objects since the list is called a dataPacketList, we
```

```
// are in trouble.

obj = dataPacketList.Pop(); // popping a listMember

// now, we cast obj to a dataPacket! How are we
// to know - the list is called a dataPacketList!!

dp = (dataPacket *) obj;

// And we call Length() on an object which is not
// really a dataPacket!

cout << "Length of data packet : " <<
    dp->Length() << "\n";
```

The above code fragment illustrates the kind of problem that can arise because we are bypassing the safety of type-checking that C++ is good enough to provide.

One way to overcome this is to be able to have `list` classes, and `listMember` classes which are specific to the type we desire. Something like:

```
class dataPacketList {
public:
    dataPacketMember *Pop();
    //....
};
```

Unfortunately, this entails writing entire class definitions and declarations for each class which needs to be in a list!

Fortunately, C++ provides a new language features called "template" which allows us to write generic class descriptions, and the language will take care of the rest. Unfortunately, "templates" are not universally available yet. Fortunately, we can simulate templates.

6.2.7 Simulating Templates

Using Shapiro's [6] design, we'll define two macros - `DefineListMember` and `DefineList` - to provide a solution.

```
/*
 * Macro : DefineListMember
 *
 * Description : This macro defines a type-safe sub-class
 * of the listMember class.
 */

#define DefineListMember(TYPE)                          \
                                                        \
```

```
class name2(TYPE,Member) : public listMember {   \
 public:                                          \
    name2(TYPE,Member) () : listMember() {}       \
    virtual ~name2(TYPE,Member) () {}             \
                                                  \
    TYPE *Next() {return (TYPE *)_next;}          \
    TYPE *Prev() {return (TYPE *)_prev;}          \
};
```

name2() is a macro that is provided in the generic.h header file. The macro takes two arguments and concatenates them to form one identifier.

```
name2(one,two)
```

evaluates to:

```
onetwo
```

Thus, if we wanted a dataPacket to be a list member, we would use the DefineListMember macro as follows:

```
DefineListMember(dataPacket);
```

```
// this now defines a class dataPacketMember which is
// now ready to be a part of a type safe list.
```

The actual class dataPacket, instead of inheriting from listMember, would now inherit from dataPacketMember.

But, we still need a type safe list class. A similar macro, DefineList, does the trick for us.

```
/*
 * Macro : DefineList
 *
 * Description : This macro defines a type-safe sub-class
 * of the list class.
 */
```

```
#define DefineList(TYPE)                        \
                                                \
class name2(TYPE,List) : public list {          \
 public:                                        \
    name2(TYPE,List) () : list() {}             \
    virtual ~name2(TYPE,List) () {}             \
                                                \
    TYPE *Tail()                                \
        {return (TYPE *) _tail; }               \
    TYPE *Head()                                \
        {return (TYPE *) _head;}                \
```

```
      TYPE *Pop()                                    \
          { return (TYPE *)list::Pop(); }            \
      TYPE *Top()                                    \
          { return (TYPE *) _tail; }                 \
      TYPE *GetNthMember(int n)              \
          { return (TYPE *)list::GetNthMember(n); }        \
      name2(TYPE,List)& Append(name2(TYPE,Member) *l) \
          {                                          \
              list::Append(l);                       \
              return *this;                          \
          }                                          \
      name2(TYPE,List)& Prepend(name2(TYPE,Member) *l)\
          {                                          \
              list::Prepend(l);                      \
              return *this;                          \
          }                                          \
      name2(TYPE,List)& Remove(name2(TYPE,Member) *l) \
          {                                          \
              list::Remove(l);               '       \
              return *this;                          \
          }                                          \
      name2(TYPE,List)& Push(name2(TYPE,Member) *l)   \
          {                                          \
              list::Push(l);                         \
              return *this;                          \
          }                                          \
  };
```

This allows us to do the following:

```
class dataPacket;              // Forward declaration
DefineListMember(dataPacket);  // Define a type-safe list member
DefineList(dataPacket);        // Define a type-safe list

class dataPacket : public dataPacketMember {
 // ..
};

dataPacketList dpList;

dataPacket *dp = new dataPacket;

dpList.Push(dp); // This is all right!
```

Now try pushing a non dataPacketMember into a dataPacketList.

```
listMember *lmp = new listMember;

dpList.Push(lmp); // Compile Time Error!
```

Here's what my compiler screams:

"error: no standard conversion of listMember * to dataPacketMember *".

Well, with the help of a generic list class, and a couple of macros, we are now capable of creating a list, queue or stack of any type of object. And type-safe too! Files `list.h` and `list.C` contain the entire source for the list module.

6.3 Inter-layer Data Transfer

Figure 6.4 Inter-layer data transfer

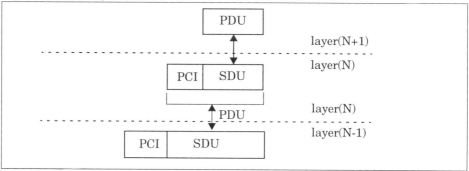

Figure 6.4 refreshes our memory about how data is exchanged between layers. It's time to concentrate on the implementation.

We can have a straightforward, but inefficient, implementation, where each layer copies data from the layer above or below into its own buffers, modifies it, and either uses it or passes it on.

What if the layers were to exchange data in the form of objects, say `data-Packet` objects? We can develop a complex, but efficient mechanism with the following properties:

- A `dataPacket` is an object which makes its way up or down a stack

- It is created once in a layer which first needs it

- It is destructed only when there is no more use for it

- Each layer modifies the data packet as appropriate, uses it, or passes it on

- The implementation minimizes allocation and freeing of buffers

As a first cut, the `dataPacket` class should provide methods to:

- Create a `dataPacket` object with some data (constructor)

- Prepend data to a `dataPacket` (e.g., the data-link layer prepends a header flag, a control byte and an address byte to the network layer data).

- Append data to a `dataPacket` (e.g., the data-link layer appends the FCS and a trailing flag to the network layer data)

- Pre-strip data from a `dataPacket` (e.g., the data-link layer needs to strip the header flag, control byte, and address byte from the PDU, before passing on the data to the network layer)

- Post-strip data from a `dataPacket` (e.g., the data-link layer needs to strip the FCS and the trailing flag from the PDU, before passing on the data to the network layer)

What about the data structure inside a `dataPacket` object which minimizes allocation, and freeing of memory? A linear buffer of a certain maximum possible size can be allocated upfront in a `dataPacket`. Figure 6.5 shows how such a buffer functions. The `dataPacket` has pointers to the allocated buffer, the head and the tail. The first data is inserted in the middle of the buffer. The head and tail pointers are moved around as data is appended, prepended, pre-stripped, or post-stripped. If we allocate enough memory to begin with, subsequent operations on the buffer will only require realigning the pointers. When will we need to allocate more memory?

Figure 6.5 Buffer operation

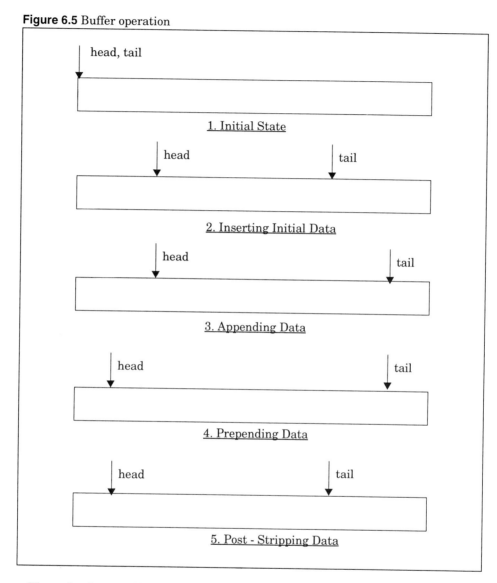

The only time we'll need to allocate more memory is when the head and tail pointers overrun the beginning or end of the buffer, respectively. We will not worry about this in our implementation. In real-world implementations the strategy used is to always allocate large enough buffers to begin with (e.g., over ethernet, a buffer size of 1516 bytes will suffice, over FDDI, a buffer size of 4096 bytes will be enough). This is not a memory efficient mechanism but works well under Unix, which has very few memory constraints.

6.3.1 Additional dataPacket Properties

Knowing what we do about the dataPacket, let us enumerate its properties in greater detail.

- Any one layer will first create a dataPacket object.

- No layer can destroy a dataPacket object (why?)

- This dataPacket object will be passed on to an adjacent layer.

- Any layer might wish to keep the dataPacket object for further use (example - retransmissions).

- If a layer wishes to maintain the dataPacket for its use, it should Register its interest with the dataPacket object.

- When a layer no longer needs the dataPacket object, it should Deregister its interest with the dataPacket object.

- The dataPacket object keeps track of how many layers (or users) are interested in it. When the last layer expresses that it needs to Deregister, then the dataPacket object deletes itself.

- No one layer can call the destructor, because other layers might be using the same dataPacket object. Hence, we need a private destructor.

6.3.2 Class dataPacket

Here's a C++ declaration of the dataPacket class. Notice that we are using the macros defined in the list module for defining a dataPacketMember class. Since a dataPacket object is an ideal candidate for being in a list somewhere, we make sure that it inherits the listMember functionality.

```
// File : dataPacket.h

class dataPacket;
/*
 * Use macros to create type safe listMember and list
 * classes.
 */

DefineListMember(dataPacket);
DefineList(dataPacket);

/*
 * Class : dataPacket
 *
 * Description : The dataPacket class provides an
 * implementation of a buffer. Functions to
 * Append, Prepend, PreStrip and PostStrip are provided.
```

```
 * The dataPacket keeps track of how many clients are
 * using it. When the last client has deregistered, the
 * dataPacket deletes itself.
 *
 * Attributes:
 * unsigned char *_buf : Pointer to allocated buffer.
 * unsigned char *_head : The head of the circular buffer.
 * unsigned char *_tail : The tail of the circular buffer.
 * int _count : The number of users of this dataPacket.
 */

class dataPacket : public dataPacketMember {

public:

    dataPacket();
    dataPacket(const unsigned char *data, int len);

    Boolean  Prepend(const unsigned char *data, int len);
    Boolean  Append(const unsigned char *data, int len);
    Boolean  PreStrip(int len);
    Boolean  PostStrip(int len);

    int    Length() const { return (_tail - _head ); }
    const unsigned char *GetData() const { return _head; }

    void  Register();
    void  Deregister();
    void  Print();

protected:

    unsigned char *_buf;
    unsigned char *_head;
    unsigned char *_tail;
    int    _count;

private:
    ~dataPacket();
    Boolean  InsertNewData(const unsigned char *data,
            int len);
};
```

Most of the methods are self-explanatory. Notice the two different types of constructors. The default constructor allocates some default buffer space, and initializes the pointers. The second constructor inserts data into the buffer, and initializes the pointers.

The Register() method increments the _count data member. Deregister() has to do a bit more work.

```
void
dataPacket::Deregister()
{
    _count--;

    if (  _count <= 0 )
        delete this; // Only way a dataPacket can be deleted!
}
```

The implementation of the dataPacket class can be found in files data-Packet.h and dataPacket.C. While the actual implementation is tedious, the manipulation of pointers is simple, and can be easily understood by examining the code. It was the interface that needed to be understood, and we have done that.

6.4 Summary

6.4.1 Class Developed

- trace and traceManager

- listMember and list

- dataPacket

The trace module is a utility which provides dynamic control for printing diagnostic information in a program (referred to as tracing in this book). The printing of information can be controlled by:

- Setting the tracing on or off.

- Dividing up a program into various modules, where the tracing for each module can be performed independently of other modules.

- Dividing up the tracing within a module into levels, so that various levels can be turned on or off.

The trace class provides the functionality for controlling the tracing for each module. One trace instance exists for each module. The traceManager class provides a way of managing all the trace objects in a system. It allows the user to access trace objects, and modify their attributes in order to affect the tracing status of a given module. Macros, DECLARE_TRACE_MODULE and DEFINE_TRACE_MODULE, can be used to declare and define trace instances for different modules.

The list module provides classes and macros which support creating of type-safe lists of objects. The basic classes are:

- The listMember class - Which is the base class from which all classes that have to be in list will have to inherit. Each listMember instance has pointers to next and prev listMember instances. The instance itself has no knowledge of a list. This allows for a generic `list` class which can manipulate `listMember` instances.

■ The `list` class - Which provides the functionality for manipulating `listMember` instances. Functionality includes being able to append, prepend, remove, push, and pop `listMember` instances.

These base classes in themselves are not type-safe. Macros `DefineListMember` and `DefineList` provide support for creating type-safe lists of any given class.

The `dataPacket` class provides support for inter-layer data transfer. It allows for an efficient exchange of data between layers by using a linear buffer which is pre-allocated to a pre-determined maximum length. Adding and removing data from the buffer involves only manipulation of pointers. The `dataPacket` class provides methods to prepend, append, pre-strip and post-strip data from the buffer.

6.4.2 Source Files

■ trace.h and trace.C

■ list.h and list.C

■ dataPacket.h and dataPacket.C

6.5 Exercises

1. Examine the differences between using templates and using macros to provide type safety in the list module. Would there be a reason for preferring one over the other?

2. Even though we created a stack by providing methods to pop and push `listMember` objects, the stack's integrity can be easily violated. How can this happen? Do we need a separate stack class to preserve its integrity?

3. Augment the `dataPacket` class to handle situations that can occur when the head and tail pointers overrun the buffer and more memory needs to be allocated.

4. Implement the `dataPacket` class using a circular buffer instead of a linear buffer. What advantages does a circular buffer provide over the linear buffer?

5. The register/deregister mechanism for the dataPacket class is not foolproof. What problems can you identify with the mechanism? Provide a more robust solution.

7

Asynchronous Programming

7.1 Introduction

One of the road blocks I encountered while working on my first data communications software project was the lack of an adequate and consistent programming paradigm. I was writing the X.25 data link layer for a hardware platform that supported X.21 (the physical layer standard for X.25). The software I had designed was essentially synchronous in nature. In our context, synchronous software would be a piece of software which, conceptually, never relinquishes control from the moment it is invoked, to the moment it terminates.

Of course, the hardware was intended to communicate with remote equipment, and this inherently introduced a delay between the time a command was issued on one end of the communication channel, and the time an eventual response was transmitted back from the remote end of the channel. So, as part of the data link layer implementation, software had to be written which could account for this delay, or, to use more appropriate terminology - asynchronous system behavior.

Thus, unintentionally, I had complicated my software implementation, by designing for both modes of behavior - synchronous and asynchronous - in the same piece of software.

It is said, "One who doesn't learn from history is condemned to repeat it". To avoid similar mistakes, we will examine and understand the domain in which we are going to develop our software, and identify the mode of programming that best meets our needs.

In this chapter, we'll examine asynchronous behavior in data communications systems. We will also study the nature of asynchronous systems themselves, and set about the task of identifying and developing a set of classes that will allow us to program for asynchronous behavior.

First, let's examine synchronous and asynchronous behavior in software systems. (To avoid any confusion it should be mentioned that we are not discussing asynchronous or synchronous communications.)

7.1.1 Synchronous Programming

Consider a small program that takes in user input, processes it, and produces an output. If we were to program the system in a synchronous fashion, we would implement a program loop that:

- Reads in user input

- Processes user input

- Produces the necessary output

Figure 7.1 Synchronous program loop

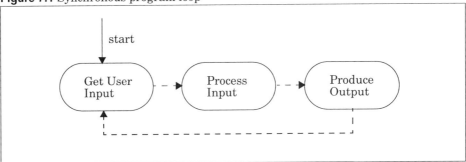

Figure 7.1 depicts such a system. The module *Get User Input* will block on input from an user, i.e., it will wait indefinitely till the user provides input. Once the user provides input, it is processed, and an output is produced. The system then goes back to waiting for user input. The entire software, thus, proceeds in a synchronous fashion. The dotted line shows the thread of execution in the program.

Even though the nature of user input is asynchronous, the programming is done as if the whole process were synchronous. Does this create problems? No, not in this particular case. But, consider the case when the program might need to process two users, each providing input from independent sources.

Figure 7.2 Multi-user input

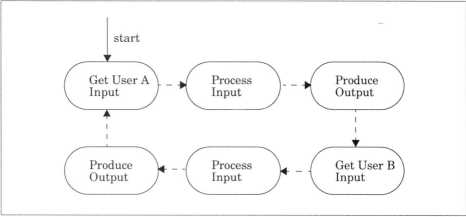

Figure 7.2 shows the case when we have to program for processing input from two users - A and B. Essentially, we have modified the loop to process input from User A first, and then input from User B. Again, if this is the behavior we desire, it is perfectly okay to program in this manner. But, more often than not, this is not all that we require of our software systems. Can you identify any potential issues, or problems that can arise in our particular example?

- Who has higher priority - User A or User B?

- What if User A never responds?

- Can input from User A preempt input from User B?

- What if we need to add more users?

All these are pertinent questions, and they are very difficult to provide solutions for in our example. The difficulty arises primarily because we have chosen to model our system as if it were synchronous, whereas, the system is essentially asynchronous. Let us modify our model to incorporate the nature of the environment in which the system is performing.

7.2 Asynchronous Programming

Consider a system which is functionally identical to the synchronous system, but is designed such that the program does not wait indefinitely for user input. The following would be considerations in designing such a system:

- Respond to user input as and when it occurs.

- Have a main program loop that is waiting for user input to occur, but it is not waiting exclusively for any specific user to input data.

- Provide a module that processes user input.

- Provide a mechanism for the main program loop to notify the input-processing module whenever user input occurs.

Figure 7.3 An asynchronous model

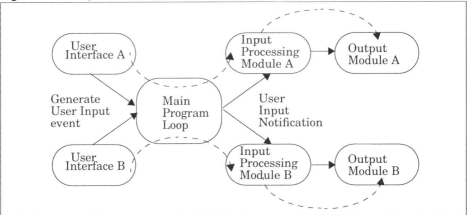

Figure 7.3 depicts an asynchronous system. The main loop is responsible for receiving user input events from the user interfaces, and notifying the appropriate module which needs to process that event.

The system is called asynchronous because there are multiple threads of execution (shown by the dotted lines) in the program. The main loop will respond to any user input, as and when it occurs, and notify the appropriate input processing module. The system is designed around the asynchronous nature of user input.

Notice that if one user never responds, the system is still available to process the other user.

The other concerns we had about priority, preemption and adding more users are still valid, but they are easier to solve in our current system. The main program loop can now be solely responsible for scheduling, which incorporates the concepts of priority, and preemption. It can be designed in a modular fashion, so that adding additional users does not change the main program loop. Adding additional users might merely be a matter of duplicating the user interface module, and the input processing module.

7.2.1 Elements of Asynchronous Programming

By examining the previous example, we should be able to identify the basic elements of asynchronous programming:

- The main loop - usually called *main event loop*, since it is receiving and dispatching events. This module also performs the function of a scheduler.

- The module which generates events for the main loop, or notifies the main loop, in some manner, of events. In our example, the events of interest would be keyboard input. Usually, this module is tightly coupled to the operating system environment. The main event loop uses the services provided by the OS to find out about events that might have occurred.

- The module which receives notification from the main event loop about events that have occurred. The notification is termed a *callback*. This module can be called an *Event Handler* (analogous to the input processing module in the previous example).

- A mechanism to let the main event loop know of all events that it needs to monitor. Thus each *Event Handler* should be able to notify the main event loop about the event it represents.

Figure 7.4 shows the model for asynchronous programming.

Figure 7.4 Model for asynchronous programming

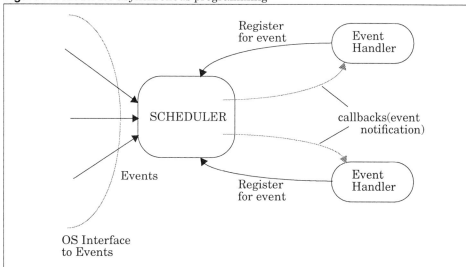

7.2.2 Data Communications and Asynchronous Systems

Since we are going to implement a data communications system, it is important that we understand its essential nature. Consider a protocol suite like OSI stack. On the bottom of the stack is the *physical layer* which is responsible for the actual data transmission, and on the top is some *application layer* protocol which interacts with the user.

The physical layer on one host computer transmits data to the peer layer on the other end of the communication link. After transmitting data, a physical layer should be in a position to receive commands from either the data link layer above it, or data from the peer layer. It cannot service one entity to the exclusion of the other. The physical layer is essentially functioning in an asynchronous mode. (Again, please note that we are not discussing asynchronous communication in the physical layer.)

The same is true of the application layer. After accepting commands from the user, the application layer passes information down to the *presentation layer* in order to pass the information to its peer. Once the application layer has serviced a certain user command, it should be capable of receiving additional commands from the user, and/or receive responses from its peer, via the layer below. This again entails that the layer function in an asynchronous manner.

Figure 7.5 Asynchronous behavior in layers

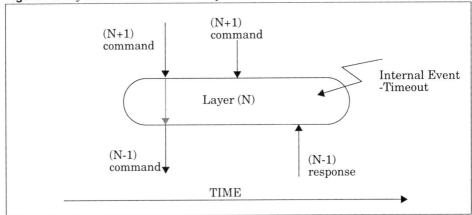

Figure 7.5 illustrates that the behavior can be generalized for any layer. Any given layer N should be capable of receiving commands/responses from the layer above and layer below at any given time. It should not, as far as possible, be devoted to exclusively servicing any one layer. All layers should also be able to handle timers. We recognize this as asynchronous behavior, and it seems prudent to develop our programming paradigm which will allow us to handle this requirement gracefully.

7.3 Asynchronous Framework Design

This section will concentrate on designing a set of classes which will form the framework for our asynchronous model of programming. Any design we arrive at will have to account for the specific environment in which we are going to program. A domain-analysis is in order at this point.

7.3.1 Domain Analysis

Figure 5.1 (see Chapter 5) shows our analysis of the problem with reference to the environment in which we are going to work. What are the asynchronous aspects of this system?

- The interaction with the user. In Unix, this can be viewed as input on the STDIN file descriptor.

- The incoming messages on the Unix IPC mechanism we choose to use. Again, in Unix, this can be viewed as input on a file descriptor.

- Timeout of the timer T1 in the data-link protocol

Earlier we noted that the scheduler is notified of events by mechanisms provided by the operating system, or environment. Unix provides a convenient system call which allows us to monitor inputs on files, and implement timers.

```
// The select system call
select(int width, fd_set *read_fds,
fd_set *write_fds, fd_set *except_fds,
    struct timeval *timeout);
```

The `select` system call will allow us to specify what file descriptors we are interested in, what kind of activity on each descriptor we want to monitor (read, write etc.), and how long it should wait for the desired activity. The first argument `width` allows us to specify the number of file descriptors we want to monitor.

The last argument `timeout` is a pointer to a timeval structure which allows us to specify how long `select` should wait.

```
struct timeval {
    long tv_sec; // seconds
    longtv_usec;// microseconds
};
```

Passing a NULL pointer as a value for the `timeout` argument causes `select` to wait forever. Passing a pointer to a valid timeval structure with both seconds and microseconds set to zero causes the `select` to check for activity on the specified files and return immediately. Any other value in the timeval structure will cause `select` to return either after waiting for activity until the specified amount of time, or when any file descriptor is ready for input, whichever is earlier.

The arguments `read_fds`, `write_fds` and `except_fds` are pointers to descriptor sets. These sets allow us to specify which file descriptors we are interested in for reading, writing and exception conditions. These descriptor sets are stored in an `fd_set` data type. We don't need to know what the `fd_set` data type is all about. Macros are available which allow us to manipulate it. Here's some example code demonstrating their use.

```
fd_set rset;
int fd;

// Macro to zero out the data structure

FD_ZERO(&rset);

// Macro to set a bit in rset for the descriptor fd. Used
```

```
// before calling select to inform select that we are interested
// in the file descriptor fd.

FD_SET(fd,&rset);

// Select returns with the descriptor sets
// containing information about files that are
// ready for reading, writing etc. We can check
// for a specific file descriptor using Macro FD_ISSET

if (FD_ISSET(fd,&rset))
{

    // Activity on fd. Data to be read.

}
```

Since we are going to be concerned only with input on files, we have sufficient information to use the `select` call. How about implementing timers? We can use `select` to help us with timers. Suppose we had three timers running which needed to timeout in 3, 4 and 9 seconds respectively. Obviously, we cannot wait for input on files indefinitely. `Select` should return within 3 seconds, in order for us to process the first timer. After processing the 3 second timer, the two timers left will have to timeout in 1 and 6 seconds respectively. `Select` will now have to return in a maximum of 1 second, allowing us to process the second timer. This can go on as long as there are timers that need to be processed. Of course, if any input arrived in the first one second, `select` would return, but none of our timers would have timed out. We would still have 2, 3 and 8 seconds left on the timers. So the next call to `select` should wait only for 2 seconds before returning, allowing us to process the first timer.

We have identified a suitable interface with the operating system which will notify us of input on files, and allow us to determine when a certain amount of time has elapsed. The next step will be to start designing classes which use this, and aid us in asynchronous programming.

7.3.2 Identifying Classes, Attributes and Behavior

From our knowledge of the problem domain, and the desired solution, the following classes are good candidates:

- `scheduler` - Implements the main event loop, using the select call.

- `inputHandler` - Process input on files.

- `timerHandler` - Processes a timeout.

The `scheduler` needs the following attributes:

- A list of `inputHandler` objects.

- A list of `timerHandler` objects.

The scheduler's lists will be empty when it is created. We have to provide mechanisms for `timerHandler` and `inputHandler` objects to notify the `scheduler` of their existence. This leads to:

- Method to add an `inputHandler` to the scheduler's list

- Method to add a `timerHandler` to the scheduler's list

It seems logical that each `inputHandler` object should keep information about which file it is monitoring. The `scheduler` should be able to query each `inputHandler` object in its list, pass it a `fd_set` structure, and ask it to specify its file descriptor.

Each `timerHandler` object should keep information about when it is going to timeout. The `scheduler` should be able to query each `timerHandler` object in its list, and find out how much time needs to elapse before it times out. The `scheduler` will then have to wait for the amount of time required for the smallest timer.

Finally, when the select system call returns, the `scheduler` has one of two options when it comes to input on files:

- It can check the fd_set data structure to determine which file descriptor is ready for input and notify the `inputHandler` object responsible for that file.

- It can pass the fd_set data structure to each `inputHandler` object in its list, and let the `inputHandler` figure out if input on its file is ready. We choose to implement this option.

Similarly, when it comes to time-outs, the `scheduler` has a few options:

- It can query each `timerHandler` object in its list to find out when its going to time out, and check that time against the current time. If the timer has expired, it can notify the `timerHandler` object.

- Or, it can pass the current time to each `timerHandler` object and let it figure out if the timer has expired. We choose to implement this option.

All this leads us to the following methods:

- `SetInput()` for `inputHandler`. This method takes a pointer to a `fd_set` structure, and sets the bit which represents its file descriptor.

- `SetTimeout()` for `timerHandler`. This method takes a pointer to a timeval structure and sets it to the time remaining for the timer to elapse.

- `InputReadyCallback()` for `inputHandler`. This method processes input.

- `CheckInput()` for `inputHandler`. This method takes a pointer to a `fd_set` structure returned by select, and checks to see if input is ready on its file descriptor. It calls `InputReadyCallback` to process any input.

- `TimeoutCallback()` for `timerHandler`. This method processes a time-out.

- `CheckTimeout()` for `timerHandler`. This method examines the current time passed to it in a timeval structure, and checks if it has timed out. If it has timed out, it calls `TimeoutCallback`.

Here's a first cut at the class declarations:

```
class scheduler {
 public:

    void Run(); // Invoking this starts the main loop!

    AddInputHandler(inputHandler *ihdl);
    DeleteInputHandler(inputHandler *ihdl);

    AddTimerHandler(timerHandler *thdl);
    DeleteTimerHandler(timerHandler *thdl);

 private:

    inputHandlerList  *_inputHandlerList;
    timerHandlerList  *_timerHandlerList;

};

class inputHandler {
 public:
   virtual void InputReadyCallback();
   void SetInput(fd_set *rfds);
   void CheckInput(fd_set *rfds);

 private:
   int _fd; // the file descriptor
};

class timerHandler {
 public:
   virtual void TimerReadyCallback();
   void SetTimeout(timeval *timeout);
   void CheckTimeout(timeval *curtime);

 private:
   timeval _nextto; // time at which the timer expires
};
```

7.3.3 Generalizing the Solution

Our scheduler is very specific! It knows only about `inputHandler` and `tim-`

erHandler objects. What if we had to extend the scheduler to incorporate outputHandler and exceptionHandler objects? We cannot do that without modifying the scheduler. It seems appropriate to design a generic scheduler at this stage, in order to account for future changes.

First things first. Instead of maintaining individual lists of inputHandlers, timerHandlers, etc., in the scheduler, let us maintain a list of objects called eventHandlers. The scheduler does not need to know what kind of event each object represents. All it needs is two generic methods that it can invoke on each eventHandler object:

■ SetEvent()- to let the scheduler know if the eventHandler is interested in any file descriptor, or if it needs to timeout.

■ CheckEvent()- the scheduler will call this method to allow the eventHandler to check for activity on its file descriptor, or process a timeout.

Also, we need:

■ EventCallback()- to be called when there is any activity to process on a file descriptor, or in the case of a timeout.

Here's a class declaration for an eventHandler:

```
/*
 * First - create type-safe lists of eventHandler objects
 */

class eventHandler;
DefineListMember(eventHandler); //define eventHandlerMember class
DefineList(eventHandler);

/*
 * Class : eventHandler
 *
 * Description : This class is the base class for all types
 * of event handlers. Sub-classes inheriting from
 * eventHandler will provide special functionality for
 * handling input, timers etc.
 */

class eventHandler : public eventHandlerMember {

public:

    eventHandler();
    virtual ~eventHandler();

    virtual void EventCallback();
```

```
virtual void SetEvent(fd_set *readfds,
    fd_set *writefds, fd_set *exceptfds,
    struct timeval *timeout) = 0;

virtual void CheckEvent(fd_set *readfds,
    fd_set *writefds, fd_set *exceptfds,
    struct timeval *curtime) = 0;
};
```

Note that SetEvent() and CheckEvent() are generic enough to handle read, write, and exception file descriptor sets, and also a timeval structure for time-outs. The eventHandler class will have to be subclassed to provide specific functionality. An inputHandler subclass would only be looking at the readfds argument, while a timerHandler subclass would only be interested in the timeout argument. Each subclass will also redefine EventCallback(), which will provide the processing necessary for the particular event that occurred. Figure 7.6 shows the new class hierarchy and relationships between the classes.

Figure 7.6 Class hierarchy and relationships

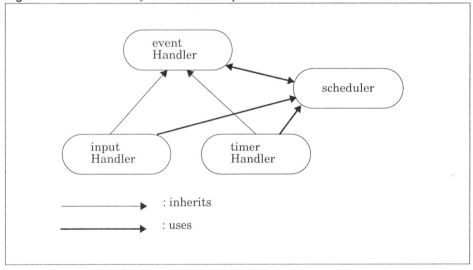

The scheduler does not need to know about what kind of eventHandler it has in its list. Here is the class declaration for the scheduler:

```
class scheduler {
 public:
    scheduler();
    ~scheduler();

    void    Run();
```

```
void      AddEventHandler(eventHandler *hdl);

void      DeleteEventHandler(eventHandler *hdl);

static      scheduler * GetScheduler()
   { return _scheduler; }

int      NumOfEventHandlers();

private:

static scheduler * _scheduler;
eventHandlerList *_eventHandlerList;
};
```

The constructor initializes the list, and the destructor cleans up.

```
scheduler::scheduler()
{
   _eventHandlerList = new eventHandlerList;
   _scheduler = this;
}

scheduler::~scheduler()
{
   if ( _eventHandlerList )

       delete _eventHandlerList;
}
```

Methods `AddEventHandler()` and `DeleteEventHandler()` add and delete `eventHandler` objects.

```
void
scheduler::AddEventHandler(eventHandler *hdl)
{
   _eventHandlerList->Append(hdl);
}

void
scheduler::DeleteEventHandler(eventHandler *hdl)
{
   _eventHandlerList->Remove(hdl);
}
```

Method `Run()` implements the main event loop, using the select call.

```
void
scheduler::Run()
{
```

```
while ( 1 ) { // Infinite loop....

    fd_set rset, wset, eset;

    // initialize file descriptor sets.
    FD_ZERO(&rset);
    FD_ZERO(&wset);
    FD_ZERO(&eset);

    timeval timeout;
    timeout.tv_sec = timeout.tv_usec = -1;

    eventHandler *es = _eventHandlerList->Head();
    timeval temp;
    temp.tv_sec = -1;

    /*
     * For every event handler, call SetEvent
     * Choose lowest timeout value.
     */

    while ( es != 0 ) {
        es->SetEvent(&rset,&wset,&eset,&temp);
        if ( temp.tv_sec >= 0 &&
          ( timeout.tv_sec == -1 ||
                temp.tv_sec < timeout.tv_sec )) {
            timeout.tv_sec = temp.tv_sec;
            timeout.tv_usec = 0;
        }

        es = es->Next();
    }

    /*
     * If timeout.tv_sec is still -1, then it means there
     * is no timeout needed. Wait indefinitely for a
     * read/write/exception
     */

    if ( timeout.tv_sec == -1 ) {
        if ( select (10, &rset, &wset, &eset, 0) == -1 ) {
            perror("Error calling select");
        }
    }
    else {
        // We have a timeout value
        if ( select (10, &rset, &wset, &eset, &timeout)
                        == -1 ) {
            perror("Error calling select");
        }
```

```
        }
        /*
         * Now, run through list of event handlers again, and
         * call CheckEvent on each.
         */

        es = _eventHandlerList->Head();

        while ( es != 0 ) {

            struct timezone t;
            timeval curtime;

            (void)gettimeofday(&curtime,&t);
            if ( curtime.tv_usec >= 500000 )
                curtime.tv_sec++;

            es->CheckEvent(&rset,&wset,&eset,&curtime);

            es = es->Next();
        }
        /*
         * Some event handlers might have marked themselves up
         * for deletion - call CleanUpMarked on list to delete
         * them.
         */

        _eventHandlerList->CleanUpMarked();
    }
}
```

Now that we have a generic scheduler, and a base class for handling events, let's provide the subclasses `inputHandler` and `timerHandler`. Note that these will provide attributes specific to each type of event, and also redefine `SetEvent()` and `CheckEvent()`. The `EventCallback()` method will not be redefined in either subclass because we still do not know what has to be done in the case of an event. Thus, both `inputHandler` and `timerHandler` become base classes for further use. If we need two `inputHandler` objects, one to process input from STDIN, and one to process input from Unix IPC, we'll subclass `inputHandler` to form two more classes. For example, `ipcInputHandler` and `stdinInputHandler`. Both these classes will only need to redefine `EventCallback()` to handle the input appropriately. Well, on to the class declarations and definitions.

```
  class inputHandler : public eventHandler {
   public:
      inputHandler(int fd) { _fd = fd; }
```

```
        int GetFd() { return _fd; }

        void SetEvent(fd_set *readfds,
            fd_set *writefds, fd_set *exceptfds,
            struct timeval *timeout);

        virtual void CheckEvent(fd_set *readfds,
            fd_set *writefds, fd_set *exceptfds,
            struct timeval *curtime);

    protected:
        int _fd;
    };
```

The inputHandler now has an attribute _fd, which is the file descriptor
for the input file it is monitoring. That descriptor should be available when
the inputHandler object is being created.

Method SetEvent() will use FD_SET to set its file descriptor in the input
argument readfds. It ignores all other arguments.

```
void
inputHandler::SetEvent(fd_set *readfds,
    fd_set *, fd_set *, struct timeval *)
{
    FD_SET(_fd,readfds);
}
```

Method CheckEvent() will use FD_ISSET to check if input is ready on its
file descriptor. It also ignores all other arguments. If input is ready, it calls
EventCallback(), which will be implemented in a subclass.

```
void
inputHandler::CheckEvent(fd_set *readfds, fd_set *,
    fd_set *, struct timeval *)
{
    if ( FD_ISSET(_fd,readfds) ) {
        EventCallback();
    }
}
```

The timerHandler class:

```
class timerHandler : public eventHandler {

    public:
        timerHandler(int timeout);
        virtual ~timerHandler();
        virtual void EventCallback();
        void Disable();
```

```
    void SetEvent(fd_set *readfds,
        fd_set *writefds, fd_set *exceptfds,
        struct timeval *timeout);

    virtual void CheckEvent(fd_set *readfds,
        fd_set *writefds, fd_set *exceptfds,
        struct timeval *curtime);

 private:

    Boolean _disable;
    timeval _nextto;
};
```

The `timerHandler` has an attribute `_nextto` which represents the absolute time at which the timeout will occur. This is calculated in the constructor.

```
timerHandler::timerHandler(int timeout) : _disable(FALSE)
{
    struct timezone t;
    (void )gettimeofday(&_nextto,&t);

    if ( _nextto.tv_usec >= 500000 )
        _nextto.tv_sec++;

    _nextto.tv_sec += timeout;
}
```

Method `SetEvent` will calculate the time left for the timer to elapse, and set the timeval structure to that value. It ignores all other arguments.

```
void
timerHandler::SetEvent(fd_set *,
        fd_set *, fd_set *,
        struct timeval *timeout)
{
    struct timezone t;
    timeval curtime;

    /*
     * Get time of day..
     */

    (void)gettimeofday(&curtime,&t);

    if ( curtime.tv_usec >= 500000 )
        curtime.tv_sec++;

    /*
     * If timer has already timed out, set timeout to 0,
```

```
 * else to the required timeout value in seconds.
 */

timeout->tv_usec = 0;
long temp = _nextto.tv_sec - curtime.tv_sec;
(temp > 0 ) ?  (timeout->tv_sec = temp)
             : (timeout->tv_sec = 0);

}
```

Method `CheckEvent()` will check the `_nextto` attribute against the `curtime` argument to determine if the timer has timed out. If it has, then the method `EventCallback()` is invoked. Notice that the callback is invoked only if the timer is not disabled. The `_disable` flag allows us to disable timers before they timeout without removing them from the scheduler's list.

```
void
timerHandler::CheckEvent(fd_set *, fd_set *, fd_set *,
        struct timeval *curtime)
{
    if ( curtime->tv_sec >= _nextto.tv_sec ) {

        if ( _disable == FALSE)
            EventCallback();
        SetMarked(); // Mark it for deletion.
    }
}
```

7.3.4 Example Program

Now that we have the framework to do some asynchronous programming, let's get started. Imagine a (contrived) problem. We need an application which waits 10 seconds after start-up and then start taking input from the user and echoing it.

We need a subclass for both the `timerHandler` class, and the `inputHandler` class.

```
class startTimer : public timerHandler {
 public:
    startTimer(int timeout) : timerHandler(timeout) {}
    void EventCallback();
};

class echoInput : public inputHandler {
 public:
    echoInput(int fd) : inputHandler(fd) {}
    void EventCallback();
};
```

Notice, we only have to redefine the EventCallback() method for both the subclasses. In the startTimer::EventCallback() method we will have to create a echoInput object, and add it to the scheduler. In the echoInput::EventCallback() method we will have to read the standard input, and echo the user input.

```
void
startTimer::EventCallback()
{
    /*
     * Create a echoInput object to handle
     * input on STDIN.
     */
    echoInput *in = new echoInput(STDIN_FILENO);

    // Get address of scheduler
    scheduler *sch = scheduler::GetScheduler();

    if ( sch ) {
        // Add the input handler to the scheduler
        sch->AddEventHandler(in);
    }
    else {
        // We are in deep trouble!
        // A scheduler was never created!
    }

    // Request for input and exit the timer
    cout << "Please type in input: " << flush;

}

void
echoInput::EventCallback()
{
    char buf[MAXLINE];

    // We know input is ready on our file
    // if this callback has been invoked

    int bytes;

    if (( bytes = read(_fd,buf,MAXLINE)) == -1 ) {
        perror("");
        return;
    }

    buf[bytes] = '\0';

    // Echo the input
```

```
        cout << "Input read : " << buf << "\n";
        // Request for more input and exit the callback
        // When there is more input waiting, this method
        // will be called again.

        cout << "Please type in input : " << flush;
    }
```

Well, we have the necessary classes. How do we put a program together to use all of this? Here's a main function that will do it for us.

```
main(int argc, char *argv[])
{
    // Create a scheduler
    scheduler *sch = new scheduler;

    // Create a 10 second timer
    startTimer *tm = new startTimer(10);

    // Add timer to scheduler
    sch->AddEventHandler(tm);

    // Kick off the main event loop
    sch->Run();
}
```

The program starts a 10 second timer, and enters a main event loop. When the timer elapses, it creates an echoInput object and adds that to the scheduler. The echoInput object will process input whenever the user types in anything on the keyboard. This is a simple example, and could have been done in a synchronous manner, but this implementation leaves us with the option of adding more users and more timers. Further chapters will use the framework developed in this chapter.

7.4 Summary

Asynchronous programming is very relevant to data communication systems. The asynchronous model of programming can be thought of as a framework which has a main event loop, OS event generators, event handlers, callbacks and event registration facilities.

7.4.1 Classes Developed

The following classes form the framework for asynchronous programming in this book:

■ scheduler - This class implements the main event loop. Event Handlers inform the scheduler of their existence, and the events they are monitoring. The `scheduler`, in turn, informs the event handlers when the event occurs.

- `eventHandler` - This is the base class for all event handlers in our system. The `eventHandler` has a generic interface `SetEvent()`, which allows the `scheduler` to determine what events a given `eventHandler` instance is monitoring. The interface also provides for generic callback methods `CheckEvent()` and `EventCallback()`, which process any event reported by the scheduler.

- `inputHandler` - This is a sub-class of the `eventHandler` class and it provides functionality specific to handling input on files. This class can be further sub-classed and the `EventCallback()` method rewritten to take specific action when input is ready on a given file.

- `timerHandler` - This is a sub-class of the `eventHandler` class and it provides functionality specific to handling timers. This class can be further sub-classed and the `EventCallback()` method rewritten to take specific action when a timer expires.

7.4.2 Source Files

- scheduler.h and scheduler.C

- eventHandler.h and eventHandler.C

- inputHandler.h and inputHandler.C

- timerHandler.h and timerHandler.C

7.5 Exercises

1. If your Unix system supports microsecond resolution, modify the scheduler code to take advantage of that.

2. Modify the example program in section 7.3.4 to incorporate a 2 minute timer, which, on expiration, will remove the echoInput object from the scheduler, and terminate the program.

3. Who is it that we quote on the first page - "One who doesn't learn from history is condemned to repeat it" - Churchill?

4. Implement a new class - `outputHandler`, which models an event handler where the event is a file that is ready to write to. Where can you use such a class?

5. Differentiate between asynchronous programming examined in this chapter and asynchronous data transmission.

8

Finite State Machines
and the Support Layers

8.1 Introduction

For beginning C programmers the whole topic of pointers has an esoteric quality. Until they are tackled hands-on, pointers seem slightly beyond comprehension. Finite state machines (FSMs) seem to induce a similar state of mind among programmers not used to the term, or unfamiliar with their implementations. Good implementations of FSMs do involve a fair amount of pointer manipulation, so the concern in not entirely unfounded. Well, as we now know, pointers are no mystery, and neither are FSMs. We begin this chapter with a brief look at a traditional FSM implementation technique popular in procedural programming. Then we go on to study an implementation using an object-oriented technique. FSMs form an integral part of any protocol implementation, and a good understanding of the implementation techniques will allow for a better modeling of protocol behavior and implementation. This chapter is based on an article on object-oriented state machines by Faison [14], to which the reader may refer for a more detailed analysis and references for further reading.

Once FSMs are understood we will use them in an implementation of the physical layer. The physical layer will provide all the primitives needed by a data-link layer, and will provide the functionality to exchange data between two unix processes. Finally, we will introduce the driver layer/user interface. In this chapter we will develop the framework for the user interface, allowing us to test out the physical layer. Both the physical layer and the driver layer will be inheriting from the `inputHandler` class developed in Chapter 7, since both will be monitoring input on Unix files (Unix IPC and standard input, respectively).

8.2 Finite State Machines

Any program which is executing is said to have a state at any given time. The state is uniquely identified by the value of all the variables, and the stack pointer for the program. The program changes states because of events that occur, both internal and external. When a program changes state it is called a transition. Usually, a useful program would also perform tasks as part of the transition. If we can identify all the states, events and transitions for a certain program we will have what is essentially a finite state machine model for the program. Figure 8.1 shows a very simple example of a FSM. The system can be in one of three states, State A, State B or State C. A set of events - Event A, Event B and Event C - can cause transitions as shown. Notice that for each state, some events cause a transition and some result in no transition.

Figure 8.1 An example of a FSM

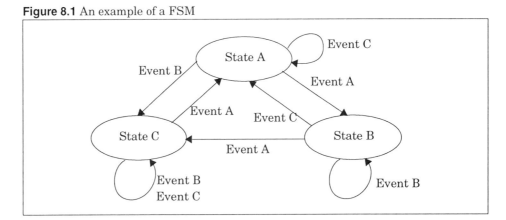

8.2.1 Traditional Design

Figure 8.2 shows a schematic for a traditional FSM implementation for a system which can be in one of three states (0, 1, or 2) and has to handle two types of events (0 or 1). The following modules are typically needed:

- Transition handlers - These are functions that are executed in order to bring about transitions. Typically, they change the state of the system, and perform any necessary function associated with the state transition.

- State table - This is usually a two-dimensional array which contains pointers to transition handlers. For a given state and a given event, one can index into the array and get the pointer of the function to execute.

- Event handler - The event handler indexes into the state table using the current state and the type of event that has occurred, retrieves the transition handler pointer, and executes the function.

Figure 8.2 State table driven implementation

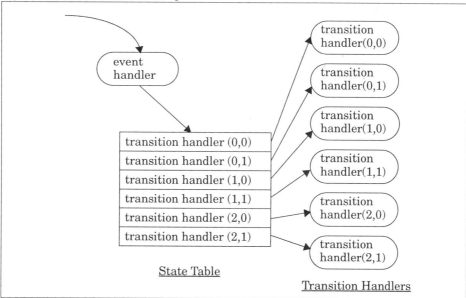

A crucial element is the state variable, i.e., a variable that holds the state of the system. The event handler uses it to figure out which handler to invoke, and the handler changes the state variable to the next appropriate value. The state variable is globally accessible.

8.2.1.1 Implementation

Here's an implementation of the FSM shown in Figure 8.1 using the above design. File state.h contains the constants, function prototypes and a declaration for the state table.

```
/*
 * File state.h
 */

const int MaxStates = 3;
const int MaxEvents = 3;

const int StateA = 0;
```

```
const int StateB = 1;
const int StateC = 2;

const int EventA = 0;
const int EventB = 1;
const int EventC = 2;

int Noop();
int StateAEventA();
int StateAEventB();
int StateBEventA();
int StateBEventC();
int StateCEventA();

typedef int (*Action)(); // Pointer to a function which takes
                         // no arguments and returns an int

// sm is a two-dimensional array of pointers to functions of
// type Action.
extern Action sm[MaxStates][MaxEvents];

// An extern declaration for the state variable.
extern int state;
```

File state.C initializes the state table with the appropriate pointers and defines the transition handlers. Note that each transition handler returns a value for the next state. An alternative implementation would be to set the state variable to the new value in the transition handler itself.

```
#include <iostream.h>
#include "state.h"

/*
 * Initialize pointers in the state table
 */
Action sm[MaxStates][MaxEvents] = {
      {StateAEventA, StateAEventB, Noop},
      {StateBEventA, Noop,         StateBEventC},
      {StateCEventA, Noop,         Noop }
};

int state; // Global variable

int Noop()
{
    cout << "No transition\n" << flush;
    return state;
}

int StateAEventA()
```

```
{
    cout << "Transitioning from state A to state B\n";
    return StateB;
}
int StateAEventB()
{
    cout << "Transitioning from state A to state C\n";
    return StateC;
}
int StateBEventA()
{
    cout << "Transitioning from state B to state C\n";
    return StateC;
}
int StateBEventC()
{
    cout << "Transitioning from state B to state A\n";
    return StateA;
}
int StateCEventA()
{
    cout << "Transitioning from state C to state A\n";
    return StateA;
}
```

File main.C contains the event loop, which receives events (in this case, a simple input from the user) and indexes into the state table to get a pointer to the transition handler, and invokes the function. Note that the state variable is set to the value returned by the transition handler.

```
#include <iostream.h>
#include "state.h"

main(int argc, char *argv[])
{
    int event;

    // Initialize state..
    state = StateA;

    // Go into event loop..ask user for events..
    // Execute transition...come back for events

    // This is the Event Handler..

    while ( 1 ) {

        cout <<   "Type Event : ";
        cin >> event;
        if(event >= 0 && event < MaxEvents )
```

```
                       // Index into state table...

                    state = sm[state][event]();
              else
                    cout << "Unknown event\n";
        }
    }
```

8.3 Object-Oriented FSM Design

Object-oriented(OO) state machine implementations have been touted as being superior to traditional implementations. One familiar argument against the previous implementation is that the state variable and the state table have to be accessible outside the state machine module, and, hence, vulnerable to corruption. This argument is not correct. Encapsulation of the state table can definitely be enforced. Sure the state variable is exposed, but as we'll see there is an analogous variable in the object-oriented implementation which is similarly vulnerable. The OO implementation does provide a more structured and intuitive approach to implementing FSMs, and the benefits seem to accrue as the FSM gets larger.

Figure 8.3 Object-oriented FSM schematic

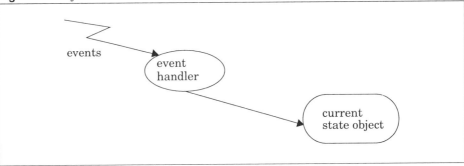

If you examine the previous FSM, it is clear that the state of the system can be defined in terms of a mapping of the set of events (that can occur in any given state) to the set of states that the system can transition to. For example, State A can be defined as:

```
{(Event A, State B), (Event B, State C), (Event C, State A)}
```

The state table developed for the previous implementation reflects this definition. In object-oriented design, it is convenient to think of encapsulating this state information into a single object. In such a situation, the state of a system will be represented by a single object - called the current state object. Figure 8.3 shows how the event handler sends all the events directly to the current state object. The current state object will process the event.

A few questions arise at this point:

- What do we mean by sending events to the current state object?

- Who creates and accesses the current state object?

- If the current state object represents the state of the system, what does changing state mean in this context?

Sending events, in OOP parlance, is equivalent to invoking methods on the current state object. This means that for every event that can occur, the event handler should be able to invoke a given method. Suppose the current state object is an instance of class `stateRoot`. It is created at system initialization prior to processing events.

```
stateRoot *curState = new stateRoot;
```

The variable `curState` is analogous to the variable `state` in the previous implementation. The variable value reflects the current state of the system. In the OO implementation, `curState` is a pointer to an instance. Hence, the type of object `curState` is pointing to represents the state of the system. Changing state in such a situation involves changing the value of the `curState` pointer, i.e., it points to an instance of a different class. Since the event handler should not know anything about the state of the system (i.e., what kind of object the current state object is) it is mandatory that all state objects share the same interface. This means all state object classes must inherit from a common base class which provides the interface. Furthermore, if each state is represented by a different object, then it is clear that we can translate a FSM into state class hierarchies.

Figure 8.4 State class hierarchy

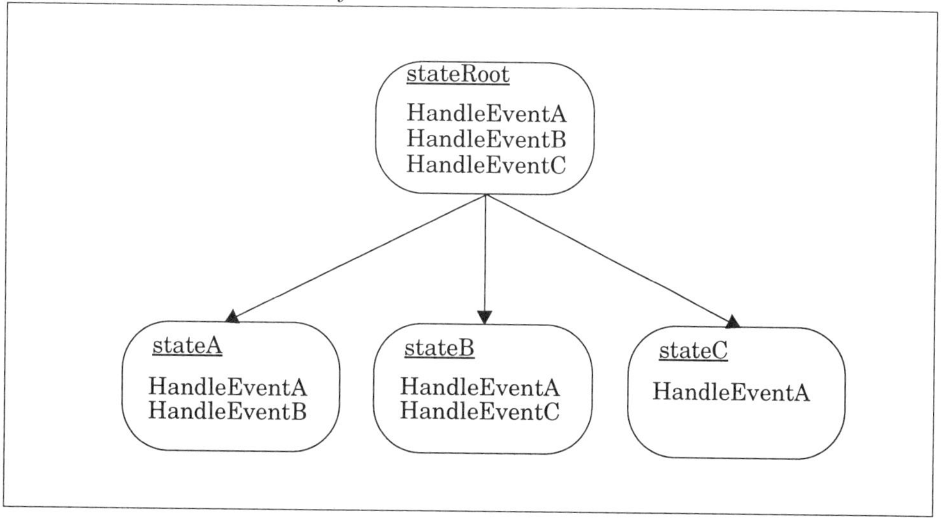

The following steps can be followed in designing the classes:

- Identify all events that need to be handled.

- For each event, provide a method in the base class to handle the event. This base class (call it the `stateRoot` class) now provides the interface to the state objects.

- For each state in the FSM, define a sub-class which inherits from the state-Root class. Redefine those methods for which the state needs to provide specialized event handling.

- If the derived class does not redefine a particular method, then it inherits that event handling capability from its parent class.

Figure 8.4 shows the state class hierarchy needed for our example FSM. The base class `stateRoot` needs three methods to handle each of the three possible events. The three states of the FSM are each represented by a sub-class of the `stateRoot` class, and they redefine methods for which they need to provide specialized functionality.

When events occur and methods are invoked on the current state object it has the ability to change itself to a new state object. This confusing statement is best clarified by looking at source code.

8.3.1 Implementation

Let us begin with a look at the base class `stateRoot`. Give particular attention to the return value of the methods. This is our clue to how the current state object changes itself.

```
/*
 * File stateRoot.h
 */

const int EventA = 0;
const int EventB = 1;
const int EventC = 2;


class stateRoot {
 public:
    virtual stateRoot *HandleEventA()
        { return this; }

    virtual stateRoot *HandleEventB()
        { return this; }

    virtual stateRoot *HandleEventC()
        { return this; }
```

```
      virtual void PrintState() = 0;
};
```

File states.h contains the declarations for the sub-classes, each representing a state in the FSM. Only certain methods are redefined in each sub-class, depending on which events affect transitions for a given state.

```
/*
 * File states.h
 */

#include "iostream.h"
#include "stateRoot.h"

class stateA : public stateRoot {
 public:

    virtual stateRoot *HandleEventA();
    virtual stateRoot *HandleEventB();
    virtual void PrintState()
       { cout << "Entered StateA\n"; }
};

class stateB : public stateRoot {
 public:

    virtual stateRoot *HandleEventA();
    virtual stateRoot *HandleEventC();
    virtual void PrintState()
       { cout << "Entered StateB\n"; }
};

class stateC : public stateRoot {
 public:

    virtual stateRoot *HandleEventA();
    virtual void PrintState()
       { cout << "Entered StateC\n"; }
};
```

File states.C contains the redefinitions of methods for each of the sub-classes.Notice that in the base class, all the event handlers returned a pointer this, i.e., the current object. In the redefined event handlers, pointers to other types of state objects are returned.

```
/*
 * File states.C
 */
```

```
#include "states.h"

/*
 * Redefine member functions for stateA
 */

stateRoot * stateA::HandleEventA()
{
    delete this;
    return new stateB;
}

stateRoot * stateA::HandleEventB()
{
    delete this;
    return new stateC;
}
/*
 * Redefine member functions for stateB
 */

stateRoot * stateB::HandleEventA()
{
    delete this;
    return new stateC;
}

stateRoot * stateB::HandleEventC()
{
    delete this;
    return new stateA;
}

/*
 * Redefine member functions for stateC
 */

stateRoot * stateC::HandleEventA()
{
    delete this;
    return new stateA;
}
```

Notice the analogy between the implementation of the traditional event handling functions and the methods of the state classes. The `Noop()` is similar to the base class event handlers - both return the current state of the system. In the object-oriented implementation the current state happens to be an object.

Finally, we have the `main()` function. This is our event handler. We have a current state object, which at start-up is initialized to be a `stateA` instance. When events are received (entered by the user), the handler invokes the appropriate method on the current state object. The current state object pointer gets assigned to the value returned by the method. And voila! Our current state object changes depending on what type of object pointer the method returns.

```
/*
 * File main.C
 */

#include <iostream.h>
#include "states.h"

main(int argc, char *argv[])
{
int event;

/*
 * Create a stateA object as the initial state object.
 */
stateRoot *currentState = new stateA;

/*
 * This is our event handler ...
 */

while (1) {
    currentState->PrintState();
    cout <<  "Type Event : ";
    cin >> event;
    switch(event) {
        case EventA:
            currentState = currentState->HandleEventA();
            break;
        case EventB:
            currentState = currentState->HandleEventB();
            break;
        case EventC:
            currentState = currentState->HandleEventC();
            break;
        default:
            cout << "Unknown state\n";
    }
}
}
```

8.4 The Physical Layer

The physical layer is our first piece of design which uses some of the various classes we have developed so far. Let us examine the main areas of design.

8.4.1 Unix IPC

Our physical layer implementation is a simulation. Real-world physical layers would be using network hardware to accomplish data communications. For our purposes, Unix IPC provides quite a few mechanisms for exchanging data between processes [10]:

- pipes (half-duplex)
- FIFOs (named pipes)
- stream pipes (full duplex)
- named stream pipes
- message queues
- semaphores
- shared memory
- sockets
- streams

   Pipes are among the most widely available form of inter-process communication in the various flavors of the Unix operating system. But pipes can only be used for communication between related processes, i.e., parent and child processes. In our architecture two independent processes need to communicate. The next best form of IPC, and also quite widely available, are FIFOs (first-in first-out) or named pipes. FIFOs can be used to exchange data between unrelated processes. We can have two FIFOs in our implementation, for full duplex communication between the processes. Figure 8.5 shows how we can use a FIFO xmit for transmitting from DTE A to DTE B, and a FIFO recv for transmitting from DTE B to DTE A.

Figure 8.5 Named pipes between processes for full-duplex communication

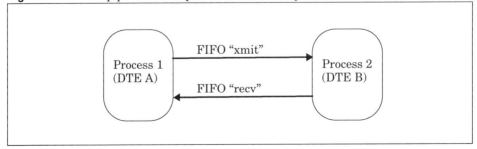

8.4.1.1 Creating a FIFO

A FIFO is a type of file and can be created using a `mknod` system call.

```
int mknod(path, mode, device)
    char *path;   // file to be created
    int mode; // mode of new file
    int device;   // device number
```

In the `mode` argument, the rightmost nine bits are the permissions, and the leftmost bits are for signifying whether you want to create a FIFO, an ordinary file, a directory etc. The `device` argument is the device number - we can use "0" for our purposes (see [10] for details). So the system call to create the "recv" FIFO would be:

```
mknod("recv", S_FIFO | 0666, 0);
```

8.4.1.2 Opening a FIFO

The FIFO needs to be opened just like a file for reading or writing. We can use the standard `open` system call.

```
int fd;
fd = open("recv", O_RDONLY | O_NDELAY );
```

Also, the `read` and `write` system calls can be used to read from and write to a FIFO.

8.4.1.3 Implementing messages

A hardware physical channel is able to check for delimiting flags to know when a data-link frame begins and ends. We can emulate the hardware by reading a byte at a time and checking for flags, or by implementing a more useful messaging system. We can implement the following scheme to enable us to read data in the blocks they were transmitted:

- Before writing a piece of data on to the FIFO, write an integer which contains the size of the following data.

- While reading, first read an integer value to figure out the size of the following message, and then read in only that many bytes of data.

In terms of designing the physical layer class, it is important to note that the physical layer needs to monitor and read input from a file. The `inputHandler` class defined in Chapter 7 provides the basic functionality for such behavior. Thus, the physical layer will be a type of `inputHandler`. The method `EventCallback()` will have to be redefined to handle input from the file being monitored.

8.4.1.4 Physical layer activation and deactivation

Physical layer activation and deactivation are again hardware specific functions which we will simulate. As far as we are concerned, once the pipes are open for reading and writing, the physical channel is activated. But, to keep it interesting, we can simulate activation and deactivation. A character "a" preceded by an integer of value 1, i.e., a message size of one byte can be transmitted to indicate channel activation; a character "b" preceded by an integer of value 1 can be transmitted to indicate channel deactivation.

8.4.2 Implementing primitives

The physical layer needs to implement primitives for use by the data-link layer. The interface provided by the physical layer should be consistent with the `layer` interface developed in Chapter 3. We will have to redefine the appropriate `Command()` methods.

Figure 8.6 Class phlayer inheritance

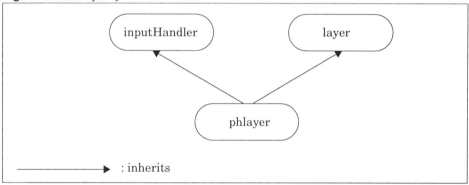

Figure 8.6 shows the inheritance tree for the `phlayer` class. The physical layer is both an `inputHandler` and a `layer`.

8.4.3 Physical Layer FSM

Our finite state machine for a physical layer is a simple one. The layer can be in one of two states:

- Inactive

- Active (i.e. capable of data transfer)

The events that can trigger transitions in the physical layer can be initiated either by the data-link layer (by invoking primitives) or by the data being read in from the FIFO. The primitives which result in events are:

- Ph_ActivateReq

.cation primitives are not regarded as events to the phys-

e events to the data-link layer. When data is read in from

ve one of three events:

: character "a" was received.

The character "b" was received.

: frame was received.

the states, events and transitions.

Figure 8.7 Physical Layer FSM

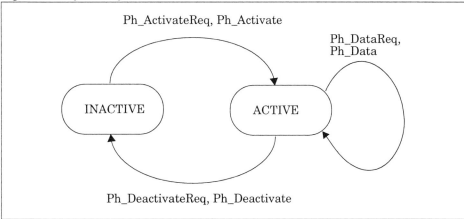

8.4.4 The Implementation

Knowing what we do about the physical layer, we can come up with a class declaration for it. Or at least the public interface for the class. Here's the complete declaration of the phlayer class.

```
class phlayer : public layer, public inputHandler {

  friend class phStateMachine;// The root state machine class
  friend class phActive; // class for ACTIVE state
  friend class phInactive; // class for INACTIVE state

  public:
    phlayer(char *xmitLink, char *recvLink);
    ~phlayer();

    virtual void Command(int cmd, int & errorCode);
    virtual void Command(int cmd, int & errorCode,
```

```
                          int reason);
          virtual void Command(int cmd, int & errorCode,
                    dataPacket *data);

          virtual void EventCallback();
          int       Init();

    private:
       int          Initialize();
       phStateMachine    *_sm;

       void  ProcessEvent(int event, int &errorCode);
       int   SendCommand(unsigned char cmd);
       int   OpenLink(char *,int);
       void  CloseLink();
       int   DataRequest(dataPacket *data);

       dataPacket *_lastRecdPkt;
       dataPacket *_pktToSend;

       int       _xmitfd, _recvfd;
       char  *_xmitLinkName;
       char  *_recvLinkName;
    };
```

Before we proceed any further with the phlayer class, let us look at the phStateMachine class. The phlayer has a private data member _sm, which is a pointer to the current state object. Here is the phStateMachine class declaration:

```
class phStateMachine {
 public:

    phStateMachine(phlayer *ph) : _ph(ph) {};
    virtual ~phStateMachine() {};

    virtual phStateMachine *PhActivateReq(int &errorCode)
       { errorCode = codeSuccessful; return this; }
    virtual phStateMachine *PhDataReq(int &errorCode)
       { errorCode = codeSuccessful; return this; }
    virtual phStateMachine *PhDeactivateReq(int &errorCode)
       { errorCode = codeSuccessful; return this; }

    virtual phStateMachine *PhActivate(int &errorCode)
       { errorCode = codeSuccessful; return this; }
    virtual phStateMachine *PhData(int &errorCode)
       { errorCode = codeSuccessful; return this; }
    virtual phStateMachine *PhDeactivate(int &errorCode)
       { errorCode = codeSuccessful; return this; }
```

```
        virtual void PrintState() = 0;

    protected:
        phlayer *_ph;
    };
```

There is a method to handle each event that can occur at the physical layer. We need two subclasses - phActive and phInactive to represent the two states the physical layer can be in. Notice that phStateMachine, phInactive and phActive are all declared friends of the phlayer class. This is because the state machine objects will need to access the private methods and data of the phlayer class.

Let us get back to the phlayer class. The constructor takes the names of two FIFO's, one for receiving and one for transmitting. So, if we are creating two processes with a physical layer in each, the constructors should be called such that the transmit FIFO for one is the receive FIFO for the other, and vice-versa. The constructor initializes the data members. The destructor deletes allocated memory.

```
phlayer::phlayer( char *xmitLink, char *recvLink ) :
    inputHandler(-1),
    _pktToSend(0),
    _lastRecdPkt(0),
    _xmitfd(-1),
    _recvfd(-1)
{
    _xmitLinkName = new char[strlen(xmitLink)+1];
    strcpy(_xmitLinkName,xmitLink);

    _recvLinkName = new char[strlen(recvLink)+1];
    strcpy(_recvLinkName,recvLink);

}

phlayer::~phlayer()
{
    if ( _sm )
        delete _sm;
    CloseLink();
    delete _xmitLinkName;
    delete _recvLinkName;
}
```

The Init() method creates a phInactive object as the current state object, and proceeds to create and open the FIFOs.

```
int
phlayer::Init()
{
```

```
            _sm = new phInactive(this);
            return(Initialize());
    }

    int
    phlayer::Initialize()
    {
        /*
         * Make the FIFO for receiving.
         */
        if ( mknod(_recvLinkName, S_IFIFO | 0666, 0) == -1
                    && errno != EEXIST ) {
            perror("mknod failed");
            return -1;
        }

        /*
         * Make the FIFO for transmitting.
         */

        if ( mknod(_xmitLinkName, S_IFIFO | 0666, 0) == -1
                        && errno != EEXIST ) {
            perror("mknod failed");
            return -1;
        }

        /*
         * Now open the FIFO's. Use O_NDELAY for the receive end
         * so as not to wait for the transmitting end.
         */

        if ( (_recvfd = OpenLink(_recvLinkName,O_RDONLY |
                        O_NDELAY)) == -1 ) {
            return -1;
        }
        /*
         * Now, wait till the receive end is open. This ensures
         * that both ends of the IPC are active.
         */
        if ( (_xmitfd = OpenLink(_xmitLinkName,O_WRONLY))
                        == -1 ) {
            return -1;
        }

        /*
         * Now start monitoring input by adding this
         * to the scheduler.
         */

        _fd = _recvfd; // Now monitor input on the receiving FIFO
```

```
    scheduler *schd = scheduler::GetScheduler();
    schd->AddEventHandler(this);
    return 0; // Successful
}

int
phlayer::OpenLink(char *link, int flag)
{
    int fd;
    if ( (fd = open(link, flag)) == -1 ) {
        perror("Error opening link");
        return -1;
    }
    else
        return fd;
}
```

Once a physical layer object has been created it can handle events, i.e., primitives invoked by the data-link layer or incoming data on the FIFO. Here's how the ProcessEvent method (the event handler for phlayer) handles the events:

```
void
phlayer::ProcessEvent(int event, int &errorCode)
{
    switch ( event )
        {
    case PH_ActivateReq:
        _sm = _sm->PhActivateReq(errorCode);
        break;
    case PH_DataReq:
        _sm = _sm->PhDataReq(errorCode);
        break;
    case PH_DeactivateReq:
        _sm = _sm->PhDeactivateReq(errorCode);
        break;
    case PH_Activate:
        _sm = _sm->PhActivate(errorCode);
        break;
    case PH_Data:
        _sm = _sm->PhData(errorCode);
        break;
    case PH_Deactivate:
        _sm = _sm->PhDeactivate(errorCode);
        break;
    default:
        errorCode = codeGeneralFailure;
        break;
        }
}
```

The Command() methods are redefined to implement the request primitives.

```
void
phlayer::Command(int cmd, int & errorCode)
{
    switch ( cmd )
        {
    case PH_ActivateReq:
        ProcessEvent(PH_ActivateReq,errorCode);
        break;
    case PH_DeactivateReq:
        ProcessEvent(PH_DeactivateReq,errorCode);
        break;
    default:
        ProcessEvent(PH_Unknown,errorCode);
        break;
    }
}
void
phlayer::Command(int cmd, int &errorCode, dataPacket *data)
{
    _pktToSend = data;
    _pktToSend->Register();

    switch ( cmd )
        {
    case PH_DataReq:
        ProcessEvent(PH_DataReq,errorCode);
        break;

    default:
        ProcessEvent(PH_Unknown,errorCode);
        break;
        }

    _pktToSend->Deregister();
    _pktToSend = 0;
}
```

Note how the phlayer registers with the dataPacket object as long as it needs to use it. Now, we need to examine how the data is received from the FIFO, and converted into events. Recall that the phlayer is a sub-class of inputHandler and needs to redefine EventCallback() in order to read the FIFO and take action.

```
void
phlayer::EventCallback()
{
    unsigned char buf[MAXLINE];
```

```
    int event;
    int bytes;

    if ( read(_recvfd,&bytes,sizeof(int))   != sizeof(int)) {
        TRACE(phlayerModule,1,("Error in phlayer::read\n"));
        perror("");
        return;
    }

    int rbytes;
    if ( (rbytes = read(_recvfd,buf,bytes)) != bytes ) {
        perror("");
        return;
    }
    /*
     * Create a dataPacket and set _lastRecdPkt to point
     * to it. Also, register with the dataPacket.
     */

    _lastRecdPkt = new dataPacket(buf,bytes);
    _lastRecdPkt->Register();

    if ( _lastRecdPkt->Length() == 1 ) {
        unsigned char c = *(_lastRecdPkt->GetData());

        if ( c == PH_ACTIVATE ) {
            event = PH_Activate;
        }
        else if ( c == PH_DEACTIVATE ) {
            event = PH_Deactivate;
        }
        else {
            event = PH_Unknown;
        }
    }
    else {
        event = PH_Data;
    }
    int errorCode = codeSuccessful;
    if ( _blockRecv == FALSE )
        ProcessEvent(event,errorCode);

    // Deregister with the data packet

    _lastRecdPkt->Deregister();
    _lastRecdPkt = 0;
}
```

The `EventCallback()` reads the FIFO and determines what type of event has occurred, and calls `ProcessEvent()` to take care of the event. Note that if the `_blockRecv` flag is set, then the event is not processed, i.e., the message is dropped.

We have seen how data is received. How about transmission? The methods `DataRequest()`, which transmits a `dataPacket`, and `SendCommand()`, which transmits a character, accomplish the task. These will be used by the state machine objects. `DataRequest()` transmits the length of the `data-Packet` before the `dataPacket` itself to implement the messaging system we discussed earlier.

```
int
phlayer::DataRequest(dataPacket *data)
{
    unsigned char lenBuf[4];
    int *intPtr;

    if ( _blockXmit == TRUE )
      return 0; // Drop the transmission

    /*
     * First, append an integer to the dataPacket whose value
     * equals the length of the dataPacket. This implements
     * messaging on the FIFO.
     */

    intPtr = (int *)lenBuf;
    *intPtr = data->Length();

    data->Prepend(lenBuf,sizeof(int));

    /*
     * Now write it out.
     */

    if ( write(_xmitfd,data->GetData(),data->Length())
            != data->Length() ) {
      perror("error transmitting data");
      return -1;
    }

    /*
     * Strip the integer that was added.
     */
    data->PreStrip(sizeof(int));
    return 0;
}

int
phlayer::SendCommand(unsigned char cmd)
{
```

```
    dataPacket *pkt = new dataPacket(&cmd,1);
    pkt->Register();
    int retVal = DataRequest(pkt);
    pkt->Deregister();
    return retVal;
}
```

Finally, let us look at the sub-classes of the phStateMachine class, which implement the FSM. First, the phInactive class.

```
class phInactive : public phStateMachine {
 public:

    phInactive(phlayer *ph) : phStateMachine(ph) {};
    virtual ~phInactive() {};

    virtual phStateMachine *PhActivateReq(int &errorCode);
    virtual phStateMachine *PhDataReq(int &errorCode)
        { errorCode = codeGeneralFailure; return this; }

    virtual phStateMachine *PhActivate(int &errorCode);
    virtual phStateMachine *PhData(int &errorCode)
        { errorCode = codeGeneralFailure; return this; }

    virtual void PrintState();
};
```

The phInactive class returns failure for PhDataReq and PhData. These were defined to return success in the base class. The three methods which really do something are:

```
phStateMachine *
phInactive::PhActivateReq(int &errorCode)
{
    _ph->SendCommand(PH_ACTIVATE);
    errorCode = codeSuccessful;
    return new phActive(_ph);
}

phStateMachine *
phInactive::PhActivate(int &errorCode)
{
    layer *dl = _ph->GetNPlus1Layer();
    if (dl )
        dl->Command(PH_ActivateInd,errorCode);
    return new phActive(_ph);
}

void
phInactive::PrintState()
```

```
{
    TRACE(phSmModule,2,("State Inactive\n"));
}
```

The phActive class implements the state in which the physical layer can transmit data.

```
class phActive : public phStateMachine {
 public:
    phActive(phlayer *ph) : phStateMachine(ph) {};
    virtual ~phActive() {};

    virtual phStateMachine *PhDataReq(int &errorCode);
    virtual phStateMachine *PhDeactivateReq(int &errorCode);

    virtual phStateMachine *PhData(int &errorCode);
    virtual phStateMachine *PhDeactivate(int &errorCode);
    virtual void PrintState();
};

phStateMachine *
phActive::PhDataReq(int &errorCode)
{
    if (_ph->DataRequest(_ph->_pktToSend) == 0 )
        errorCode = codeSuccessful;
    else
        errorCode = codeGeneralFailure;
    return this;
}

phStateMachine *
phActive::PhDeactivateReq(int &errorCode)
{
    _ph->SendCommand(PH_DEACTIVATE);
    _ph->CloseLink();
    errorCode = codeSuccessful;
    return new phInactive(_ph);
}

phStateMachine *
phActive::PhData(int &errorCode)
{
    layer *dl = _ph->GetNPlus1Layer();
    if ( dl )
        dl->Command(PH_DataInd,errorCode,_ph->_lastRecdPkt);
    else
        errorCode = codeGeneralFailure;
    return this;
}
```

```
phStateMachine *
phActive::PhDeactivate(int &errorCode)
{
    layer *dl = _ph->GetNPlus1Layer();
    if (dl )
        dl->Command(PH_DeactivateInd,errorCode);
    _ph->CloseLink();
    return new phInactive(_ph);
}

void
phActive::PrintState()
{
    TRACE(phSmModule,2,("State Active\n"));
}
```

The source is in files phEvents.h, phlayer.[Ch], phStateMachine.[Ch], phInactive.[Ch], and phActive.[Ch].

Now that we have a physical layer, let us develop a useful user interface (which will also serve as a driver layer, so that the data-link layer can invoke indication primitives on it).

8.5 The Driver Layer/User Interface

The physical layer is both a layer and an inputHandler, and hence it inherits from both classes. The driver layer will also be a layer and an inputHandler. Why it needs to be a layer is obvious - the data-link layer needs to invoke indication and response primitives on it. Thus, the driver layer should have the same interface as the network layer. It needs to be an inputHandler because it will be receiving inputs from the standard input (STDIN) - which will be the source of user input. We'll call our class nwlayer. In this chapter, we'll develop the user interface part of the nwlayer class. Even the user interface is only partially developed, since the only modules we have implemented so far are the tracing module and the physical layer. As we proceed with the implementation, we'll augment the nwlayer class presented here to provide more menu options, and to also be able to receive indication primitives from the data-link layer. Here's the first cut at the class declaration:

```
class nwlayer : public inputHandler , public layer {

public:
    nwlayer(int aFd);
    ~nwlayer();
    virtual void EventCallback();

private:
    void Parse(char *);
```

```
    void PrintCommands();
    void Trace(Boolean);
    void PhysicalLayerCommands();
};
```

The constructor calls the base class constructor, and invokes `PrintCommands` to print out the menu.

```
nwlayer::nwlayer(int aFd) : inputHandler (aFd)
{
    PrintCommands();
}

void
nwlayer::PrintCommands()
{
    cout << "\nThe following commands are available\n";
    cout << "Use the integer in brackets to invoke
                                    the given command\n";

    cout << "\n";
    cout << "Set TRACE                (1)\n";
    cout << "Unset TRACE              (2)\n";
    cout << "Physical Layer commands (3)\n";

    cout << "Please type in (integer) command : " << flush;
}
```

Note that the `nwlayer` doesn't know or care what file descriptor it's monitoring. When we create the `nwlayer` object, we'll invoke the constructor with STDIN as an argument.

Once the menu has been displayed, the user will type in a response. This response will result in `EventCallback()` being called. This method is redefined here to parse the response and take appropriate action.

```
void
nwlayer::EventCallback()
{
    char buf[MAXLINE];
    int bytes;
    if ( (bytes = read(_fd,buf,MAXLINE))  == -1 ) {
        perror("Error in read");
        return;
    }

    buf[bytes] = '\0';
    Parse(buf);
}
```

```
void
nwlayer::Parse(char *buf)
{
    int cmd = atoi(buf);

    switch (cmd )
        {
    case 1:
        Trace(TRUE);
        break;
    case 2:
        Trace(FALSE);
        break;
    case 3:
        PhysicalLayerCommands();
        break;
    default:
        cout << "Unknown command\n" << flush;
        }
    PrintCommands(); // Print menu again
}
```

Tracing can be turned on or off in various modules. Trace() queries the user for a module number and a level if tracing is to be turned on, or it just queries for a module number if tracing is to be turned off.

```
void
nwlayer::Trace(Boolean set)
{
    int module, level;

    cout << "\n";
    traceManager::PrintModules(); // Prints list of modules
    cout << "Type Module :";
    cin >> module;

    trace *info = traceManager::GetModule(module);

    if ( info == 0 )
        return;

    if ( set == TRUE ) {
        cout << "Type Level :";
        cin >> level;
        info->SetTrace(level);
    }
    else
        info->ResetTrace();
}
```

Selecting to execute physical layer commands from the main menu causes another more specific menu to be displayed. PhysicalLayerCommands() displays the detailed menu, and takes the appropriate action on user input. The user can activate and deactivate the physical layer, transmit data, and block and unblock transmission/reception. Real-world network layer implementations would not have access to the physical layer.

```cpp
void
nwlayer::PhysicalLayerCommands()
{
    int cmd;
    unsigned char msg[100];
    cout << "\n              Activate Physical Layer    (1)";
    cout << "\n              Deactivate Physical Layer  (2)";
    cout << "\n              Send Data                  (3)";
    cout << "\n              Block transmission         (4)";
    cout << "\n              Block reception            (5)";
    cout << "\n              Unblock transmission       (6)";
    cout << "\n              Unblock reception          (7)";
    cout << "\n              \nType in command :" << flush;
    cin >> cmd;
    layer *ph = _nMinus1->GetNMinus1Layer();
    int errorCode = codeSuccessful;
    switch (cmd )
        {
    case 1:
        ph->Command(PH_ActivateReq,errorCode);
        break;
    case 2:
        ph->Command(PH_DeactivateReq,errorCode);
        break;
    case 3:
        cout << "\n        Type in message: " << flush;
        cin >> msg;
        dataPacket *pkt =
            new dataPacket(msg,strlen((char *)msg));
        pkt->Register();
            ph->Command(PH_DataReq,pkt,errorCode);
        pkt->Deregister();
        break;
    case 4:
        ph->BlockXmit();
        break;
    case 5:
        ph->BlockRecv();
        break;
    case 6:
        ph->UnblockXmit();
        break;
```

```
    case 7:
        ph->UnblockRecv();
        break;
    default:
        cout << "Unknown command\n";
        }

    if ( errorCode != codeSuccessful )
        cout << "Error return : " << errorCode << "\n";
    }
```

The source for the driver layer is in files nwlayer.h and nwlayer.C.

8.5.1 A Simple Main Program

We now have enough to start two processes and communicate. We can also play around with the tracing utility. Here's a simple main program to start off with.

```
main(int argc, char *argv[] )
{
    if ( argc != 3 ) {
        printf("Please supply all the arguments\n");
        exit(1);
    }

    // Create a scheduler...
    scheduler *sch = new scheduler;

    // Create a physical layer and initialize it.
    phlayer *ph = new phlayer(argv[1],argv[2]);
    ph->Init();

    // Create a dummy data link layer - default base class
    layer *dl = new layer();

    // Create a driver layer - monitor Standard input
    nwlayer *nw = new nwlayer(STDIN_FILENO);

    // Set up the layer pointers
    ph->SetNPlus1Layer(dl);
    dl->SetNPlus1Layer(nw);
    dl->SetNMinus1Layer(ph);
    nw->SetNMinus1Layer(dl);

    // Add the nwlayer inputHandler to the scheduler.
    // The inputHandler for the FIFO is added to the
    // Scheduler by the phlayer itself.
```

```
        sch->AddEventHandler(nw);

        // Of we go!
        sch->Run();

    }
```

Compile all the files discussed until now with this main program. If your executable is called dl (mine is!), then executing dl with the following arguments
creates two processes which can communicate with each other.

```
csh> dl comm recv
csh> dl recv comm
```

Note that the arguments, which are names for the FIFOs, are reversed for the
two processes. Here's the menu you'll see once both processes are running.

```
The following commands are available
Use the integer in brackets to invoke the given command

Set TRACE                 (1)
Unset TRACE               (2)
Physical Layer commands   (3)
Please type in (integer) command :
```

8.6 Summary

Traditional FSM implementations are state table driven, whereas object-oriented FSMs involve manipulation of state objects. The current state of a system is represented by a current state object, and, as the state of the system
changes, the type of the current state object changes. Events are handled by
the system by invoking methods on the current state object.

8.6.1 Class Developed

The physical layer implementation is a simulation using FIFOs. The layer
provides the interface necessary for the data-link layer to invoke primitives
and exchange data between peer layers. The following classes implement the
functionality of the physical layer:

- phlayer - This class inherits from both the inputHandler class (to han-
  dle input on unix IPC) and layer class (to provide the interface to a layer).
  The class implements the functionality for the Ph_ActivateReq,
  Ph_DeactivateReq and Ph_DataReq primitives. These primitives are
  invoked by the data-link layer. The phlayer class uses the phState-
  Machine class and its sub-classes to fully realize its functionality.

- phStateMachine - This is the base class for implementing the FSM for the physical layer. The physical layer can be in one of two states - ACTIVE or INACTIVE.

- `phActive` - This class inherits from the `phStateMachine` class and provides functionality for the physical layer when it is in the ACTIVE state.

- `phInactive` -This class inherits from the `phStateMachine` class and provides functionality for the physical layer when it is in the INACTIVE state.

The driver layer, which doubles as a user interface, provides the functionality to interface with the tracing module and also to access the physical layer directly.

- `nwlayer` - This class implements the driver layer (which provides the network layer interface to interact with the data-link layer), and also provides the user interface. This class inherits from the `inputHandler` class (to handle input on STDIN) and also from the `layer` class.

8.6.2 Source Files

- phEvents.h

- phlayer.h and phlayer.C

- phStateMachine.h and phStateMachine.C

- phInactive.h and phInactive.C

- phActive.h and phActive.C

- nwlayer.h and nwlayer.C

8.7 Exercises

1. Modify the traditional state machine implemented in the chapter, so that the state table is completely encapsulated.

2. The current state machine object is changed in the methods of the state objects. But it is also possible to change it in the main() program, thus messing up the FSM. Is there a way to prevent this?

3. If the physical layer was to be implemented with real hardware, what changes would have to be made to support the hardware? Would the design need to change? Keep in mind that reading and writing would involve interrupt service routines.

4. Extract the source files we have studied so far from the diskette. Modify nwlayer.[Ch] to include only the code discussed in this chapter. Create an executable program with the main() program presented at the end of this chapter and execute it.

5. The user interface is a simple implementation, and is not truly asynchronous. In situations where `cin` is used, the user interface is blocking while waiting for input. The user interface is not blocking on user input when it is expecting a response at the main menu level. Modify the user interface so that it is completely asynchronous at all times.

3

THE PROTOCOL IMPLEMENTATION

Our efforts so far have been spent in building a framework to aid in implementing and testing the data-link layer protocol. The chapters that follow discuss the guts of the protocol implementation. We begin Chapter 9 by designing a finite state machine for the protocol, and a high-level design of the classes we will need to complete the implementation.

Chapter 10 focuses on the procedures for connection management. Chapter 11 discusses the implementation aspects of information transfer and flow control. Chapter 12 is devoted to implementing procedures for error detection and error recovery.

Chapter 13 explains the remaining aspects of the user interface/driver layer.

9

Data-link Layer Design

9.1 Introduction

Chapter 8 introduced the concept of finite state machines and an object-oriented implementation of FSMs. We even implemented a rather trivial FSM for the physical layer. In this chapter we will explore the design and implementation of FSMs in greater detail for the more challenging data-link layer. Designing FSMs for complex systems is not a trivial task, and the art lies in trying to optimize between the total number of states and the amount of work that needs to be done in each state. We will go through the analysis required to develop a solution for the data-link layer. The following steps will be followed in the design process:

- Identify events.

- Identify states.

- Iterate through the first two steps to refine the state machine. This might involve changes in the number and types of events, and also in the number of states.

- Identify the transitions.

In this chapter we will develop the set of events and states. The actual state transitions will be identified in subsequent chapters. The latter part of this chapter will be devoted to designing classes required for our remaining implementation.

9.2 Events

The first step in designing a FSM would be identifying all the events that can occur. We need to look at three different sources of events:

- Events at the physical-data-link layer boundary.

- Events at the data-link-network layer boundary.

- Events occurring internally in the data-link layer.

9.2.1 Physical-Data-link Boundary

The only types of events that can occur at this interface are related to the indication primitives in the physical layer service definition:

- PH_ActivateInd

- PH_DeactivateInd

- PH_DataInd

The first two events are straightforward. The PH_DataInd event is not just a single event. It is an indication of a data-link frame that has been received from the peer layer. This event expands into the following events:

- Received SABM

- Received DISC

- Received UA

- Received DM

- Received FRMR

- Received RR

- Received RNR

- Received REJ

- Received Iframe

Apart from valid frames, frames can also be received which cause a frame reject condition (see Section 4.16).

- A frame with an unimplemented or undefined control field.

- A frame with an invalid n(r) value.

- A I-frame with an information field exceeding the maximum established length.

- A frame with an information field which is not permitted, or a frame of incorrect length (for e.g., an info. field in a SABM frame).

- Unsolicited response frames with the F(final) bit set to 1.

Finally, frames can be received with error conditions for which no error recovery is possible:

- An error with the trailing and leading flags in a frame.

- A frame which contains less than 32 bits between the flags.

- A frame which has a wrong address field.

- A frame with a frame check sequence (FCS) error.

9.2.2 Network-Data-link Boundary

The events that can occur at this layer boundary are related to the request and response primitives in the data-link layer service definition. Here's the list (pretty straightforward):

- DL_ConnectReq

- DL_ConnectRes

- DL_DataReq

- DL_ResetReq

- DL_ResetRes

- DL_DisconnectReq .

9.2.3 Internal Events

The only asynchronous events that can occur internal to the data-link layer are timer-related events. All timers that are used in our data-link implementation for monitoring timeouts are T1 timers (as specified in ISO 7776). The number of timers that we need to distinguish as distinct events depends upon the number of different timers that can be operational in any given state of the data-link operation. We have one obvious candidate for now:

- t1Timer expired (see Section 4.17)

9.3 States

Let's move on to identifying the states. Some of the main states are easy to recognize:

- Disconnected
- Link setup pending
- Information transfer
- Link reset pending
- Link disconnect pending
- Frame reject

Consider the link setup pending state. Figure 9.1 shows the transitions that can occur from the disconnected state to the link setup pending state.

Figure 9.1 Preliminary transitions to link setup pending state

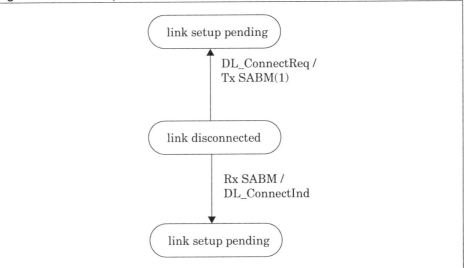

The link setup pending state reached in the two cases above are semantically different states. One is an outgoing link setup pending state, and the other is an incoming link setup pending state. A similar reasoning holds true for the link reset pending state. Thus the two states - link setup pending and link reset pending - expand to the following four states:

- Outgoing link setup pending
- Incoming link setup pending
- Outgoing link reset pending
- Incoming link reset pending

What is the difference between the four new states that we have identified? In both of the outgoing states, a SABM frame has been sent because of:

- a DL_ConnectReq, or

- a DL_ResetReq, or

- an internal reset condition

The same response is expected from the peer data-link layer in any of the three situations - a UA frame. The difference between the states is in the action taken when the response (a UA) is received:

- In the first case, a DL_ConnectCnf needs to be invoked.

- In the second case, a DL_ResetCnf needs to be invoked.

- In the third case, a DL_ResetInd needs to be invoked.

It is possible to model the two outgoing states as one state and an extra flag to keep track of what caused the reset/setup to be initiated. This allows us to work with one less state, and hence less complex FSMs. Of course, there will be a little extra processing that will need to be done in the single state. In our case, the trade-off is worth the effort, but it might not always be the case. It is up to the designer of the FSM to decide which is appropriate. Getting back to our single state (when a UA is received), the flag determines what action should be taken (one of the three mentioned above).

Now, consider the two incoming states. The states are entered because:

- A SABM has been received, and a DL_ConnectInd has been invoked.

- A SABM has been received, and a DL_ResetInd has been invoked.

In the first case, a DL_ConnectRes is expected from the network layer, which results in a UA being transmitted. In the second case, a DL_ResetRes is expected from the network layer, which also results in a UA being transmitted. Again, we can merge the two states into one and use a flag to discriminate the type of network layer response to process.

Here's our final cut of the main states:

- Disconnected: The data-link is in a disconnected state.

- Outgoing setup pending: An outgoing link setup/reset is pending, and a response is expected from the peer data-link layer.

- Incoming setup pending: An incoming link setup/reset is pending, and a network layer response is expected.

- Information transfer: The link is setup and is in the active data transfer phase.

- Frame reject: A FRMR has been sent, and a response is expected from the peer data-link layer.

- Disconnect pending: A DISC has been sent, and a response is expected from the peer data-link layer.

Notice that we have referred to the above states as "main" states. We still have other states that need to be identified, which the data-link can enter while in the information transfer phase.

Figure 9.2 Information transfer between primary and secondary entities

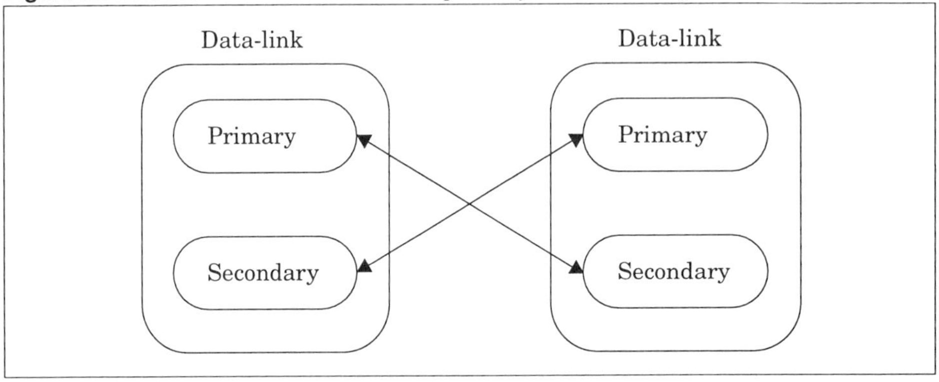

9.3.1 Information Transfer

During information transfer the data-link layer can be thought of as two logically distinct entities:

- The primary entity - Which is responsible for transmitting information frames.

- The secondary entity - Which is responsible for receiving information frames.

Figure 9.2 shows how the primary entity in one data-link layer will be communicating with the secondary entity in the peer data-link layer, and vice-versa.

The primary entity can be in one of the following states:

- Information transfer: Data is being transferred normally.

- Remote secondary busy: A RNR has been received, and the remote secondary is not ready to receive any more I-frames.

- Timer T1 checkpointing: Timer T1 has expired, and no acknowledgment has been received for a previously transmitted I-frame.

The secondary entity can be in one of the following states:

- Information transfer: Normal data transfer.

- Busy condition: The secondary has sent a RNR and is not ready to receive any I-frames.

- REJ condition: The secondary has sent a REJ and is expecting the primary on the peer side to initiate recovery by transmitting a particular I-frame.

Let's see if we can simplify our states. Consider the primary states. The only difference between the information transfer state and the remote secondary busy state is that the primary entity cannot transmit any I-frames when the remote entity is busy. We don't really need a separate state to model the remote busy condition - a flag, which contains the remote entity state, should suffice.

Similarly, when the primary is in a checkpointing cycle (i.e., a T1 timer has been started after transmitting an Iframe with P=1) it cannot transmit any more Iframes until the previous Iframes are acknowledged. We don't need a separate state to model the checkpointing cycle. The presence of a t1Timer that is running will be enough to stop the primary from transmitting any more Iframes. The primary entity can be modeled by only one state:

- Information transfer - along with variables which indicate whether the remote secondary is busy or a checkpointing cycle is in progress.

For a given data-link layer, if we combine the primary and secondary entities, we get the following states:

- Information transfer: Full-duplex data transfer in effect.

- Receiver busy: Can send I-frames, cannot receive I-frames.

- Reject condition: Can send I-frames, cannot receive I-frames except for the I-frame with the requested sequence number.

Note that I-frames can be transmitted in all three states subject to the following conditions: the remote secondary cannot be busy nor can the t1Timer be running.

The data link enters a reject condition after it has received an out-of-sequence I-frame, and it has transmitted a REJ frame. A timer is also started at this point. Let's call it the rejTimer. Note that in the reject state the rejTimer is started by the secondary entity in the data-link (i.e. that part of the data-link that is receiving I-frames) and the t1Timer mentioned above is started by the primary entity (i.e. the entity that is transmitting I-frames). Thus, both the rejTimer and the t1Timer can be active at the same time. This is the only state when two timers with different functions need to be active. Also, note that both are timers of type T1.

We have managed to collapse the primary and secondary entities into one entity represented by three states, but we have expanded the set of internal events that can occur. The t1Timer expired event that was mentioned earlier is now equivalent to:

- t1Timer expired (for monitoring responses to SABMs, DISCs, FRMRs, RRs, RNRs and I-frames)

- rejTimer expired (for monitoring responses to REJ frames)

9.4 The FSM Classes

Designing the base class for the state machine is a simple effort - just provide a method to handle each of the events. File dlEvents.h defines some of the events:

```
/*
 * File : dlEvents.h
 */


/*
 * Implementation specific constants
 */

const int DL_ConnectReq      = 200;
const int DL_ConnectInd      = 201;
const int DL_ConnectRes      = 202;
const int DL_ConnectCnf      = 203;

const int DL_DataReq         = 204;
const int DL_DataInd         = 205;

const int DL_ResetReq        = 206;
const int DL_ResetInd        = 207;
const int DL_ResetRes        = 208;
const int DL_ResetCnf        = 209;

const int DL_DisconnectReq   = 210;
const int DL_DisconnectInd   = 211;

const int t1TimerExp         = 212;
const int rejTimerExp        = 213;
```

Here's the class declaration for dlStateMachine:

```
/*
 * File : dlStateMachine.h
 */

class dlStateMachine {

public:

    dlStateMachine(dllayer *dl);
    virtual ~dlStateMachine() {}

    // The physical layer indications
```

```
    virtual dlStateMachine *PhActivateInd(int &errorCode);
    virtual dlStateMachine *PhDeactivateInd(int &errorCode);

    // The network layer requests and responses

    virtual dlStateMachine *DlConnectReq(int &errorCode);
    virtual dlStateMachine *DlConnectRes(int &errorCode);
    virtual dlStateMachine *DlDisconnectReq(int &errorCode);
    virtual dlStateMachine *DlDataReq(int &errorCode);
    virtual dlStateMachine *DlResetReq(int &errorCode);
    virtual dlStateMachine *DlResetRes(int &errorCode);

    // Frames from the peer data-link layer

    virtual dlStateMachine *HandleIframe(int &errorCode);
    virtual dlStateMachine *HandleSabm(int &errorCode);
    virtual dlStateMachine *HandleDisc(int &errorCode);
    virtual dlStateMachine *HandleDm(int &errorCode);
    virtual dlStateMachine *HandleUa(int &errorCode);
    virtual dlStateMachine *HandleRr(int &errorCode);
    virtual dlStateMachine *HandleRnr(int &errorCode);
    virtual dlStateMachine *HandleRej(int &errorCode);
    virtual dlStateMachine *HandleFrmr(int &errorCode);
    virtual dlStateMachine *HandleUndefined(int &errorCode);
    virtual dlStateMachine *HandleUnsolFBit(int &errorCode);
    virtual dlStateMachine *HandleIncorrectLength(
            int &errorCode);
    virtual dlStateMachine *HandleIfrLengthExcess(
            int &errorCode);

    // Internal events

    virtual dlStateMachine *HandleT1Timer(int &errorCode);
    virtual dlStateMachine *HandleRejTimer(int &errorCode);


    virtual void PrintState();
  protected:
    dllayer *_dl;
};
```

Figure 9.3 FSM class inheritance tree

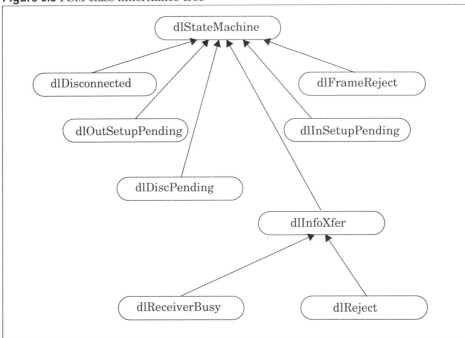

Sub-classes for the all the main states inherit from the base class dlState-Machine. Figure 9.3 shows the various classes needed to represent each state and their hierarchy. Most of the hierarchy is straightforward, except for the dlReceiverBusy and dlReject classes. Why don't those two inherit from the dlStateMachine like the other FSM classes?

The reason is that both the sub-states of the information transfer phase differ very slightly from the main information transfer state. Most of their functionality is identical to the information transfer state except:

■ The dlReceiverBusy state differs only in the manner in which it handles I-frames that are received (it cannot accept them), and in the manner in which it processes a RR command frame (it needs to reply with a RNR instead of a RR). Thus, the dlReceiverBusy class can inherit from dlInfoXfer class and redefine the HandleIframe() and HandleRr() methods.

■ The dlReject state also differs in the manner in which it handles I-frames that are received (it is looking for an I-frame with a specific sequence number). In addition, it also has to process the rejTimer. Thus, the dlReject class can inherit from the dlInfoXfer class and redefine the HandleIframe() and HandleRejTimer() methods.

The inheritance strategy illustrates another powerful mechanism that can be used while developing object-oriented state machines. Behavior which is shared between states can be abstracted into a common class. This simplifies the state machine, reducing the number of states and transitions. Of course code duplication is also avoided. As FSMs get more and more elaborate this strategy of creating super-states (like the dlInfoXfer state) becomes very useful in managing the complexity. A super-state is one which encapsulates behavior for more than one state[14]. In our case, the dlInfoXfer state provides the behavior for itself, and most of the behavior for dlReceiverBusy and dlReject states.

Let us now refer back to the base class dlStateMachine. Here are some of the methods defined in the base class.

```
/*
 * File : dlStateMachine.C
 */

/*
 * Function : dlStateMachine()
 *
 * Description : This is the constructor. It initializes
 * private variables.
 */

dlStateMachine::dlStateMachine(dllayer *dl) : _dl(dl)
{
}

/*
 * Function : PhDeactivateInd()
 *
 * Description : This function handles the primitive
 * PH_DeactivateInd invoked by the physical layer.
 * It invokes the DL_DisconnectInd primitive on the
 * network layer, and changes state to Disconnected.
 */

dlStateMachine *
dlStateMachine::PhDeactivateInd(int &errorCode)
{
    _dl->_nPlus1->Command(DL_DisconnectInd,errorCode,
            peerDisconnect);
    CHANGE_STATE(dlDisconnected);
}
```

Note the CHANGE_STATE macro used in the method above. This macro is defined in dlStateMachine.h and provides a convenient way of changing states.

```
/*
 * MACRO : CHANGE_STATE
```

```
 *
 * Description : Convenience macro to change state.
 * The argument to the macro is the new state class.
 * Creates a new state object, deletes the current
 * object, returns the new state object.
 */

#define CHANGE_STATE(a)                           \
    dlStateMachine *newState = new a(_dl);   \
    delete this;                                  \
    return newState;
```

The dlStateMachine class mostly provides default behavior, which in some cases can be returning with an error code of codeSuccessful or with an error code codeGeneralFailure. The default behavior is chosen so as to minimize the number of redefinitions that might be needed in the sub-classes. Of course this is true only when the sub-classes only need to set the error code (which is what the base class does). The following methods illustrate the point.

```
/*
 * The following functions provide the default
 * implementations for the event handling functions -
 * merely printing out messages.
 */

dlStateMachine *
dlStateMachine::DlConnectReq(int &errorCode)
{
    TRACE(dlSmModule,1,("Ignoring Connect Request\n"));
    errorCode = codeGeneralFailure;
    return this;
}

dlStateMachine *
dlStateMachine::HandleSabm(int &errorCode)
{
    TRACE(dlSmModule,1,("Discarding SABM\n"));
    errorCode = codeSuccessful;
    return this;
}
```

We'll stop our discussion of states, events, the dllayer class and the data-link state machine classes until we examine the state transitions in each state in the forthcoming chapters.

9.5 Identify Other Classes

The next step in the data-link layer design would be to identify the classes that would complete the implementation. Here is a list which gives an intuitive reasoning for each class:

- class `dllayer`: The first candidate is a class for the data-link layer itself. No mystery here.

- class `frame`: A class to encapsulate all the functionality related to data-link layer frames (SABMs, DISCs, IFRAMEs, etc.)

- class `t1Timer`: A class to implement the timer required for monitoring I-frame transmissions, replies for SABM, DISC, RR commands and FRMR responses.

- class `rejTimer`: A class to implement the timer required to monitor the reject state.

- class `window`: A class to encapsulate the behavior of sliding window protocols (see Chapter 4).

Of course, we have the `dlStateMachine` class and all its subclasses.

- class `dlStateMachine`

- class `dlDisconnected`

- class `dlOutSetupPending`

- class `dlInSetupPending`

- class `dlDiscPending`

- class `dlFrameReject`

- class `dlInfoXfer`

- class `dlReceiverBusy`

- class `dlReject`

9.6 Class frame

A lot of effort will be spent in the data-link layer forming frames for transmission, and parsing frames that are received. It would be convenient to have the knowledge of encoding and decoding frames encapsulated in a single class.

Figure 9.4 Use of frame objects in inter-layer data transfer

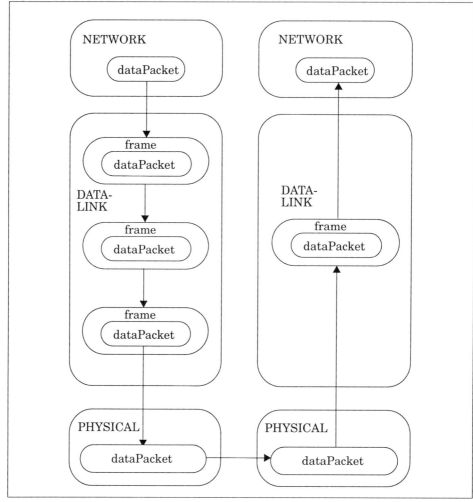

Figure 9.4 shows a scenario of how frame objects are used in the data-link layer. A dataPacket object is handed down to the data-link layer by the net-work layer. A frame object is created around the dataPacket. This frame object is essentially a wrapper around the dataPacket with data-link specific information like leading and trailing flags, address field, control field, frame check sequence (FCS), etc.

Notice that the frame objects might be queued up in the data-link layer. When the frame is ready for transmission, the data is extracted (which is the data-link frame, as opposed to the frame object) and passed to the physical layer as a dataPacket. This dataPacket is different from the dataPacket handed down to the data-link layer, in that it now contains some data-link specific information along with the original dataPacket. On the other side of the physical channel, the physical layer reads the data into a dataPacket object and passes it to the data-link layer. A `frame` object is formed around the `dataPacket`, and the data is analyzed to figure out what type of data-link frame has been received. If it is an IFRAME (as it is in Figure 9.4) then the `frame` is stripped of flags, address byte, control byte, and FCS bytes and forwarded to the network layer as a `dataPacket` object (assuming an error-free scenario). Note that the transmitting data-link layer might create frame objects which represent frames other than I-frames such as SABMs, DISCs, etc. These are created when necessary and transmitted without any queuing. Queuing is necessary for I-frames because they might need to be retransmitted in case of loss of data, or because of flow control.

Let us examine in greater detail what kind of interface the `frame` class should provide:

- It should have data members to represent the data-link frame parameters like frame type, n(r), n(s), p/f bit and, of course, any `dataPacket` (information) associated with the frame.

- We should be able to determine whether the `frame` is a command or a response `frame`.

- On the transmitting side, a `frame` object should be able to take data-link parameters (including any network layer information) and form a `dataPacket` for transmission.

- On the receiving side, the frame object should be able to take an incoming `dataPacket` object, parse it, validate it and determine what kind of data-link frame it is. It should also extract the various parameters like n(s), n(r), p/f bit, etc., and store them.

Given all the above requirements, here is the declaration for the `frame` class.

```
/*
 * File : frame.h
 */

/*
 * Some flags, and masks.
 * The flags and masks depend on the encoding format described
 * in ISO 7776. See Chapter 4 for a description of encoding
 * formats for the various frames.
 */

unsigned const char FLAG = 0x7e;

const char   MASK     = 0x01;
const char   SUP_MASK = 0x0f;
const char   UNUM_MASK  = 0xef;

const char   PF_MASK = 0x10;
```

```
const char   NS_MASK = 0x0e;
const char   NR_MASK = 0xe0;


/*
 * Literal values for frames
 */

const unsigned char IFRAME   = 0x00;
const unsigned char RR     = 0x01;
const unsigned char RNR    = 0x05;
const unsigned char REJ    = 0x09;
const unsigned char SABM   = 0x2f;
const unsigned char DISC   = 0x43;
const unsigned char UA     = 0x63;
const unsigned char DM     = 0x0f;
const unsigned char FRMR   = 0x87;

/*
 * Some error conditions
 */

// an undefined frame
const unsigned char UNDEFINED   = 0xaa;

// an invalid frame
const unsigned char INVALID      = 0xbb;

// Info in I-frame exceeds max.
const unsigned char IfrLengthExcess = 0xcc;

// Frame has invalid length.
const unsigned char IncorrectLength = 0xdd;

/*
 * FCS Defines. See Appendix A for FCS computation algorithm.
 */

const unsigned short FCS_INIT = 0xffff;
const unsigned short FCS_RECV = 0xf0b8;

class dataPacket;
class frame;
class dllayer;

/*
 * Define frameMember and frameList - since
 * frame objects will definitely be in a list.
 */
```

```
DefineListMember(frame);
DefineList(frame);


/*
 * Class : frame
 *
 * Description : The frame class encapsulates all the
 * functionality needed to form data-link frames for
 * transmission, and parse incoming data-link frames to
 * determine the frame parameters like n(r), n(s), p/f
 * fields, and whether it's a command or response, and of
 * course the frame type. The class also has the ability to
 * calculate frame check sequences (FCS) for frames to
 * be transmitted, and verify FCS for received frames.
 * Methods are provided to access frame parameters, and also
 * to form frames for transmission.
 *
 * Attributes :
 * dataPacket *_data :Pointer to the data-packet which holds
 *    data.
 * unsigned char _cntl : The control byte for this frame.
 * unsigned char _ft: The frame type.
 * unsigned int _pf : The P/F bit
 * unsigned int _ns : The N(s) value
 * unsigned int _nr : The N(r) value
 * Boolean _cmd : True means this frame is a COMMAND frame.
 * Boolean _formed : True means this frame has already been
 *    formed (i.e. flags, address, control bytes, etc., are
 *    in place.)
 */

class frame : public frameMember {

 public:
    frame();
    frame(dataPacket *aData, Boolean xmit);
    ~frame();

    void SetParams(unsigned char ft, int pf,
                        int nr = 0, int ns = 0)
      { _pf = pf; _ns = ns; _nr = nr; _ft = ft; }

    void FormFrame(Boolean isCmd);

    dataPacket *   GetDataPacket() { return _data; }
    unsigned char  GetFrameType() { return _ft; }

    Boolean IsCmd() { return _cmd; }
    unsigned int GetNr() { return _nr; }
```

```
        unsigned int GetNs() { return _ns; }
        unsigned int GetPf() { return _pf; }
        unsigned char GetCntl() { return _cntl; }
        void SetNs(int ns) { _ns = ns; }
        void SetNr(int nr) { _nr = nr; }
        void SetPF(int pf) { _pf = pf; }

        void  PrintParams();
    protected:
        void  ExtractParams();
        void  AppendFCS();
        Boolean CheckValid();
        unsigned short CalculateCksum(unsigned short crc,
                const unsigned char *s, int n);

        dataPacket *_data;
        unsigned char _cntl;
        unsigned char _ft;
        unsigned int _pf : 1;
        unsigned int _ns : 3;
        unsigned int _nr : 3;
        Boolean _cmd;
        Boolean _formed;
    };
```

There are two constructors. The default constructor merely creates an empty dataPacket, and initializes the rest of the variables to default values. The frame object also registers with the dataPacket object to ensure that the dataPacket is not deleted before the frame object. This constructor is used whenever the data-link layer needs to create frames without any network layer data (i.e., non I-frames).

```
frame::frame() :
_data(0),
_pf(0),_ns(0),_nr(0),_formed(FALSE),_cmd(FALSE)
{
    _data = new dataPacket();
    _data->Register();
}
```

The second constructor is used to create a frame object when a dataPacket is received either from the network layer or from the physical layer.

- When a dataPacket is received from the network layer, it is meant for transmission. The dataPacket is merely stored in the frame object for future use.

- When a dataPacket is received from the physical layer it is parsed and the frame parameters are extracted. First the frame is checked to see if it is valid (see Section 9.2.1)

```
frame::frame(dataPacket *aData, Boolean xmit) :
_data(aData),
_pf(0),_ns(0),_nr(0),_formed(FALSE),_cmd(FALSE)
{
    _data->Register();
    if (xmit == FALSE ) {

        if ( CheckValid() == FALSE ) {
            _ft = INVALID;
        }
        else {
            _ft = UNDEFINED;
            ExtractParams();
        }
    }
}
```

The destructor calls `Deregister()` on the `dataPacket` object contained in the `frame`.

```
frame::~frame()
{
    _data->Deregister();
}
```

The `ExtractParams()` method parses the received `dataPacket`. It identifies any error conditions like frames with incorrect length, frames with undefined or unimplemented control byte, etc.

```
void
frame::ExtractParams()
{
    unsigned char  add;
    add = *(_data->GetData()); // The address byte

    _data->PreStrip(1); // Remove the address byte

    _cntl = *(_data->GetData()); // the control byte
    _data->PreStrip(1);  // Remove the control byte
    _data->PostStrip(2); // remove the FCS

    _pf = (_cntl & PF_MASK) >> 4;


    _cmd = (add == cmdAddress) ? FALSE : TRUE;

    if ( !(_cntl & MASK )) {

        // An I-frame..
```

```
            _ft = IFRAME;
            _ns = (_cntl & NS_MASK) >> 1;
            _nr = (_cntl & NR_MASK) >> 5;
            if ( _cmd != TRUE )
               _ft = UNDEFINED;
            else if (_data->Length() > MaxIframeLength ) {
               _ft = IfrLengthExcess;
            }
        }

        else if (!(_cntl & ( MASK << 1))) {

            // A supervisory frame..

            _ft = _cntl & SUP_MASK;
            _nr = (_cntl & NR_MASK) >> 5;
            if ( _ft != RR && _ft != RNR && _ft != REJ )
               _ft = UNDEFINED;
            else
               if (_data->Length() != 0) {//No data field allowed
                  _ft = IncorrectLength;
               }
        }

        else {

            _ft = _cntl & UNUM_MASK;

            // Check for proper command and response frames

            if ( _ft != SABM && _ft != DISC && _ft != UA &&
                    _ft != DM && _ft != FRMR )
               _ft = UNDEFINED;
            else if ( (_ft == SABM || _ft == DISC ) &&
                    _cmd != TRUE )
               _ft = UNDEFINED;
            else if ( (_ft == UA || _ft == DM || _ft == FRMR )
                    && _cmd != FALSE)
               _ft = UNDEFINED;
            else {
               if ( ( _ft != FRMR && _data->Length() != 0 ) ||
                  ( _ft == FRMR && _data->Length() != 3 )) {
                  _ft = IncorrectLength;
               }
            }
        }
    }
}
```

When a frame needs to be transmitted, first the frame object is created with
either a default constructor (for supervisory and unnumbered frames) or with

the constructor with arguments (for information frames). Then methods `Set-Params()` and `FormFrame()` are invoked on the newly created frame object to create a `dataPacket` which has all the data-link parameters.

`FormFrame()` checks to see if the frame is being formed for the first time.If it is a frame that already has data-link specific information, then it deletes them, and starts anew.

```
void
frame::FormFrame(Boolean isCmd)
{
    if ( _formed == TRUE ) {

        // If it has old control byte,address byte, etc.,
        // strip them
        _data->PreStrip(3); // flag, control byte and address
        _data->PostStrip(3); // FCS and flag
    }

    _formed = TRUE;
    _cntl = _ft | ( _pf << 4 ) | ( _ns << 1 ) | ( _nr << 5 );
    _cmd = isCmd;

    unsigned char add;
    (isCmd == TRUE ) ?   (add = cmdAddress) :
                    (add = resAddress);

    _data->Prepend(&_cntl,1);
    _data->Prepend(&add,1);
    _data->Prepend(&FLAG,1);
    AppendFCS();
    _data->Append(&FLAG,1);
}
```

`AppendFCS()` appends a frame check sequence to the data, and `CheckValid()` checks a received frame for leading and trailing flags, minimum frame size, correct FCS sequence and proper address field encoding. It returns TRUE if the frame is valid. Both methods use `CalculateCksum()` to compute the FCS. See Appendix A for a detailed explanation of the algorithm.

```
void
frame::AppendFCS()
{
    unsigned short fcs;
    // First, calculate checksum

    fcs = CalculateCksum(FCS_INIT,
            _data->GetData(),_data->Length());

    // Now take a one's complement of the fcs
```

```
        // and append it to frame.

        unsigned char fcsbuf[2];
        unsigned short tmp = ~fcs;
        fcsbuf[0] = tmp & 0xff;
        fcsbuf[1] = (tmp >> 8) & 0xff;
        _data->Append(fcsbuf,2);
}

Boolean
frame::CheckValid()
{
    const unsigned char *data = _data->GetData();
    int len = _data->Length();
    if ( len < 2 || *(data) != FLAG ||
                    *(data+len-1) != FLAG ) {
        // Flags are messed up
        return FALSE;
    }

    if ( _data->Length() < 6 ) {
        // i.e. less than 32 bits between flags
        return FALSE;
    }

    unsigned short fcs;
    if ( (fcs = CalculateCksum(FCS_INIT,data,len-1))
                != FCS_RECV ) {
        // FCS is messed up
        return FALSE;
    }

    data += 1;
    if ( *data != addressA && *data != addressB ) {
        // incorrect address encoding
        return FALSE;
    }

    _data->PreStrip(1); // Remove the leading flag.
    _data->PostStrip(1); // Remove the trailing flag.
    return TRUE;
}
```

Here's a small fragment of code that demonstrates how I-frames, supervisory frames and unnumbered frames can be created.

```
/*
 * Creating a Command RNR, with P/F = 1, n(r) = 4
 */
```

```
frame *rnr = new frame(); // No information data.
rnr->SetParams(RNR, 1, 4);
rnr->FormFrame(TRUE); // TRUE for command

/*
 * Creating a Response REJ, with P/F = 0, n(r) = 3
 */

frame *rej = new frame();
rej->SetParams(REJ, 0, 3);
rej->FormFrame(FALSE); // FALSE for response

/*
 * Creating a SABM command, with P/F = 1
 */

frame *sabm = new frame();
sabm->SetParams(SABM,1);
sabm->FormFrame(TRUE);

/*
 * Creating an I-frame with dataPacket from the network
 * layer, P/F = 1, n(r) = 3, n(s) = 6
 */

dataPacket *nwlayerData; // From the network layer
frame *iframe =
       new frame(nwlayerData, TRUE); // TRUE for transmit
iframe->SetParams(IFRAME, 1, 3, 6);
iframe->FormFrame(TRUE);
```

9.7 Class dllayer

The public interface for the `dllayer` class is simple to design. It is a layer, and hence inherits from the `layer` class, and redefines the `Command()` methods to provide the implementation for the primitives. Like the `phlayer` class, it needs a `ProcessEvent()` method (the event handler), and a current state machine object (which is of type `dlStateMachine`). Here's a preliminary class declaration:

```
/*
 * File : dllayer.h
 */

class dllayer : public layer {

    // All state machine classes are friends since
    // they need to access the private data of dllayer
```

```
          friend class dlStateMachine;
          friend class dlDisconnected;
          friend class dlInSetupPending;
          friend class dlOutSetupPending;
          friend class dlInfoXfer;
          friend class dlDiscPending;
          friend class dlFrameReject;
          friend class dlReceiverBusy;
          friend class dlReject;
          friend class timerT1;
      public:

          dllayer();
          virtual ~dllayer();

          virtual void Command(int cmd, int &errorCode);
          virtual void Command(int cmd, int &errorCode,
                    dataPacket *data);
          virtual void Command(int cmd, int &errorCode,
                    int reason);
          int Init();
      private:
          dlStateMachine *_sm;
          void  ProcessEvent(int event, int &errorCode);
          void XmitFrame(int &errorCode, Boolean cmd,
                  int frameType, int pf,int nr = 0, int ns = 0);
      };
```

The dllayer class declares all the state machine classes to be friends - this is just as well, since they will all need to access private data members of the dllayer class. A timerT1 class is also declared to be a friend. The reason will become clear later in this chapter.

The Init() method creates a current state machine object, and also invokes the PH_ActivateReq primitive on the physical layer. The initial state is dlDisconnected (we'll examine this class in the next chapter - it's sufficient to know that it inherits from dlStateMachine).

```
int
dllayer::Init()
{
    // Start the data-link layer in the dlDisconnected state
    _sm = new dlDisconnected(this);

    // Activate the physical layer
    int errorCode = codeSuccessful;

    _nMinus1->Command(PH_ActivateReq,errorCode);

    if ( errorCode != codeSuccessful )
```

```
        cout << "Physical layer activation failed\n";

    return errorCode;
}
```

The `Command(int, int)` method used to handle all primitives, except DL_DataReq and PH_DataInd, is simple.

```
void
dllayer::Command(int cmd,int &errorCode)
{
    ProcessEvent(cmd,errorCode);
}
```

ProcessEvent() is just a big switch statement. It checks the event and invokes the appropriate method on the current state object. The following code is just a partial implementation. The code to handle events PH_DataInd and DL_DataReq will be introduced later.

```
void
dllayer::ProcessEvent(int event, int &errorCode)
{
    _sm->PrintState();
    switch ( event )
        {
    case DL_ConnectReq:
        _sm = _sm->DlConnectReq(errorCode);
        break;
    case DL_ConnectRes:
        _sm = _sm->DlConnectRes(errorCode);
        break;
    case DL_ResetReq:
        _sm = _sm->DlResetReq(errorCode);
        break;
    case DL_ResetRes:
        _sm = _sm->DlResetRes(errorCode);
        break;
    case DL_DisconnectReq:
        _sm = _sm->DlDisconnectReq(errorCode);
        break;
    case PH_DeactivateInd:
        _sm = _sm->PhDeactivateInd(errorCode);
        break;
    case t1TimerExp:
        _sm = _sm->HandleT1Timer(errorCode);
        break;
    case rejTimerExp:
        _sm = _sm->HandleRejTimer(errorCode);
        break;
```

```
        default:
          errorCode = codeGeneralFailure;
          break;
          }
      _sm->PrintState();
  }
```

XmitFrame() is a utility function used to transmit a data-link frame. It sets the frame parameters as provided and invokes PH_DataReq on the physical layer. This method will be used extensively by the state machine classes. Ignore the _expFBit variable for now. Its use will become clear when we discuss unsolicited F-bits.

```
void
dllayer::XmitFrame(int &errorCode, Boolean cmd, int frameType,
                 int pf, int nr, int ns)
{
    frame fr;
    fr.SetParams(frameType,pf,nr,ns);
    fr.FormFrame(cmd);
    _nMinus1->Command(PH_DataReq, errorCode, fr.GetDataPacket());
    if ( errorCode == codeSuccessful )
        if ( cmd == TRUE )
            _expFBit = pf;
    return;
}
```

We will develop the rest of the dllayer class as we go along, examining at each stage only what is relevant and required. For now, let us move on to the other classes to get a more complete picture of the design.

9.8 Timer Classes

As discussed earlier, we need two timers. Recollect that these timer classes will inherit from the timerHandler class and redefine the EventCallback() method. Functionally, when each timer expires it should call ProcessEvent() method on the data-link layer. This should be done in the EventCallback() method. Let us begin with the t1Timer class.

```
extern int T1; // contains value of T1 timer

class t1Timer : public timerHandler {
 public:
    timerT1(dllayer *dl, int timeout = T1) :
          timerHandler(timeout), _dl(dl) {}

    void EventCallback();
```

```
private:
   dllayer *_dl;
};

void
t1Timer::EventCallback()
{
   int errorCode = codeSuccessful;
   _dl->ProcessEvent(t1TimerExp, errorCode);
}
```

The constructor invokes the base class constructor, and initializes the private data member _dl (which is the pointer to the data-link layer which created this timer). The EventCallback() method merely invokes the ProcessEvent() method on the layer, with the event set to t1TimerExp.

The class definition of rejTimer will be identical, except for the Event-Callback() method. It will invoke ProcessEvent() with event type set to rejTimerExp. Do we really need two separate classes for these timers? We could have a single class timerT1 with an attribute _event which identifies the type of event that will occur when the timer expires.

```
/*
 * File : timerT1.h
 */

class timerT1 : public timerHandler {
 public:

    timerT1(int event, dllayer *dl, int timeout = T1);
    virtual ~timerT1();
    virtual void EventCallback();

 private:

    int    _event;
    dllayer *_dl;
};
```

The constructor invokes the base class constructor and initializes data members.

```
timerT1::timerT1(int event, dllayer *dl, int timeout) :
_event(event), _dl(dl), timerHandler(timeout)
{
}
```

The EventCallback() method uses the _event data member while invoking ProcessEvent().

```
/*
 * File : timerT1.C
 */

void
timerT1::EventCallback()
{
    int errorCode = codeSuccessful;
    _dl->ProcessEvent(_event,errorCode);
}
```

Thus, when the timer is created it is supplied with an event type - which would be the event that would occur when the timer expires. This relieves the timer of any particular knowledge of data-link events. Since the timer needs to access a private function `ProcessEvent()` it needs to be a friend of the `dllayer` class.

9.8.1 Timer-Related Functionality for dllayer

Now that we have a generic timer class, we need to augment the functionality of the `dllayer` class to handle timers. The attributes required in the dllayer class would be:

- The t1Timer

- The rejTimer

- The retry count associated with the t1Timer

- The retry count associated with the rejTimer

The behavior related to timers is also simple to foresee:

- Methods to start and stop t1Timer

- Methods to start and stop rejTimer

Here's an incremental addition to the `dllayer` class to handle the timer functionality:

```
/*
 * File : dllayer.h
 */

class dllayer : public layer {

    // ...
 private
   void StartT1Timer(Boolean continueRetry);
   void StartRejTimer(Boolean continueRetry);
```

```
    void StopT1Timer();
    void StopRejTimer();

    timerT1 * StartTimer(int event);

    timerT1 *_t1Timer;
    timerT1 *_rejTimer;
    int      _t1RetryCount;
    int      _rejRetryCount;

};
```

Here's the code for StartTimer(), StopT1Timer(), and StartT1Timer(). The other methods are similar.

```
/*
 * File : dllayer.C
 */

timerT1 *
dllayer::StartTimer(int event)
{
    timerT1 *t = new timerT1(event,this);
    scheduler *sch = scheduler::GetScheduler();
    sch->AddEventHandler(t);
    return t;
}

void
dllayer::StopT1Timer()
{
    if ( _t1Timer ) {
        _t1Timer->Disable(); //timer will delete itself on timeout
        _t1Timer = 0;
        _t1RetryCount = 0;
    }
}

void
dllayer::StartT1Timer(Boolean continueRetry)
{
    scheduler *sch = scheduler::GetScheduler();

    if ( continueRetry == TRUE ) {
        // timer's already running,override it

        if ( _t1Timer == 0 ) { // Error!
            return;
        }
        _t1Timer = StartTimer(t1TimerExp);
```

```
            _t1RetryCount++;
        }

        else {
            if ( _t1Timer != 0 ) {
                StopT1Timer();
            }

            _t1Timer = StartTimer(t1TimerExp);
            _t1RetryCount = 0;
        }
    }
```

The above design of the dllayer class and the timerT1 class has been a demonstration of the iterative nature of object-oriented design. We reduced the timer classes from two to one by using a useful data member. The timer related data members and methods of the dllayer class became apparent as we developed our design of the timerT1 class.

9.9 class window

The window class will be used for implementing sliding window protocols. A description of this class is best deferred until we start discussing flow control. We don't need to know anything about the window class for the next chapter on connection management, since sliding windows are used for data transfer only.

9.10 State Machine Classes

Earlier in this chapter we developed the base class for the state machine - dlStateMachine. The sub-classes which will provide functionality for each of the data-link states will be dealt with in subsequent chapters, with each chapter addressing only those sub-classes that it needs to. The procedure also illustrates the possible modular development of state machines using an object-oriented design.

9.11 Summary

Developing good finite state machines can be an iterative process. An optimal solution involves minimizing the number of states in a FSM without making the task of each state unreasonably large.

The following are the main states for the data-link layer:

- Disconnected

- Outgoing setup pending

- Incoming setup pending

- Information transfer

- Frame reject

- Disconnect pending

Information transfer can be decomposed into three states:

- Information transfer

- Receiver busy

- Reject condition

The following events can occur in the data-link layer:

- PH_ActivateInd

- PH_DeactivateInd

- PH_DataInd (which decomposes into events which represent the various types of valid and invalid data-link frames)

- DL_ConnectReq

- DL_ConnectRes

- DL_DataReq

- DL_ResetReq

- DL_ResetRes

- DL_DisconnectReq

- t1Timer timeout

- rejTimer timeout

9.11.1 Classes Developed

- dlStateMachine - the base class for the data-link layer FSM. Provides default methods to handle all the events. Sub-classes will be defined to handle processing for each of the above mentioned states.

- dllayer - the data-link layer. This chapter developed only the initialization methods, the ProcessEvent() method and the functionality related to timers.

- frame - this class provides functionality to encapsulate all the behavior necessary to handle data-link frame encoding and decoding.

- timerT1 - this class provides the T1 timer functionality. It inherits from the timerHandler class and is used by the dllayer class to implement both the t1Timer and rejTimer.

9.11.2 Source Files

- dllayer.h and dllayer.C
- frame.h and frame.C
- dlStateMachine.h and dlStateMachine.C
- timerT1.h and timerT1.C

9.12 Exercises

1. The `frame` class has a data member which is a pointer to the `dataPacket` class. Why can the `frame` class not inherit from the `dataPacket` class?

2. Modify the `dllayer` class and the `timerT1` class so that the knowledge of retry counts will remain encapsulated in the `timerT1` class. Will this require new event types?

3. Why doesn't the `dllayer` class inherit from the `inputHandler` class?

4. The `dataPacket` objects that are passed from the network layer are stored by the data-link layer in a queue. I-frames are formed by creating a `frame` object, encapsulating the network layer data. These I-frames can be modified if retransmission is necessary. The current `dataPacket` class design accommodates this requirement. If the network layer (in a real implementation) was also queueing the data, can the `dataPacket` class allow two (or more) layers to modify the same data? Will each layer need to make a copy of the data? Modify the `dataPacket` class so that each layer is allowed access to data pertinent only to itself.

10

Connection Management

10.1 Introduction

We had a detailed introduction to connection management in Chapter 4. This term encompasses the following three phases:

- Connection establishment

- Connection reset

- Connection release

This chapter will concentrate on the state machine classes which implement these phases. The `dllayer` class will be augmented to accommodate the additional functionality. At this stage in the implementation, request/response primitives will be invoked on the data-link layer, and indication/confirmation primitives will be invoked on the network layer. As a consequence, we will examine that aspect of the `nwlayer` class (our driver) which handles primitives. In this chapter, the driver layer will be referred to as the network layer (when we are talking about it from the perspective of the data-link layer) since it doesn't know the layer above is just a driver with the appropriate interface.

As far as the data-link layer FSM is concerned, we have only examined the states and events, and identified all the various classes needed to implement the FSM. To complete the picture we have to look at the state transitions for each state. In this chapter we will discuss the state transitions pertinent to connection management. We begin by looking at the dllayer class functionality needed to handle connection request and response primitives.

10.2　Primitive Implementation in Class dllayer

The layer base class from which dllayer inherits, provides three Command() methods for implementing primitives. Two of these are redefined in class dllayer (Chapter 9 examined one of the methods). The following are additions to the dllayer class in order to implement the connection management primitives:

```
/*
 * enum to differentiate between different types of reset.
 */
enum setupType { initial=0, externalReset, internalReset };

class dllayer : public layer {
  // ...
  public:
    virtual void Command(int cmd, int &errorCode,
          dataPacket *data);

  private:
    void ResetStateVariables();

    frame *_lastFrameRecd;
    int   _expFBit;
    setupType _setupType;
};
```

We have seen the implementation of the first Command() method in the previous chapter. The second Command() method, which handles PH_DataInd and DL_DataReq primitives, is of specific interest. The incoming dataPacket is stored in _lastFrameRecd. By creating a frame object we have already parsed the incoming data, and identified the frame type and other frame parameters. This will be used in the ProcessEvent() method to further analyze the event. The implementation of the DL_DataReq primitive is left for Chapter 11.

```
void
dllayer::Command(int cmd, int &errorCode, dataPacket *data)
{
    switch (cmd )
        {
    case PH_DataInd:
```

```
      if ( _lastFrameRecd )
         delete _lastFrameRecd;

      // Create a new frame object with the received
      // dataPacket.

      _lastFrameRecd = new frame(data,FALSE);
      _lastFrameRecd->PrintParams();

      // For testing - if reception is blocked, just
      // return. This will create an error situation

      if ( _blockRecv == FALSE)
         ProcessEvent(PH_DataInd,errorCode);

      break;

   case DL_DataReq:

      // This will be dealt with in the next chapter.
      break;

   default:
      errorCode = codeGeneralFailure;
      break;
   }
}
```

The ProcessEvent() method was introduced in Chapter 9, and we saw how it handled all events, except PH_DataInd and DL_DataReq. In the case of a PH_DataInd event, the frame type of the _lastFrameRecd is checked to identify the event with finer granularity.

```
void
dllayer::ProcessEvent(int event, int &errorCode)
{
   _sm->PrintState();
   switch ( event )
      {
   case PH_DataInd:

      // Check for unsolicited f-bit

      if ( (_lastFrameRecd->IsCmd() == FALSE) &&
         (_lastFrameRecd->GetPf() == 1) ) {

         if ( _expFBit == 0 ) {
         // We got unsolicited F-BIT
         _sm = _sm->HandleUnsolFBit(errorCode);
         break;
```

```
    }
    else
        // We got a solicited F bit, now clear it.
        _expFBit = 0;
    }
    switch ( _lastFrameRecd->GetFrameType() )
        {
    case INVALID:
        errorCode = codeSuccessful;
        break;
    case UNDEFINED:
        _sm = _sm->HandleUndefined(errorCode);
        break;
    case SABM:
        _sm = _sm->HandleSabm(errorCode);
        break;
    case UA:
        _sm = _sm->HandleUa(errorCode);
        break;
    case DISC:
        _sm = _sm->HandleDisc(errorCode);
        break;
    case DM:
        _sm = _sm->HandleDm(errorCode);
        break;
    case FRMR:
        _sm = _sm->HandleFrmr(errorCode);
        break;
    case IFRAME:
        _sm = _sm->HandleIframe(errorCode);
        break;
    case RNR:
        _sm = _sm->HandleRnr(errorCode);
        break;
    case REJ:
        _sm = _sm->HandleRej(errorCode);
        break;
    case RR:
        _sm = _sm->HandleRr(errorCode);
        break;
    case IfrLengthExcess:
        _sm = _sm->HandleIfrLengthExcess(errorCode);
        break;
    case IncorrectLength:
        _sm = _sm->HandleIncorrectLength(errorCode);
        break;
    default:
        _sm = _sm->HandleUndefined(errorCode);
        break;
        }
```

```
        break;
    default:
        errorCode = codeGeneralFailure;
        break;
        }
    _sm->PrintState();
}
```

Notice the use of the private variable _expFBit. This variable is set to TRUE whenever a response with a F=1 is expected, allowing us to detect unsolicited responses with the F bit set to 1.

The ResetVariables() is a convenience method which stops any timers that might be running. This method will need to be augmented as we proceed with the implementation.

```
void
dllayer::ResetStateVariables()
{
    // Stop any timers
    _expFBit = 0;
    StopT1Timer();
    StopRejTimer();
}
```

That is about all we need to implement in the dllayer class in order to handle connection management. The rest of the work will be done by the state machine classes.

10.3 Connection Establishment

Connection establishment involves going from dlDisconnected state to dlInfoXfer state. The transition involves the following intermediate states:

- dlOutSetupPending - Reached after transmitting a SABM from dlDisconnected state. The data-link layer is waiting for a response from the peer layer. The flag _setupType is set to initial.

- dlInSetupPending - Reached after invoking a DL_ConnectInd from the dlDisconnected state. The data-link layer is waiting for a response from the network layer. The flag _setupType is set to initial.

The dlInfoXfer state can be reached from both dlInSetupPending and dlOutSetupPending when the appropriate response is received. Once the data-link layer is in the dlInfoXfer state, the connection is said to be established.

10.4 Connection Reset

Once the data-link is in the dlInfoXfer state the link might be reset because of a network layer request or some internal error condition. Whatever the reason, a SABM is transmitted while in the dlInfoXfer state to set the link reset in motion - and the state is changed to dlOutSetupPending. This version of the dlOutSetupPending is distinguished from the one in connection establishment by setting the _setupType flag to externalReset.

When a SABM is received while in the dlInfoXfer state, a DL_ResetInd is invoked on the network layer, and the state is changed to dlInSetupPending. Again, this version of dlInSetupPending is distinguished from the same state reached from dlDisconnected by setting the _setupType flag to external-Reset.

The data-link layer can transition from dlInSetupPending and dlOutSetupPending to either dlInfoXfer (if the reset is accepted by either the network layer or the peer layer), or to dlDisconnected (if the reset is rejected).

10.5 Connection Release

The data-link can release the connection while in the dlInfoXfer state because of a network layer request or because of some internal error condition. During the process of connection release, the data-link will either transition to dlDiscPending (waiting for a response after transmitting a DISC), or go directly to dlDisconnected (after receiving a DISC).

Figure 10.1 Transition diagram for dlDisconnected state

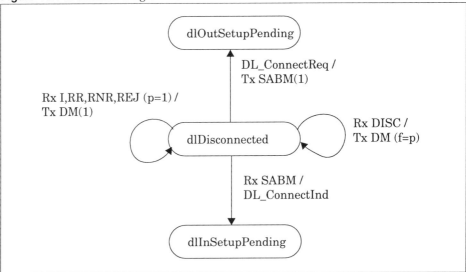

10.6 State dlDisconnected

The data-link layer begins life in the dlDisconnected state. Recall that the dllayer::Init() method creates a dlDisconnected object as the current state object. The state transition diagram for the dlDisconnected state is among the simpler ones we'll encounter.

Figure 10.1 shows the transitions in the dlDisconnected state (see Appendix B for a description of the conventions for FSMs used in this book). The dlDisconnected class implements the transitions. Here's the class declaration:

```
/*
 * File : dlDisconnected.h
 */
class dlDisconnected : public dlStateMachine {

 public:
    dlDisconnected(dllayer *dl);
    virtual ~dlDisconnected() {}
    dlStateMachine *DlConnectReq(int &errorCode);
    dlStateMachine *DlDisconnectReq(int &errorCode)
        { errorCode = codeSuccessful; return this; }

    dlStateMachine *HandleIframe(int &errorCode);
    dlStateMachine *HandleSabm(int &errorCode);
    dlStateMachine *HandleDisc(int &errorCode);
    dlStateMachine *HandleRr(int &errorCode);
    dlStateMachine *HandleRnr(int &errorCode);
    dlStateMachine *HandleRej(int &errorCode);
    virtual void PrintState();
};
```

The constructor calls ResetVariables() on the data-link layer. This ensures that the data-link is initialized correctly when it enters the dlDisconnected state.

```
dlDisconnected::dlDisconnected(dllayer *dl) :
        dlStateMachine(dl)
{
    _dl->ResetStateVariables();
}
```

Receiving a SABM causes a transition to the dlInSetupPending state. Note that the _setupType data member of dllayer is set to initial. This causes the dlInSetupPending state to take appropriate action when the network layer responds. A DL_ConnectInd primitive is invoked on the network layer.

```
dlStateMachine *
dlDisconnected::HandleSabm(int &errorCode)
{
    _dl->_nPlus1->Command(DL_ConnectInd, errorCode);
    _dl->_setupType = initial; // Setup type is initial

    CHANGE_STATE(dlInSetupPending);
}
```

A DL_ConnectReq primitive invoked by the network layer causes a SABM(p=1) to be transmitted, and a transition to the dlOutSetupPending state. Again, _setupType is set to initial. Also, timer T1 is started. The event that will occur when the timer expires is t1TimerExp.

```
dlStateMachine *
dlDisconnected::DlConnectReq(int &errorCode)
{
    // now, go ahead and send a SABM
    _dl->XmitFrame(errorCode,TRUE, SABM,1);

    if ( errorCode == codeSuccessful ) {
        _dl->StartT1Timer(FALSE); // start a new timer
        _dl->_setupType = initial; // setup type is initial
        CHANGE_STATE(dlOutSetupPending);
    }
    else
        return this;
}
```

The following methods merely transmit DM frames in order to respond to I-frames, DISCs, command RR, RNR and REJ frames.

```
dlStateMachine *
dlDisconnected::HandleDisc(int &errorCode)
{
    // Transmit a DM with F=P
    _dl->XmitFrame(errorCode,FALSE,DM,
            _dl->_lastFrameRecd->GetPf());
    return this;
}

dlStateMachine *
dlDisconnected::HandleIframe(int &errorCode)
{
    if ( _dl->_lastFrameRecd->GetPf()) // If P=1
        _dl->XmitFrame(errorCode,FALSE,DM,1);
    return this;
}

dlStateMachine *
dlDisconnected::HandleRr(int &errorCode)
{
    // Transmit a DM if RR is a command and P=1
    if ( _dl->_lastFrameRecd->IsCmd() &&
                    _dl->_lastFrameRecd->GetPf())
        _dl->XmitFrame(errorCode,FALSE,DM,1);
    return this;
}
```

```
dlStateMachine *
dlDisconnected::HandleRnr(int &errorCode)
{
    // Transmit a DM if RNR is a command and P=1
    if ( _dl->_lastFrameRecd->IsCmd() &&
                    _dl->_lastFrameRecd->GetPf())
        _dl->XmitFrame(errorCode,FALSE,DM,1);
    return this;
}

dlStateMachine *
dlDisconnected::HandleRej(int &errorCode)
{
    // Transmit a DM if REJ is a command and P=1
    if ( _dl->_lastFrameRecd->IsCmd() &&
                _dl->_lastFrameRecd->GetPf())
        _dl->XmitFrame(errorCode,FALSE,DM,1);
    return this;
}
```

That's about it for the dlDisconnected state implementation. Let us briefly take a look at the sequence of function calls needed to make a connection request.

1. The nwlayer invokes the DL_ConnectReq primitive
   dllayer::Command(DL_ConnectReq, errorCode)

2. The data-link layer processes the Event
   dllayer::ProcessEvent()

3. The dlDisconnected state object handles the event
   dlDisconnected::DlConnectReq()

4. The phlayer is asked to transmit the data (a SABM)
   phlayer::Command(PH_DataReq, errorCode, data)

5. The physical layer processes the Event
   phlayer::ProcessEvent()

6. The phActive state object handles the event
   phActive::PhDataReq()

7. The data is transmitted
   phlayer::DataRequest()

-------------- the data reaches the peer physical layer ---------

7. The peer physical layer reads in the data.
   phlayer::EventCallback()

```
6. The physical layer processes the Event
   phlayer::ProcessEvent()

5. The phActive state object handles the event
   phActive::PhData()

4. The PH_DataInd primitive is invoked on the peer data-link layer
   dllayer::Command(PH_DataInd, errorCode, data)

3. The data-link layer processes the Event - its a SABM
   dllayer::ProcessEvent

2. The dlDisconnected state object handles the event
   dlDisconnected::HandleSabm()

1. Invoke DL_ConnectInd on the network layer
   nwlayer::Command(DL_ConnectInd, errorCode)
```

When the peer network layer responds, the response works its way back to the
original network layer which initiated the request.

10.7 Invoking Primitives on the Network Layer

In the `HandleSabm()` method of the `dlDisconnected` class, the primitive
DL_ConnectInd is invoked on the network layer. The other primitives that the
data-link layer can invoke on the network layer during connection management   are   DL_ConnectCnf,   DL_ResetInd,   DL_ResetCnf,   and
DL_DisconnectInd. It's time to look at the `nwlayer` class to see how it handles
the primitives.

The network layer needs to respond to DL_ConnectInd, and DL_ResetInd. It
can respond to these with DL_ConnectRes and DL_ResetRes, respectively, if
the connection establishment/reset is to be accepted, or else it can respond
with a DL_DisconnectReq to deny the connection establishment/reset.

Since our network layer is merely a driver, it makes a decision to accept or
deny by examining the `_acceptConnReq` flag. This flag can be set from the
user interface. Also, the driver layer has to respond asynchronously. So we
create a timer `dlCmdResTimer` with zero timeout value. The timer expires
almost immediately, and it invokes the appropriate primitive on the data-link
layer.

Here's the addition to the `nwlayer` class:

```
class nwlayer : public inputHandler , public layer {

 public:

    // ...

    virtual void Command(int cmd, int &errorCode);
```

```
        virtual void Command(int cmd, int &errorCode,
                int reason);
};
```

The implementation of the `Command()` methods:

```
void
nwlayer::Command(int cmd, int& errorCode)
{
    scheduler *sch = scheduler::GetScheduler();
    int res;

    if ( _blockRecv == TRUE )
        return; // Ignore primitive

    switch(cmd)
        {
    case DL_ConnectInd:
        (_acceptConnReq == TRUE )
            ? (res = DL_ConnectRes) : (res = DL_DisconnectReq);

        // Start a timer - it will respond to the dllayer
        // when it expires.
        sch->AddEventHandler(new dlCmdResTimer(res,_nMinus1));
        errorCode = codeSuccessful;
        break;

    case DL_ConnectCnf:
        errorCode = codeSuccessful;
        break;

    case DL_ResetCnf:
        errorCode = codeSuccessful;
        break;

    default:
        errorCode = codeGeneralFailure;
        break;
        }
}

void
nwlayer::Command(int cmd, int &errorCode, int reason)
{
    if ( _blockRecv == TRUE )
        return; // Ignore primitive

    int res;
    scheduler *sch = scheduler::GetScheduler();
```

```
        switch(cmd)
            {
        case DL_ResetInd:

            if ( reason == internalError)
                return; // no need for a reset response

            (_acceptConnReq == TRUE )
                ? (res = DL_ResetRes) : (res = DL_DisconnectReq);

            // start a timer - it will respond to the dllayer when
            // it expires.
            sch->AddEventHandler(new dlCmdResTimer(res,_nMinus1));
            errorCode = codeSuccessful;
            break;

        case DL_DisconnectInd:
            errorCode = codeSuccessful;
            break;

        default:
            errorCode = codeGeneralFailure;
            break;
            }
    }
```

The Command() method which handles the DL_DataInd primitive will be redefined in Chapter 11. For now, we have all we need in the driver layer to handle connection management.

Here's the dlCmdResTimer class:

```
/*
 * File : dlCmdResTimer.h
 */

class dlCmdResTimer : public timerHandler {

 public:

    dlCmdResTimer(int cmd, layer *dl) :
        _dl(dl), _cmd(cmd), timerHandler(0) {};
    virtual ~dlCmdResTimer();
    virtual void EventCallback();

 private:
    int    _cmd;
    layer *_dl;
};
```

We need to redefine the `EventCallback()` method. It really is very trivial.

```
/*
 * File : dlCmdResTimer.C
 */

void
dlCmdResTimer::EventCallback()
{
    int errorCode = codeSuccessful;
    _dl->Command(_cmd,errorCode);
}
```

Now that we know how the `nwlayer` class responds to primitives invoked on it during connection management, let us get back to the connection establishment phase and its remaining states.

10.8 State dlOutSetupPending

The dlOutSetupPending state is an intermediate state, reached after transmitting a SABM from either the dlDisconnected state or the dlInfoXfer state. The connection is in a transition, and the data-link can either go to dlInfoXfer or dlDisconnected, depending on the response received from the peer data-link layer. As part of the transition, primitives need to be invoked on the network layer. The type of primitive depends on the `_setupType` flag. First, let us examine the transition diagram.

Figure 10.2 Transition diagram - dlOutSetupPending state

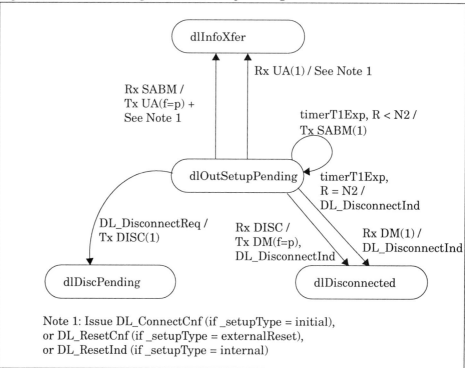

Note 1: Issue DL_ConnectCnf (if _setupType = initial),
or DL_ResetCnf (if _setupType = externalReset),
or DL_ResetInd (if _setupType = internal)

Figure 10.2 shows the transition diagram for the dlOutSetupPending state. Pay close attention to the different actions taken during transitions depending on the value of the _setupType flag. The code that follows will clarify the use of the flag. Here's the class declaration for the dlOutSetupPending class:

```
class dlOutSetupPending : public dlStateMachine {
 public:
    dlOutSetupPending(dllayer *dl) : dlStateMachine(dl) {}
    virtual ~dlOutSetupPending() {}
    virtual void PrintState();

    virtual dlStateMachine *DlDisconnectReq(int &errorCode);
    virtual dlStateMachine *HandleT1Timer(int &errorCode);
    virtual dlStateMachine *HandleUa(int &errorCode);
    virtual dlStateMachine *HandleDm(int &errorCode);
    virtual dlStateMachine *HandleDisc(int &errorCode);
    virtual dlStateMachine *HandleSabm(int &errorCode);
};
```

Methods have been redefined to process DISC, SABM, DM, and UA frames. Also, the timer T1, which was started before we entered the dlOutSetupPending state, is now a factor, and HandleT1Timer() has to be redefined. First,

let us look at the methods for handling a typical response to a SABM frame
that has been transmitted (i.e. a UA).

```
dlStateMachine *
dlOutSetupPending::HandleUa(int &errorCode)
{
    if ( !_dl->_lastFrameRecd->GetPf())
        return this; //Ignore UA with F=0,we are expecting F=1
    if ( _dl->_setupType == initial )
        _dl->_nPlus1->Command(DL_ConnectCnf,errorCode);
    else if ( _dl->_setupType == externalReset )
        _dl->_nPlus1->Command(DL_ResetCnf,errorCode);
    else
        _dl->_nPlus1->Command(DL_ResetInd,errorCode,
                                        internalError);
    CHANGE_TO_INFOXFER(TRUE);
}
```

CHANGE_TO_INFOXFER is another utility macro. We will discuss the argument taken by the macro in Chapter 11.

```
#define CHANGE_TO_INFOXFER(a)                              \
    dlStateMachine *newState = new dlInfoXfer(_dl,a);    \
    delete this;                                          \
    return newState;
```

The following methods implement the collision scenarios, i.e., a SABM colliding with a SABM or a SABM colliding with a DISC.

```
dlStateMachine *
dlOutSetupPending::HandleSabm(int &errorCode)
{
    // Transmit a UA
    _dl->XmitFrame(errorCode,FALSE,UA,
                _dl->_lastFrameRecd->GetPf());
    // Appropriately notify the network layer
    if ( _dl->_setupType == initial )
        _dl->_nPlus1->Command(DL_ConnectCnf,errorCode);
    else if ( _dl->_setupType == externalReset )
        _dl->_nPlus1->Command(DL_ResetCnf,errorCode);
    else
        _dl->_nPlus1->Command(DL_ResetInd,errorCode,
                                        internalError);
    CHANGE_TO_INFOXFER(TRUE);
}

dlStateMachine *
dlOutSetupPending::HandleDisc(int &errorCode)
{
```

```
        // Transmit a DM
        _dl->XmitFrame(errorCode,FALSE,DM,
                        _dl->_lastFrameRecd->GetPf());
        // Notify network layer
        _dl->_nPlus1->Command(DL_DisconnectInd,errorCode,
                        peerDisconnect);
        CHANGE_STATE(dlDisconnected);
}
```

The `HandleDm()` method implements the case when a DM is received.

```
dlStateMachine *
dlOutSetupPending::HandleDm(int &errorCode)
{
    // Ignore a mode setting command, i.e., DM F=0
    if ( !_dl->_lastFrameRecd->GetPf())
        return this;

    _dl->_nPlus1->Command(DL_DisconnectInd,errorCode,
                        peerDisconnect);
    CHANGE_STATE(dlDisconnected);
}
```

A DL_DisconnectReq at this stage results in a DISC being transmitted, and a transition to the dlDiscPending state.

```
dlStateMachine *
dlOutSetupPending::DlDisconnectReq(int &errorCode)
{
    _dl->XmitFrame(errorCode,TRUE,DISC,1);
    CHANGE_STATE(dlDiscPending);
}
```

Finally, the handling of the timer T1. If timer T1 expires while we are still in the dlOutSetupPending state, it means we haven't got a response from the peer layer. The SABM is transmitted again provided we haven't retransmitted it more than N2 times. After N2 retries a DL_DisconnectInd is issued to the network layer and the state is changed to dlDisconnected.

```
dlStateMachine *
dlOutSetupPending::HandleT1Timer(int &errorCode)
{
    if ( _dl->_t1RetryCount < N2 ) {
        // Transmit a SABM
        _dl->XmitFrame(errorCode,TRUE,SABM,1);

        if ( errorCode == codeSuccessful ) {
            _dl->StartT1Timer(TRUE); // re-start T1 again
            return this;
```

```
        }
        _dl->_nPlus1->Command(DL_DisconnectInd,errorCode,
                              noPeerResponse);
        CHANGE_STATE(dlDisconnected);
    }
    else {
        _dl->_nPlus1->Command(DL_DisconnectInd,errorCode,
                              noPeerResponse);
        CHANGE_STATE(dlDisconnected);
    }
}
```

That completes the code for the dlOutSetupPending state. The code for the state machines is now going to look more and more alike, since we are going to be using the same building blocks.

Figure 10.3 Transition diagram for state dlInSetupPending

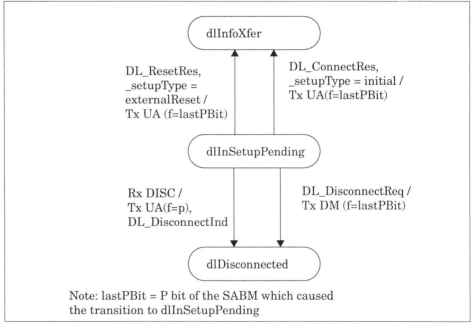

Note: lastPBit = P bit of the SABM which caused
the transition to dlInSetupPending

10.9 State dlInSetupPending

The dlInSetupPending state is an intermediate state reached after invoking a DL_ConnectInd or DL_ResetInd from the dlDisconnected state or the dlInfoXfer state. The connection is in a transition and the data-link can either go into the dlInfoXfer or the dlDisconnected state, depending on the response received from the network layer.

Figure 10.3 shows the transitions possible when the data-link is in state dlInSetupPending. Note that the P bit of the SABM (which sent the data-link into the dlInSetupPending state) should be stored, so that the F bit can be set to the appropriate value in a UA or DM response that might need to be transmitted (see Exercise 1).

We need to redefine very few methods for this state.

```
class dlInSetupPending : public dlStateMachine {

public:
    dlInSetupPending(dllayer *dl);
    virtual ~dlInSetupPending() {}
    virtual void PrintState();
    virtual dlStateMachine *DlConnectRes(int &errorCode);
    virtual dlStateMachine *DlDisconnectReq(int &errorCode);
    virtual dlStateMachine *DlResetRes(int &errorCode);
    virtual dlStateMachine *HandleDisc(int &errorCode);

private:
    int _lastPBit;
};
```

The constructor initializes the `_lastPBit` data member.

```
dlInSetupPending::dlInSetupPending(dllayer *dl) :
        dlStateMachine(dl)
{
    _lastPBit = dl->_lastFrameRecd->GetPf();
}
```

A DL_ConnectRes at this stage will result in a transition to dlInfoXfer, if the dlInSetupPending state was reached from dlDisconnected (i.e., `_setupType` = initial)

```
dlStateMachine *
dlInSetupPending::DlConnectRes(int &errorCode)
{
    // If the state was not entered because of an
    // initial link setup, ignore a DL_ConnectRes

    if ( _dl->_setupType != initial )
        return this;

    // Transmit a UA
    _dl->XmitFrame(errorCode,FALSE,UA,_lastPBit);
    CHANGE_TO_INFOXFER(TRUE);
}
```

A DL_ResetRes at this stage will result in a transition to dlInfoXfer if the dlInSetupPending state was reached because of a SABM that was received while in the dlInfoXfer state (i.e., `_setupType` = externalReset).

```
dlStateMachine *
dlInSetupPending::DlResetRes(int &errorCode)
{
    // If reset was not because of an externalReset,
    // ignore Reset Response

    if ( _dl->_setupType != externalReset )
        return this;

    // Transmit a UA
    _dl->XmitFrame(errorCode,FALSE,UA,_lastPBit);

    CHANGE_TO_INFOXFER(TRUE);
}
```

A DL_DisconnectReq invoked by the network layer is a refusal to accept a connection setup or reset. The data-link transmits a DM, and transitions to dlDisconnected state.

```
dlStateMachine *
dlInSetupPending::DlDisconnectReq(int &errorCode)
 {
    // Transmit A DM
    _dl->XmitFrame(errorCode,FALSE,DM,_lastPBit);
    CHANGE_STATE(dlDisconnected);
}
```

A DISC command received while in the dlInSetupPending state results in a DL_DisconnectInd primitive being invoked on the network layer, and a transition to the dlDisconnected state.

```
dlStateMachine *
dlInSetupPending::HandleDisc(int &errorCode)
{
    // Send UA to peer DL
    _dl->XmitFrame(errorCode,FALSE,UA,
             _dl->_lastFrameRecd->GetPf());

    // Notify NW layer of Disconnection
    _dl->_nPlus1->Command(DL_DisconnectInd,errorCode,
             peerDisconnect);

    CHANGE_STATE(dlDisconnected);
}
```

That was an extremely straightforward state to implement. The only other state left to study as part of connection management is state dlDiscPending.

10.10 State dlDiscPending

The dlDiscPending state corresponds to the connection release phase. This state is reached after a DISC is transmitted and an acknowledgment from the peer is expected.

Figure 10.4 Transition diagram for dlDiscPending state

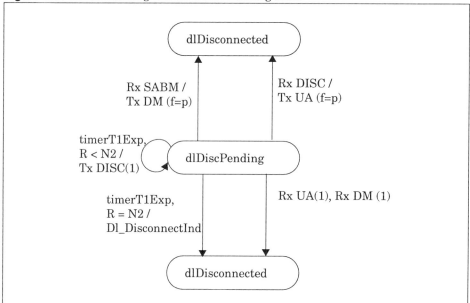

Figure 10.4 shows the transition diagram for the dlDiscPending state. There is only one transition that can happen in this state, a transition to the dlDisconnected state. A number of events can cause that transition, including collision of unnumbered commands. The timer T1 is also a factor in this state, and the DISC command can be retransmitted up to N2 times before initiating a higher level of recovery. Here's the class declaration which shows the methods that need to be redefined:

```
class dlDiscPending : public dlStateMachine {

public:
    dlDiscPending(dllayer *dl);
    virtual ~dlDiscPending() {}

    virtual dlStateMachine *HandleSabm(int &errorCode);
    virtual dlStateMachine *HandleDisc(int &errorCode);
    virtual dlStateMachine *HandleUa(int &errorCode);
    virtual dlStateMachine *HandleDm(int &errorCode);
    virtual dlStateMachine *HandleT1Timer(int &errorCode);
```

```
        virtual void PrintState();
};
```

`HandleDisc()` and `HandleSabm()` methods are redefined to handle collision situations.

```
dlStateMachine *
dlDiscPending::HandleSabm(int &errorCode)
{
    // Collision of different un-numbered commands
    // Transmit a DM
    _dl->XmitFrame(errorCode,FALSE,DM,
                 _dl->_lastFrameRecd->GetPf());

    CHANGE_STATE(dlDisconnected);
}

dlStateMachine *
dlDiscPending::HandleDisc(int &errorCode)
{
    // Collision of similar un-numbered commands.
    // Transmit a UA
    _dl->XmitFrame(errorCode,FALSE,UA,
               _dl->_lastFrameRecd->GetPf());

    CHANGE_STATE(dlDisconnected);
}
```

DM and UA responses also result in a transition to the dlDisconnected state
without any actions being taken. Since we are expecting a response with the F
bit set to 1, a UA or a DM with F = 0 is ignored.

```
dlStateMachine *
dlDiscPending::HandleUa(int &errorCode)
{
    errorCode = codeSuccessful;
    // Ignore UA with F=0!
    if ( _dl->_lastFrameRecd->GetPf() == 0 )
       return this;

    CHANGE_STATE(dlDisconnected);
}

dlStateMachine *
dlDiscPending::HandleDm(int &errorCode)
{
    errorCode = codeSuccessful;
    // Ignore a mode setting command, i.e., DM F=0
    if ( _dl->_lastFrameRecd->GetPf() == 0 )
       return this;
```

```
        CHANGE_STATE(dlDisconnected);
}
```

Finally, to handle the timer T1 we need to redefine the `HandleT1Timer()` method.

```
dlStateMachine *
dlDiscPending::HandleT1Timer(int &errorCode)
{
    if ( _dl->_t1RetryCount < N2 ) {
        // We can retransmit the DISC command, p =1

        _dl->XmitFrame(errorCode,TRUE,DISC,1);

        if ( errorCode == codeSuccessful ) {
            _dl->StartT1Timer(TRUE);
            return this;
        }

        // Transmission failed.
        _dl->_nPlus1->Command(DL_DisconnectInd,errorCode,
                noPeerResponse);

        CHANGE_STATE(dlDisconnected);
    }
    else {
        //already retransmitted N2 times,and no response recd.
        _dl->_nPlus1->Command(DL_DisconnectInd,errorCode,
                noPeerResponse);

        CHANGE_STATE(dlDisconnected);
    }
}
```

10.11 Summary

Connection management involves the following phases.

- Connection establishment
- Connection release
- Connection reset

10.11.1 Classes Developed

- `dlDisconnected` - This class inherits from the `dlStateMachine` class and provides the functionality for the dlDisconnected state of the data-link layer.

- `dlOutSetupPending` - This class inherits from the `dlStateMachine` class and provides the functionality for the dlOutSetupPending state of the data-link layer. Outgoing setup pending is a state reached after transmitting a SABM for either link setup or reset.

- `dlInSetupPending` - This class inherits from the `dlStateMachine` class and provides the functionality for the dlInSetupPending state of the data-link layer. Incoming setup pending is a state reached after receiving a SABM for either link setup or reset.

- `dlDiscPending` - This class inherits from the `dlStateMachine` class and provides the functionality for the dlDiscPending state of the data-link layer. Disconnect pending is a state reached after having transmitted a DISC.

- `dllayer` - The data-link layer class was modified to handle primitives for connection management.

- `nwlayer` - The driver layer class was modified to respond to primitives invoked by the data-link layer.

- `dlCmdResTimer` - This class implements a timer which allows the driver layer to respond asynchronously to data-link layer primitives.

10.11.2 Source Files

- dlDisconnected.h and dlDisconnected.C
- dlOutSetupPending.h and dlOutSetupPending.C
- dlInSetupPending.h and dlInSetupPending.C
- dlDiscPending.h and dlDiscPending.C
- dllayer.h and dllayer.C
- nwlayer.h and nwlayer.C
- dlCmdResTimer.h and dlCmdResTimer.C

10.12 Exercises

1. While making a transition to the dlInSetupPending state, the value of the P bit of the SABM (which caused the transition) is stored in `_lastPBit`. We could have used the `_lastFrameRecd->GetPf()` method to get the value of the P bit. Why is that solution not used?

2. Design the FSM we would need for connection management if instead of using the `_setupType` flag we use distinct states to distinguish between the various types of link setup and reset conditions.

11

Information Transfer and Flow Control

11.1 Introduction

The next phase in our implementation is information transfer. We saw in Chapter 10 how to establish a connection in order to enter the information transfer phase. This chapter will develop the classes needed to utilize the connection for data transfer.

The first part of the chapter will develop a `window` class, which will implement the sliding window protocol discussed in Chapter 4. Once we have a `window` class we will attempt full duplex data transfer during error-free conditions. This will give us a good insight into the working of sliding window protocols in general, and the `window` class in particular. Next, we will introduce the case when a receiver enters the busy state, and is unable to receive any I-frames. This will enable us to understand flow control implementation in protocols. The two states around which this chapter is organized are the dlInfoXfer and dlReceiverBusy states.

11.2 Class window

Chapter 9 introduced the `window` class. This class is needed to implement a sliding window protocol. Though our data-link implementation uses a modulo-8 sliding window and has a system parameter (K=7) which defines the maximum number of outstanding I-frames, we should design a generic class which can handle any values of the modulus and K.

11.2.1 Identifying the Attributes

The attributes mimic the various state variables needed to implement sliding window protocols. Here are the attributes we need:

- v(s) - The send state variable.

- v(r) - The receive state variable.

- Modulus - The modulus of the window.

- List of I-frames - A list of I-frames for which acknowledgments are pending, or which still haven't been transmitted.

- Number of acks pending - The number of I-frames for which acknowledgments are pending.

11.2.2 Identifying the Behavior

The window class should be the sole arbiter of sequence numbers for I-frames, acknowledgments, etc. All knowledge of such sequence numbers, whether n(s), n(r), v(s), or v(r) should be encapsulated within this class. Keeping this in mind, let us identify some basic behavior.

Firstly, the transmission aspect of the window:

- Add a new I-frame to the list of I-frames to be transmitted.

- Format a new I-frame for transmission. This will involve setting the n(r), n(s) and the P-bit of the I-frame.

- Check if the send window is full, and prevent any further transmissions.

Secondly, accepting acknowledgments:

- Process a n(r) that was received. The window should be able to remove acknowledged I-frames from its list. It should also be able to recognize invalid n(r) values.

Next, the receiving aspect of the window:

- Check the sequence number of a received I-frame (i.e., recognize any out-of-sequence I-frames).

Finally, handling retransmissions and resets:

■ The ability to reset the state variables like v(s), v(r) for retransmission, or resetting the link.

11.2.3 Identify Relationships between Classes

Figure 11.1 shows the relationships of the `window` class with other classes. The `dllayer` class will have an attribute which is an instance of the `window` class. The `window` class, in turn, will have an attribute which is a list of `frame` instances, i.e., a `frameList` instance. These are composition relationships. The classes for the three information transfer states will use the `window` class (for transmitting I-frames, processing n(s), n(r) values, etc.).

Figure 11.1 Relationships with the window class

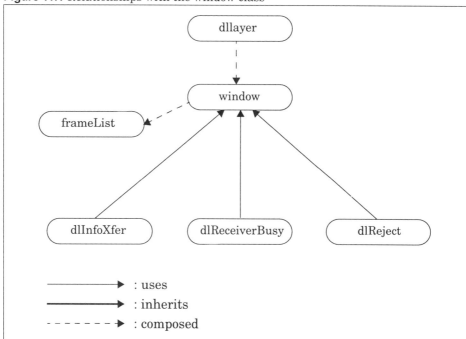

Here's the declaration for the window class:

```
class window {

public:

    window(int modulus);
    virtual ~window();
    dataPacket *GetNextToXmit();
    int ProcessAck(int nr);
```

```
        void AddFrame(dataPacket *dp);
        Boolean CheckSequence(int ns);

        int GetVr() { return _vr; }
        int GetVs() { return _vs; }
        int UnackedFrames() { return _ackPending; }
        int GetQueueLength() { return _xmitList.Length(); }
        void Reset();
        void StartRetransmission();

    private:

        void UnqueueFrames(int num);
        int      _modulus;
        int      _vs;
        int      _vr;
        int      _ackPending;
        frameList    _xmitList;
};
```

The class is really a straightforward implementation of the attributes and behavior discussed above. We can examine each method in detail to fully understand how the class functions. Let us begin with the constructor. It initializes all data members.

```
window::window(int modulus) :
_modulus(modulus),
_vs(0), _vr(0),
_ackPending(0)
{
}
```

Here's how you would add a new I-frame (which comes in as a `dataPacket` object from the network layer) for transmission:

```
void
window::AddFrame(dataPacket *dp)
{
    // Create a frame.
    frame *f = new frame(dp,TRUE);

    // And add to (FIFO)list.
    _xmitList.Prepend(f);
}
```

That was simple! What do we do with I-frames that have been queued up? Well, the data-link layer will want to transmit I-frames. We provide a function which will return a `dataPacket` object that contains a formatted I-frame ready for transmission. Also, see Exercise 5.

```
dataPacket *
window::GetNextToXmit()
{

    if ( _ackPending == K ) {
        // Window is FULL.No more I-frames can be transmitted.
        return 0; // Maximum outstanding acks
    }

    if ( _ackPending == _xmitList.Length() ) {
        // All have been transmitted, but not acknowledged.
        return 0; // All outstanding acks
    }

    // Get next in list.
    frame *f = _xmitList.GetNthMember(_ackPending);
    int pf;

    // Check if we need to set the P bit to 1 or 0.

    if ( _ackPending == (K-1))
        // It's the last one before the window gets full.
        pf = 1;

    else if ( (_xmitList.Length() - _ackPending ) == 1)
        // It's the last one in the list.
        pf = 1;

    else
        pf = 0;

    // Form the I-frame.
    f->SetParams(IFRAME,pf,_vr,_vs);
    f->FormFrame(TRUE);

    // Increment V(s) state variable.
    _vs = (_vs + 1) % _modulus; // Modulo increment

    // Increment unacked count.
    _ackPending++;

    // Return the dataPacket pointer.
    return (f->GetDataPacket());
}
```

So the data-link layer will be calling the GetNextToXmit() method for the next I-frame to transmit, until the method returns zero, signalling that either there are no more I-frames to transmit, or the send window is full. Here's an example of a fragment of code that illustrates the use of the GetNext-ToXmit() method.

```
dllayer *dl;// Pointer to some data-link layer

dataPacket *dp; // Pointer to a data packet
window *win;// A window, initialized elsewhere

while ( dp = win->GetNextToXmit() ) {

    // dp now contains a formatted I-frame
    // Transmit the I-frame
    // Use the physical layer

    dl->_nMinus1->Command(PH_DataReq,errorCode,dp);
}
```

Now that we can transmit I-frames, we should be able to process acknowledgments received in the form of the n(r) field in I-frames or supervisory frames. The `ProcessAck()` method takes an n(r) value, and if it is valid it removes all the acknowledged I-frames from its queue. Note that the received I-frame/RR/RNR/REJ frame is nowhere in the picture. The `window` class is interested only in the n(r) value received in the frame.

```
int
window::ProcessAck(int nr)
{
    if ( nr == _vs )  {

        // All Acked, remove all Iframes from queue.
        UnqueueFrames(_ackPending);
        int temp = _ackPending;
        _ackPending = 0;
        return temp;
    }

    // Check if N(r) is valid.
    int i = 1;
    int temp = 0;

    while ( i <= _ackPending ) {

        temp =  ( _vs >= i ) ?
            (_vs - i)%_modulus :
            (_modulus - i + _vs );

        if ( nr == temp )
            break;
        else
            i++;
    }
```

```
        if ( i > _ackPending ) // Wrong N(r)!
            return -1;

        // Valid NR
        int acked = _ackPending - i;
        _ackPending = i;

        UnqueueFrames(acked); // remove acked Iframes from queue
        return acked; // Return number of I-frames acknowledged.
}
```

The method `UnqueueFrames()` removes a specified number of I-frames from the `_xmitList`.

```
void
window::UnqueueFrames(int num)
{
    int i= 0;
    if ( num > _xmitList.Length() ) {
        return;
    }
    while ( i < num ) {

        frame *f = _xmitList.Top();
        if ( f != 0 )
            _xmitList.Remove(f);
        i++;


    }
}
```

Method `CheckSequence()` checks the validity of the sequence number of a received I-frame. Note that the received I-frame is nowhere in the picture and it is just the n(s) value we are interested in (see Exercise 3).

```
Boolean
window::CheckSequence(int ns)
{
    if ( ns != _vr )
        return FALSE;

    _vr = (_vr+1)%_modulus;
    return TRUE;
}
```

It is possible that the data-link layer might need to retransmit I-frames for which acknowledgments are pending. This requires a resetting of state variables or in other words, resetting the sliding window parameters. The method `StartRetransmission()` accomplishes just that.

```
void
window::StartRetransmission()
{
    // Start of retransmission cycle
    if ( _ackPending == 0 )
    return;

    // Else we need to modify v(s), which will be the
    // sequence number for the next I-frame to be
    // transmitted.

    if ( _vs > _ackPending )
        _vs = _vs - _ackPending;
    else
        _vs = ( _modulus - _ackPending ) + _vs;

    _ackPending = 0;
}
```

Note that the method does not retransmit any I-frames; it merely resets the window for retransmission. When the method `GetNextToXmit()` is called to get the next I-frame to be transmitted, it will have the appropriate n(s) value, and the window parameters will also reflect the fact that I-frames are being retransmitted.

`Reset()`, as the name suggests, resets the window, not for retransmission, but, a complete reset (for the case when a data-link connection is being reset). All the queued up I-frames are discarded. It is the higher layer's responsibility to recover from any loss of data.

```
window::Reset()
{
    _vr = _vs = 0;

    if ( _xmitList.Length() > 0 )
        UnqueueFrames(_xmitList.Length());

    _ackPending = 0;
}
```

Finally, the destructor.

```
window::~window()
{
    // Remove all frames from the queue.
    UnqueueFrames(_xmitList.Length());
}
```

The other methods in the class are useful accessor methods which return values of data members. We now have a complete implementation of a `window` class. Note that the implementation will work for any value of K and the modulus.

11.3 Augmenting Class dllayer

Here's how the dllayer class will use the window class.

```
// Constants defined in types.h

const int MODULO = 8; // Modulo of sliding window
const int K = 7; // Max. number of unacknowledged I-frames

class dllayer : public layer {
    // ...
 private:
    window _win; // a window object
};
```

The constructor initializes the window with the defined modulus value.

```
dllayer::dllayer() :
_t1Timer(0),
_rejTimer(0),
_lastFrameRecd(0), _expFBit(0),
_win(MODULO),_remoteBusy(FALSE)
{
}
```

The Command() method handles a DL_DataReq primitive by first adding the newly received dataPacket to the window's queue, and then invoking ProcessEvent().

```
void
dllayer::Command(int cmd,int &errorCode, dataPacket *data)
{
    switch (cmd )
        {
    case PH_DataInd:
        // dealt earlier.

    case DL_DataReq:

        // Add new data to be transmitted to window queue.
        // And call ProcessEvent.

        _win.AddFrame(data);
        ProcessEvent(DL_DataReq,errorCode);
        break;
```

```
        default:
            // dealt earlier.
    }
```

The `ResetStateVariables()` method resets the window.

```
void
dllayer::ResetStateVariables()
{
    // Stop any timers
    _expFBit = 0;
    StopT1Timer();
    StopRejTimer();
    _win.Reset(); // Drops any i-frames in the queue.
}
```

That's the extent of the interaction between the `window` and the `dllayer` classes. The FSM classes `dlInfoXfer`, `dlReceiverBusy` and `dlReject` interact more extensively with the `window` class. It's time to take a look at the main information transfer class - `dlInfoXfer`.

11.4 State dlInfoXfer

The dlInfoXfer state is entered from either the dlInSetupPending state or the dlOutSetupPending state. When the data-link enters the dlInfoXfer state, it is ready for full-duplex data transfer.

The state transition diagram for the dlInfoXfer state is more complex than the previous ones. We will have to attempt it in stages. Let us begin by looking at the transitions involved to the major states dlDiscPending, dlDisconnected, dlInSetupPending, and dlOutSetupPending. The transition to dlFrameReject is examined in Chapter 12, since it belongs in the realm of error detection and error recovery.

Figure 11.2 shows the state transitions among the major states. Note that the state transition diagram is partial and does not show the transmission or reception of I-frames. The `dlInfoXfer` class implements the corresponding state. The class will also have to be dealt with in a piece-meal manner, since we are dealing with information transfer in a phased manner. Therefore, the code for some of the methods might not be completely shown in any one place.

Figure 11.2 Major state transition diagram for dlInfoXfer state

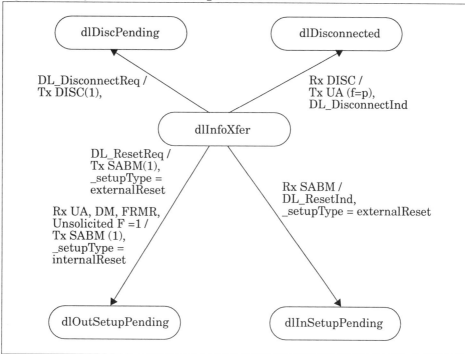

Here's the `dlInfoXfer` class which handles the state transitions introduced so far:

```
class dlInfoXfer : public dlStateMachine {

public:
    dlInfoXfer(dllayer *dl, Boolean reset);
    virtual ~dlInfoXfer() {}
    virtual dlStateMachine *DlResetReq(int &errorCode);
    virtual dlStateMachine *DlDisconnectReq(int &errorCode);

    virtual dlStateMachine *HandleSabm(int &errorCode);
    virtual dlStateMachine *HandleDisc(int &errorCode);
    virtual dlStateMachine *HandleUa(int &errorCode);
    virtual dlStateMachine *HandleDm(int &errorCode);
    virtual dlStateMachine *HandleFrmr(int &errorCode);

    virtual dlStateMachine *HandleUnsolFBit(int &errorCode);

    virtual void PrintState();

protected:
    dlStateMachine *LinkReset(int &errorCode);
};
```

Notice the constructor takes an additional argument reset in addition to the argument required by the base class dlStateMachine. If reset is TRUE, then the data-link state variables are reset. It would be useful to mention at this stage where we might need this. We know that a transition to the dlInfoXfer state can happen from dlInSetupPending or dlOutSetupPending. In either case, reset needs to be TRUE, since we need to start with a squeaky clean data-link connection. What we don't know at this stage (and this is the problem with introducing a solution piece-meal) is that we can transition to dlInfoXfer from two other minor information transfer states - dlReceiverBusy, and dlReject. In those situations we don't want to reset the data-link state variables. Instead, we want to continue with the current state variables of the data-link layer. In such a case, the dlInfoXfer object will be created with reset set to FALSE.

```
dlInfoXfer::dlInfoXfer(dllayer *dl, Boolean reset):
    dlStateMachine(dl)
{
    if ( reset == TRUE )
        _dl->ResetStateVariables();
}
```

Here's how the DL_DisconnectReq and DL_ResetReq primitives are handled while in the dlInfoXfer state.

```
dlStateMachine *
dlInfoXfer::DlDisconnectReq(int &errorCode)
{
    // Transmit a DISC, P=1, and start timer T1

    _dl->XmitFrame(errorCode,TRUE,DISC,1);
    if ( errorCode == codeSuccessful ) {
        _dl->StartT1Timer(FALSE);
        CHANGE_STATE(dlDiscPending);
    }
    else
        return this;
}

dlStateMachine *
dlInfoXfer::DlResetReq(int &errorCode)
{
    // now, go ahead and send a SABM

    _dl->XmitFrame(errorCode,TRUE,SABM,1);

    if ( errorCode == codeSuccessful ) {
        // Start T1 timer, and change state.
        _dl->StartT1Timer(FALSE);
        _dl->_setupType = externalReset;
```

```
        CHANGE_STATE(dlOutSetupPending);
    }
    else
        return this;
}
```

An incoming SABM frame results in a transition to the dlInSetupPending state in the `HandleSabm()` method. A DL_ResetInd primitive is invoked on the network layer.

```
dlStateMachine *
dlInfoXfer::HandleSabm(int &errorCode)
{
    _dl->_nPlus1->Command(DL_ResetInd,errorCode,peerReset);
    _dl->_setupType = externalReset;
    CHANGE_STATE(dlInSetupPending);
}
```

The `HandleDisc()` method processes a DISC command frame that was received. The state is changed to dlDisconnected, and a DL_DisconnectInd primitive is invoked on the network layer.

```
dlStateMachine *
dlInfoXfer::HandleDisc(int &errorCode)
{
    // First, transmit a UA
    _dl->XmitFrame(errorCode,FALSE,UA,
            _dl->_lastFrameRecd->GetPf());

    // Notify the network layer
    _dl->_nPlus1->Command(DL_DisconnectInd,errorCode,
            peerDisconnect);

    // Change state..
    CHANGE_STATE(dlDisconnected);
}
```

A DM, UA, FRMR frame, or a response frame with an unsolicited F bit equal to 1 are all reasons for a link reset. Note that a state change to dlOut-SetupPending is this case has a setup type equal to `internalReset` which is different from the setup type for a DL_ResetReq.

```
dlStateMachine *
dlInfoXfer::HandleUa(int &errorCode)
{
    return (LinkReset(errorCode));
}

dlStateMachine *
```

```
dlInfoXfer::HandleDm(int &errorCode)
{
    return (LinkReset(errorCode));
}

dlStateMachine *
dlInfoXfer::HandleFrmr(int &errorCode)
{
    return (LinkReset(errorCode));
}

dlStateMachine *
dlInfoXfer::HandleUnsolFBit(int &errorCode)
{
    return (LinkReset(errorCode));
}

dlStateMachine *
dlInfoXfer::LinkReset(int &errorCode)
{
    _dl->XmitFrame(errorCode,TRUE,SABM,1);

    if ( errorCode == codeSuccessful ) {

        _dl->StartT1Timer(FALSE);
        _dl->_setupType = internalReset;
        CHANGE_STATE(dlOutSetupPending);
    }
    else
        return this;
}
```

So far we have examined transitions from the dlInfoXfer state to dlDisc-
Pending, dlDisconnected, dlOutSetupPending and dlInSetupPending states.
All these states have been examined in detail in the previous chapter.

Figure 11.3 Transmitting I-frames

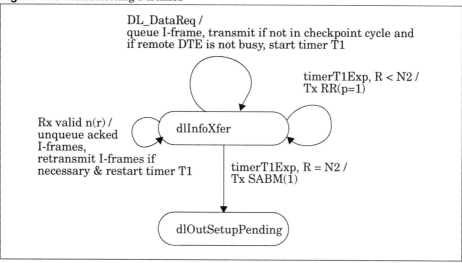

11.5 Transmitting I-Frames

I-frames need to be transmitted when DL_DataReq primitives are invoked by the network layer. Figure 11.3 shows what happens when a DL_DataReq is received while the data-link is in the dlInfoXfer state. Two concepts - those of checkpointing and flow control - need to be examined before we can go any further.

11.6 Checkpoint Cycle

Checkpointing is a procedure initiated by the sender of I-frames to ensure that the I-frames have been received and acknowledged. A checkpoint cycle begins with the transmission of an I-frame with P=1, and ends either:

- with the receipt of a supervisory response frame with the F-bit set to 1, or

- when the timer T1 (which was started after the I-frame with P=1 was transmitted) expires

Recall that the `window` object controls the maximum number of I-frames that can be transmitted without receiving an ack, and that the last I-frame transmitted has a P bit set to 1. In our implementation, the checkpoint begins after the last I-frame allowed by the `window` object has been transmitted and `_t1Timer` has been started. How do we know if the data-link is in a checkpoint cycle? We merely check to see if the `_t1Timer` is running. If it is, a checkpoint cycle is in progress. Thus, when a DL_DataReq is received, the I-frame is transmitted only if the `_t1Timer` is not running. Otherwise, the I-frame is queued to be transmitted at a later time.

The checkpoint cycle ends with no error conditions, if all the outstanding I-frames are acked before the _t1Timer expires. Figure 11.3 also shows the actions taken when the timer expires. A supervisory command frame (in this case, a RR) is transmitted with P=1. This is to solicit a response from the remote DTE. Once the supervisory command has been transmitted N2 times, a link-reset procedure is initiated.

11.6.1 Receiving Acknowledgment

Figure 11.3 also shows what happens when a valid n(r) is received. All the acknowledged I-frames are removed from the queue (in the window object), and any I-frames are retransmitted if necessary. Note that I-frames are retransmitted at the end of a checkpoint cycle, if a RR response with F=1 is received or if a REJ frame is received. A n(r) field received in an I-frame or a RNR frame does not result in retransmissions.

We will deal with the case of an invalid n(r) in Chapter 12 as part of error detection and error recovery.

11.7 Flow Control

When a RNR frame is received from the remote DTE it is said to be in a busy condition. This is our first introduction to implementing flow control. By transmitting a RNR the remote DTE is indicating that it is incapable of receiving any more I-frames until its busy condition is cleared.

When a RNR is received, the data-link layer sets a flag to indicate that the remote DTE is busy. This flag is checked every time an I-frame needs to be transmitted. The dllayer class contains a data member to represent the remote DTE status.

```
class dllayer : public layer {

    // ..
  private:

     Boolean    _remoteBusy;
};
```

The constructor of the dllayer class will initialize this flag to FALSE. The flag is set to TRUE whenever a RNR is received while the data-link is in the dlInfoXfer state. The flag is cleared (i.e. set to FALSE) when a RR or REJ is received from the remote DTE.

Why would a receiver go into the busy state? There could be any number of reasons - prominent among them being running out of buffer space to store any incoming I-frames. Unfortunately, in our implementation it is almost impossible to run out of buffer space, or to encounter any condition which makes the data-link go into a busy state. So, in order to learn how to deal with such a situation, if it were to arise, we will have to simulate the busy condition. A global variable `receiverBusy` can be used to monitor the local DTE's busy state.

```
Boolean receiverBusy;
```

Figure 11.4 Flow control transitions

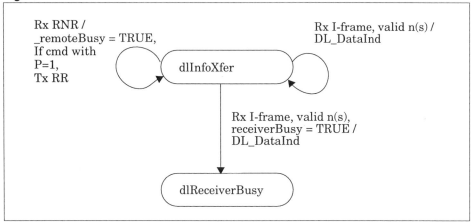

This variable can be set from the user interface to either TRUE or FALSE. If set to TRUE, it is equivalent to the condition that the receiver has run out of buffer space, and can accept no more I-frames. Figure 11.4 shows how the data-link can transition from the dlInfoXfer state to the dlReceiverBusy state when an I-frame is received, and the `receiverBusy` flag is TRUE. Real-world implementations which have buffer constraints would have the same transitions, only they would not use any dummy variable.

11.8 State dlReceiverBusy

The dlReceiverBusy state differs from the dlInfoXfer state only in the manner in which it processes I-frames and RR frames that are received.

Figure 11.5 Transition diagram - dlReceiverBusy state

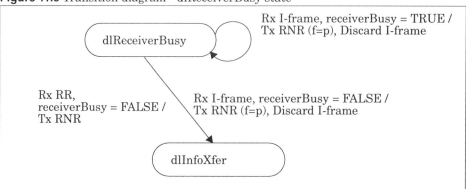

Figure 11.5 shows the state transitions for the dlReceiverBusy state. Note that the dlReceiverBusy class, which implements the state, actually inherits from the dlInfoXfer class, thus inheriting all other state transitions of the dlInfoXfer state except the ones shown in the figure. If the receiverBusy flag is set to FALSE while the data-link is in the dlReceiverBusy state, then a transition is made to dlInfoXfer state after a RR or an I-frame is received. The I-frame is discarded before the transition is made. The data-link would be in a position to process I-frames once it is in the dlInfoXfer state.

Before we examine the dlReceiverBusy class, let us finish looking at the aspects of the dlInfoXfer class that handle the DL_DataReq primitive, I-frames, RR and RNR frames.

```
class dlInfoXfer : public dlStateMachine {

 public:
    virtual dlStateMachine *DlDataReq(int &errorCode);


    virtual dlStateMachine *HandleIframe(int &errorCode);
    virtual dlStateMachine *HandleRr(int &errorCode);
    virtual dlStateMachine *HandleRnr(int &errorCode);

    virtual dlStateMachine *HandleT1Timer(int &errorCode);

 protected:

    virtual int   GetSupervisoryFrame();
    void          SendStateResponse();
    void          CheckT1Status();
    void          Transmit(Boolean retransmit);
};
```

Let us examine the protected utility methods. Method CheckT1Status() checks to see if the _t1Timer needs to be stopped, or restarted.

```
void
dlInfoXfer::CheckT1Status()
{
    if ( _dl->_win.UnackedFrames() != 0 ) {

        // There are unacknowledged I-frames.
        // Start T1 timer again.

        _dl->StartT1Timer(FALSE);
        _dl->_expFBit = 1;
    }

    else {
        _dl->StopT1Timer();
    }
}
```

The `Transmit()` method transmits any I-frames that are pending transmission. The window is reset for retransmission if necessary.

```
void
dlInfoXfer::Transmit(Boolean retransmit)
{
    int errorCode = codeSuccessful;

    if ( retransmit == TRUE )
        _dl->_win.StartRetransmission(); // reset V(s)

    // Query the window for I-frames to transmit.
    // The window will return I-frames with the
    // proper N(s), N(r), etc.

    dataPacket *dp;
    while ( dp = _dl->_win.GetNextToXmit() ) {

        _dl->_nMinus1->Command(PH_DataReq,errorCode,dp);

        if ( errorCode != codeSuccessful )
            return;

        _dl->_expFBit = 1; // the last I-frame has P=1
    }
    CheckT1Status(); // Start timer T1 if necessary
}
```

Method `GetSupervisoryFrame()` returns the type of supervisory frame to send. In the dlInfoXfer state, this method returns a RR.

```
int
dlInfoXfer::GetSupervisoryFrame()
```

```
{
    return RR;
}
```

Method `SendStateResponse()` uses the above method to transmit an appropriate supervisory response frame. Note that by redefining `GetSupervisoryFrame()` in classes `dlReceiverBusy` and `dlReject`, the method `SendStateResponse()` will transmit a RNR or REJ, respectively.

```
void
dlInfoXfer::SendStateResponse()
{
    // Transmit a supervisory response.
    int errorCode = codeSuccessful;
    _dl->XmitFrame(errorCode,FALSE,GetSupervisoryFrame(),
            _dl->_lastFrameRecd->GetPf(), _dl->_win.GetVr());
}
```

Now, we can examine the public methods which handle events. Here's how a DL_DataReq is handled.

```
dlStateMachine *
dlInfoXfer::DlDataReq(int &errorCode)
{
    // First check if remote DTE is busy.
    // Next check if we are in checkpointing.
    // All clear - transmit frames.

    if ( _dl->_remoteBusy == TRUE ) {

        // Remote DTE is busy.
        // As far the network layer is concerned
        // accept the data successfully for later transmission.

        errorCode = codeSuccessful;
    }

    else if ( _dl->_t1Timer != 0 ) {
        // In checkpoint cycle, cannot transmit I-frames.
        // As far the network layer is concerned
        // accept the data successfully for later transmission.

        errorCode = codeSuccessful;
    }

    else {

        // Transmit the I-frames, start timer etc.
```

```
        Transmit (FALSE) ;

    }
    return this;
}
```

How about handling I-frames? The following code is a part of the code
required for processing received I-frames. What is missing is the code required
for validating n(r) and n(s). These will be introduced in Chapter 12.

```
dlStateMachine *
dlInfoXfer::HandleIframe(int &errorCode)
{
    _dl->_lastFrameRecd->PrintParams();

    // Check for ack
    // The next chapter deals with an invalid n(r)

    int nr = _dl->_lastFrameRecd->GetNr();
    int numAcked;

    if ( (numAcked = _dl->_win.ProcessAck(nr)) == -1 )
        // Error recovery needed

    unsigned int ns = _dl->_lastFrameRecd->GetNs();

    // There will be a check here for an invalid n(s)
    // and any possible error recovery

    // Assuming a correct n(s) value

    if ( _dl->_lastFrameRecd->GetPf()) {
        // Have to send a response since P=1
        SendStateResponse();
    }
    else if ( !(_dl->_win.GetQueueLength() >
            _dl->_win.UnackedFrames())) {

        // There is no I-frame waiting to be transmitted.
        // Send a acknowledgement now in a supervisory frame.

        SendStateResponse();
    }

    // Else, the acknowledgement will be sent in the next
    // I-frame. Notify the network layer

    _dl->_nPlus1->Command(DL_DataInd, errorCode,
            _dl->_lastFrameRecd->GetDataPacket());
```

```
      // Now, if the receiverBusy flag is TRUE, we are to
      // go into a receiver busy state. Remember this is just a
      // simulation of the receiver busy condition, since our
      // software cannot really go into a busy state.

      if ( receiverBusy == FALSE )
         return this;

      // Receiver is busy - change state
      CHANGE_STATE(dlReceiverBusy);
}
```

A checkpoint cycle is started once a I-frame with P=1 is transmitted. Method CheckT1Status() starts the _t1Timer if there are I-frames pending acknowledgments. Method HandleT1Timer() processes the timeout of the _t1Timer.

```
dlStateMachine *
dlInfoXfer::HandleT1Timer(int &errorCode)
{
    if ( _dl->_t1RetryCount < N2 ) {

        // Transmit supervisory command frame
        // GetSupervisoryFrame() returns the type of
        // supervisory command to send.

        _dl->XmitFrame(errorCode,TRUE,
              GetSupervisoryFrame(),1, _dl->_win.GetVr());

        // Restart T1
        _dl->StartT1Timer(TRUE);
        return this;
    }

    else {

        // Already re-transmitted N2 times. Reset.
        return (LinkReset(errorCode));
    }
}
```

A RR frame that is received will result in the clearing of any busy condition for the remote DTE. If the RR is a response with F=1, it can also end a checkpoint cycle in progress. The HandleRr() method shown below is again missing the code for handling invalid n(r) values.

```
dlStateMachine *
dlInfoXfer::HandleRr(int &errorCode)
{
```

```
// Check for ack
// The next chapter deals with invalid n(r) values

int nr = _dl->_lastFrameRecd->GetNr();

int numAcked;
if ( (numAcked = _dl->_win.ProcessAck(nr)) == -1 )
// error recovery here.

// Okay we have a valid n(r)

Boolean cmd = _dl->_lastFrameRecd->IsCmd();

if ( _dl->_lastFrameRecd->GetPf() ) { // P/F = 1

   if ( cmd == TRUE )
      SendStateResponse();

   else if ( _dl->_remoteBusy == TRUE ||
         _dl->_t1Timer != 0 ) {

      // Remote DTE was busy
      // A checkpointing cycle just finished.
      // Retransmit any frames if necessary.

      Transmit(TRUE); // re-transmit any frames
   }
}
_dl->_remoteBusy = FALSE; // Remote DTE is no longer busy
return this;
}
```

A RNR frame received will result in the _remoteDTE flag being set to TRUE. No more I-frames can be transmitted until this flag is reset to FALSE. Method HandleRnr() processes a RNR frame.

```
dlStateMachine *
dlInfoXfer::HandleRnr(int &errorCode)
{
   // Check for ack
   // The next chapter deals with invalid n(r)

   int nr = _dl->_lastFrameRecd->GetNr();
   int numAcked;

   if ( (numAcked = _dl->_win.ProcessAck(nr)) == -1 )
      // Error recovery here.

   Boolean cmd = _dl->_lastFrameRecd->IsCmd();
```

```
// Transmit a response immediately RNR is a command
// with P = 1

if ( _dl->_lastFrameRecd->GetPf() && cmd == TRUE )
   SendStateResponse();

// Transmit a supervisory command querying for the
// remote DTE status.

_dl->XmitFrame(errorCode,TRUE,GetSupervisoryFrame(),1,
      _dl->_win.GetVr());

//Start timer T1 with a zero retry count
_dl->StartT1Timer(FALSE);

_dl->_remoteBusy = TRUE; // Remote DTE is busy now
return this;
}
```

11.9 Class dlReceiverBusy

The dlReceiverBusy class inherits most of its functionality from the dlIn-foXfer class, except for the manner in which it handles I-frames and RR frames.

```
class dlReceiverBusy : public dlInfoXfer {
 public:

   dlReceiverBusy(dllayer *dl);
   virtual ~dlReceiverBusy() {}
   virtual dlStateMachine *HandleIframe(int &errorCode);
   virtual dlStateMachine *HandleRr(int &errorCode);
   virtual void PrintState();

 protected:
   virtual int GetSupervisoryFrame();
};
```

The constructor invokes the base class constructor (See Exercise 4.). Method GetSupervisoryFrame() is redefined to return RNR.

```
dlReceiverBusy::dlReceiverBusy(dllayer *dl) :
dlInfoXfer(dl,FALSE) {}

int
dlReceiverBusy::GetSupervisoryFrame()
{
    return RNR;
}
```

Thus, all the code in the dlInfoXfer state which needs to send a supervisory response will still work as before, except that in the dlReceiverBusy state, the inherited code will be transmitting RNRs instead of RRs.

When the receiver is busy, I-frames are discarded except for the n(r) field which is processed.

```
dlStateMachine *
dlReceiverBusy::HandleIframe(int &errorCode)
{
    _dl->_lastFrameRecd->PrintParams();

    // Check for ack
    // The next chapter deals with invalid n(r) values

    int nr = _dl->_lastFrameRecd->GetNr();
    int numAcked;
    if ( (numAcked = _dl->_win.ProcessAck(nr)) == -1 )
    // error recovery here

    SendStateResponse();

    if ( receiverBusy == TRUE )
        return this;

    // Receiver is not busy anymore
    // Change back to dlInfoXfer
    // The data-link will be able to process I-frames
    // the next time it receives them.

    CHANGE_TO_INFOXFER(FALSE);
}
```

The `HandleRr()` method adds to the functionality of the `HandleRr()` method in the `dlInfoXfer` class. It transmits a RNR response, and also checks to see if the data-link needs to remain in the busy state or not.

```
dlStateMachine *
dlReceiverBusy::HandleRr(int &errorCode)
{
    // Call the base class method.
    dlInfoXfer::HandleRr(errorCode);

    // Send RNR response for cases that the base class
    // would not have responded.

    if (_dl->_lastFrameRecd->IsCmd() == TRUE &&
        _dl->_lastFrameRecd->GetPf() == 0)

        SendStateResponse();
```

```
        else if ( _dl->_lastFrameRecd->IsCmd() == FALSE ) {

            // Transmit a supervisory response.
            int errorCode = codeSuccessful;
            _dl->XmitFrame(errorCode,FALSE,
                GetSupervisoryFrame(),0, _dl->_win.GetVr());
        }

        if ( receiverBusy == TRUE )
            return this;

        // Receiver is not busy anymore.
        // Change back to dlInfoXfer.

        CHANGE_TO_INFOXFER(FALSE);
    }
```

We have examined all the code necessary to implement full duplex data transfer under error-free conditions and to implement flow control. Chapter 12 will deal with situations where invalid sequence numbers are received, or invalid n(r) fields are received as acknowledgments. Some of these are recoverable errors, others necessitate a link reset.

11.10 Summary

11.10.1 Classes Developed

- window - This class encapsulates the behavior of sliding window protocols. A list of frame objects is maintained and hence the window class has a composition relationship with the frameList class. The window class maintains state variables v(s) and v(r), and queues I-frames until they are transmitted and acknowledged. It provides methods to format the I-frames and access them for transmission. It also processes the acknowledgments received in the n(r) field of I-frame/RR/REJ/RNR frames.

- dllayer - This class was augmented to interact with the window class, and also to handle the DL_DataReq primitive. The dllayer class has a composition relationship with the window class in that it has a data member which is a window instance.

- dlInfoXfer - This class inherits from the dlStateMachine class and redefines methods to provide the functionality for the dlInfoXfer state of the data-link layer. This chapter looked at the methods needed for transmitting I-frames, checkpointing and processing acknowledgments.

- dlReceiverBusy - This class inherits from the dlInfoXfer class and redefines methods to provide the functionality for the dlReceiverBusy state of the data-link layer. In this state the data-link is unable to process I-frames because of a busy condition, which is artificially created in this implementation.

11.10.2 Source Files

- window.h and window.C

- dlInfoXfer.h and dlInfoXfer.C

- dlReceiverBusy.h and dlReceiverBusy.C

- dllayer.h and dllayer.C

11.11 Exercises

1. In the `dllayer::Command()` method for handling the DL_DataReq primitives, the incoming `dataPacket` is first inserted into the window's queue, and then the `ProcessEvent()` method is called. Find the potential bug in this implementation.

2. Think of an alternative way of simulating and implementing the local DTE receiver busy condition.

3. In our implementation we queue all the I-frames to be transmitted. Why don't we queue the I-frames that are received?

4. Why does the dlReceiverBusy constructor invoke the dlInfoXfer constructor with the reset argument set to FALSE?

5. The `window` class implementation has a bug in the manner in which it deals with the modulus and K values. Given the relationship between the modulus and K (K = modulus - 1), identify the bug in the method `GetNext-ToXmit()`.

12

Error Detection
and Error Recovery

12.1 Introduction

We saved the best for the last. If we didn't have this chapter, our protocol would collapse at the first hint of trouble. ISO 7776 is a robust protocol, capable of detecting and recovering from a number of different types of errors. Of course, situations arise where an error is detected, but there is no possible means of recovering from it. In such cases, the protocol resorts to a link reset.

In chapters 10 and 11 we have already seen some types of error detection and recovery. For instance, during a connection setup, if a request for a link setup was not acknowledged within a timeout period T1, then the request was repeated. The ack might have been delayed for a variety of reasons, including the fact that the original request might not have reached the remote DTE, or the ack from the remote DTE might have got lost. Thus, recovery mechanisms which use the T1 timer are an integral part of error recovery. In the information transfer phase we saw how the T1 timer is used for checkpointing, which again forms part of the error detection of lost I-frames or lost acks. Error recovery during checkpointing involves retransmission of I-frames if necessary.

This chapter will deal with the following types of error detection and error recovery:

- n(s) sequence errors which cause the data-link to go into the dlReject state (after having sent a REJ frame).

- serious errors from which there is no recovery possible other than a link reset.

12.2 Transition to dlReject State

Let us first examine the conditions which cause the data-link to go into the dlReject error recovery state. The transition from dlInfoXfer to dlReject is very straightforward. Whenever the data-link receives an out-of-sequence I-frame (i.e. an I-frame whose n(s) value is not equal to receive state variable v(r)) while it is in the dlInfoXfer state, it transmits a REJ frame and transitions to the dlReject state, where it then waits for an I-frame with the correct sequence number. Meanwhile, a DTE which receives a REJ frame processes the n(r) field and retransmits any I-frames necessary. Figure 12.1 shows the transitions in the dlInfoXfer state which involve I-frame sequence errors.

Figure 12.1 I-frame sequence error handling

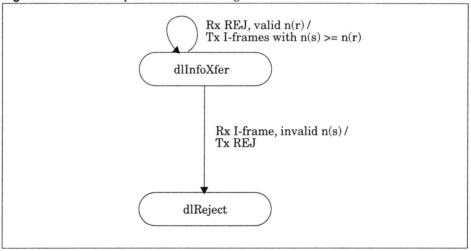

The following code fragments from the `dlInfoXfer` class demonstrate how the errors are handled.

```
class dlInfoXfer : public dlStateMachine {
    // ...
 public:

    virtual dlStateMachine *HandleRej(int &errorCode);
};
```

The HandleRej() method will retransmit any necessary I-frames. It uses Go-back-N ARQ (see Chapter 4).

```
dlStateMachine *
dlInfoXfer::HandleRej(int &errorCode)
{
    // Check for ack.
    // Invalid n(r) will be dealt with later in this chapter.

    int nr = _dl->_lastFrameRecd->GetNr();
    int numAcked;
    if ( (numAcked = _dl->_win.ProcessAck(nr)) == -1 )
        // Error recovery here.

    Boolean cmd = _dl->_lastFrameRecd->IsCmd();

    if ( cmd == TRUE && _dl->_lastFrameRecd->GetPf() )
        SendStateResponse();

    // Clear any remote DTE busy condition
    _dl->_remoteBusy = FALSE;

    // Start retransmissions if needed.
    // Note Transmit() is called with argument TRUE -
    // this causes the window to be reset for retransmission.

    Transmit(TRUE);
    return this;
}
```

The HandleIframe() method introduced in Chapter 11 needs to be augmented to handle the situation of a n(s) sequence error.

```
dlStateMachine *
dlInfoXfer::HandleIframe(int &errorCode)
{
    // All the previous code + ..

    unsigned int ns = _dl->_lastFrameRecd->GetNs();

    if ( _dl->_win.CheckSequence(ns) == FALSE ) {

        // Out of sequence I-frame
        // Transmit REJ, and go into dlReject state

        TRACE(dlSmModule,1,("Out of sequence frame\n"));

        _dl->XmitFrame(errorCode,FALSE,REJ,
            _dl->_lastFrameRecd->GetPf(),_dl->_win.GetVr());
```

```
            _dl->StartRejTimer(FALSE);
            CHANGE_STATE(dlReject);
    }

    // + all the rest of the code ...
}
```

The above two methods demonstrate how the `dlInfoXfer` class causes a transition to dlReject state, and how it handles a REJ frame received from the remote DTE.

12.3 State dlReject

The dlReject can be reached only from the dlInfoXfer state after having received an out-of-sequence I-frame. The reject condition can be cleared only after receiving the I-frame with the correct sequence number (n(s)).

Figure 12.2 State transitions for dlReject state

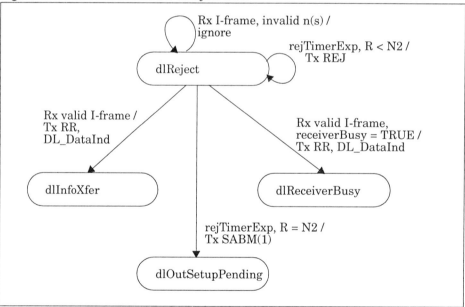

Figure 12.2 shows the state transitions for the dlReject state. Recall that the dlReject state is a special state under the dlInfoXfer state (or, in C++ terms, the `dlReject` class inherits from the `dlInfoXfer` class). Thus, most of the state transitions for the dlReject state are the same as that for the dlInfoXfer state, except for the conditions shown above. The `dlReject` class redefines the methods necessary to handle I-frames and `rejTimer` expiration.

```
class dlReject : public dlInfoXfer {

public:
   dlReject(dllayer *dl);
   virtual ~dlReject() {}
   virtual dlStateMachine *HandleIframe(int &errorCode);
   virtual void PrintState();

   virtual dlStateMachine *HandleRejTimer(int &errorCode);

protected:
   virtual int GetSupervisoryFrame();
};
```

The constructor invokes the base class constructor. Note that the second argument to the dlInfoXfer() constructor is FALSE. This means that the state variables of the data-link are not to be reset.

```
dlReject::dlReject(dllayer *dl) : dlInfoXfer(dl,FALSE)
{
}
```

Method GetSupervisoryFrame() returns a REJ. Thus, methods in dlInfoXfer class which use this method while sending a supervisory response will still work, but a REJ frame will be transmitted informing the remote DTE of the reject condition.

```
int
dlReject::GetSupervisoryFrame()
{
    return REJ;
}
```

Method HandleIframe() does most of the work. All I-frames with invalid n(s) values are discarded. This is because only one REJ condition can be maintained at any one time. Since we have already sent a REJ frame for a previously received invalid n(s), we cannot send another REJ frame for any other invalid n(s) values.

```
dlStateMachine *
dlReject::HandleIframe(int &errorCode)
{
    _dl->_lastFrameRecd->PrintParams();

    // Check for ack.
    // The case of invalid N(r) will be dealt with later

    unsigned int ns = _dl->_lastFrameRecd->GetNs();
```

```
// Discard out-of-sequence I-frame
if ( _dl->_win.CheckSequence(ns) == FALSE ) {
   TRACE(dlSmModule,1,("Out of sequence frame\n"));
   return this;
}

// Valid n(s) received.
// Acknowledge the Iframe, and clear the Reject condition.

_dl->XmitFrame(errorCode,FALSE,RR,
   _dl->_lastFrameRecd->GetPf(), _dl->_win.GetVr());


// Notify the network layer
_dl->_nPlus1->Command(DL_DataInd,errorCode,
   _dl->_lastFrameRecd->GetDataPacket());


// Check if receiver is busy or not!
if ( receiverBusy == FALSE ) {
   CHANGE_TO_INFOXFER(FALSE);
}

// Receiver is busy ...change back to dlReceiverBusy
CHANGE_STATE(dlReceiverBusy);
}
```

The `rejTimer` was started after sending the first REJ frame in the dlInfo-Xfer state and transitioning to the dlReject state. Method `HandleRej-Timer()` processes the `rejTimer` timeouts.

```
dlStateMachine *
dlReject::HandleRejTimer(int &errorCode)
{
    if ( _dl->_rejRetryCount < N2 ) {

        // Retransmit the REJ
        _dl->XmitFrame(errorCode,TRUE,REJ,1,
        _dl->_win.GetVr());

        // Restart REJ Timer
        _dl->StartRejTimer(TRUE);
        return this;
    }
    else {
        // Rej timer timed out N2 times!
        _dl->_rejTimer = 0;
        return ( LinkReset(errorCode));
    }
}
```

If the correct I-frame is not received before the `rejTimer` expires, the REJ frame is retransmitted. After retransmitting the REJ frame N2 times, a link reset is initiated.

Figure 12.3 Error conditions requiring link reset

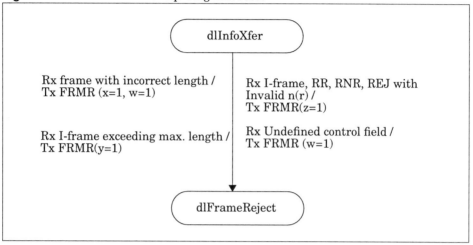

12.4 Frame Reject Conditions

If the following errors occur while the data-link is in the dlInfoXfer state (or its sub-states, dlReceiverBusy and dlReject), then the data-link transmits a FRMR frame, and enters the dlFrameReject state.

- Invalid n(r) value received in a I-frame, RR, RNR or REJ.

- Undefined control field in a frame.

- A frame contained an information field that is not permitted.

- An I-frame with the information field greater than the maximum allowed.

Figure 12.4 FRMR information field formats

<u>Unnumbered format (U)</u>

| info. field bits: | 1 | 2 | 3 | 4 | 5 | 6 | 7 | 8 |

Byte 1:   ----- rejected frame control field ---

Byte 2:   0   ----- n(s) ---   c/r   ---- n(r) ----

Byte 3:   w   x   y   z   0   0   0   0

Transmitting a FRMR frame is a desperate plea by the DTE to indicate it has encountered an irrecoverable error, and the link needs to be reset. Figure 12.3 shows the transitions from the dlInfoXfer state to the dlFrameReject state.

A FRMR frame that is transmitted requires a 3-byte information field which identifies the cause of the trouble. Figure 12.4 shows the format of each byte.

■ Byte 1 contains the control field of the rejected frame in its entirety.

■ Byte 2: n(s) is set equal to v(s) - the current send state variable of the DTE transmitting the FRMR.

■ Byte 2: c/r will be set to "1" if the frame being rejected is a response frame, and it will be set to "0" if the frame being rejected is a command frame.

■ Byte 2: n(r) will be set equal to v(r) - the receive state variable at the DTE transmitting the FRMR.

■ Byte 3: "w" will be set to "1" if the control field received and returned in byte 1 was undefined or not implemented.

■ Byte 3: "x" is set to "1" if a frame was received containing an information field which was not permitted. "w" will also be set to 1 in this case.

■ Byte 3: "y" is set to "1" to indicate that an I-frame was received with an information field length which exceeded the maximum allowed length.

■ Byte 3: "z" is set to "1" to indicate an invalid n(r) value.

Once a FRMR is transmitted, then a link reset command or request is expected from the remote DTE. If no response is received, then the same FRMR needs to be transmitted (with an information field which is identical to the first FRMR). This implies, we have to store the 3-byte information field somewhere. The dllayer class provides an ideal place to store this information field, and also the method which transmits the FRMR.

```
class dllayer : public layer {

// ..
private:

    unsigned char _frmrInfo[3];
    void    XmitFrmr(int pf,int &errorCode);
};

void
dllayer::XmitFrmr(int pf, int &errorCode)
{
    // Form the dataPacket with info. field
    dataPacket *frmrData = new dataPacket(_frmrInfo,3);

    frame fr(frmrData,TRUE); // Instantiate a frame
    fr.SetParams(FRMR,pf); // Set to FRMR frame type
    fr.FormFrame(FALSE); // Form the response frame
```

```
    // Invoke PH_DataReq on the physical layer.

    _nMinus1->Command(PH_DataReq, errorCode,
        fr.GetDataPacket());
}
```

The above method and data in the `dllayer` class is used by the `dlIn-foXfer` class, which needs some more code to handle the error conditions. We start by adding some code to the class declaration.

```
// FRMR conditions (in types.h)
enum FrmrConditionType { W=1, X = 2, Y = 4, Z = 8 };

class dlInfoXfer : public dlStateMachine {
// ...

 public:

    virtual dlStateMachine *HandleUndefined(int &errorCode);
    virtual dlStateMachine *HandleUnsolFBit(int &errorCode);
    virtual dlStateMachine *
                HandleIncorrectLength(int &errorCode);
    virtual dlStateMachine *
                HandleIfrLengthExcess(int &errorCode);
 protected:

    dlStateMachine * HandleFrmrCondition(
            FrmrConditionType type, int &errorCode);
};
```

Method `HandleFrmrCondition()` formats a FRMR frame, transmits it and transitions to the dlFrameReject state. It uses the facilities provided by the `dllayer` class to transmit the FRMR frame.

```
dlStateMachine *
dlInfoXfer::HandleFrmrCondition(FrmrConditionType type,
        int &errorCode)
{

    // Form the information field for the FRMR frame
    // First clear the bytes
    _dl->_frmrInfo[0] &= 0x00;
    _dl->_frmrInfo[1] &= 0x00;
    _dl->_frmrInfo[2] &= 0x00;

    // The first byte is the control byte of the recd. frame
    // which caused the rejection

    _dl->_frmrInfo[0] =
```

```
        _dl->_lastFrameRecd->GetCntl(); // Control byte

        // The second byte contains V(r), V(s) and info. about
        // whether the received frame was a response or
        // command frame.

        _dl->_frmrInfo[1] =
            (_dl->_win.GetVs() << 1) |
            ((_dl->_lastFrameRecd->IsCmd() == TRUE ? 0 : 1)<< 4) |
            ( _dl->_win.GetVr() << 5 );

        // The third byte..
        _dl->_frmrInfo[2] |= type; // Passed in argument

        if ( type == X )
            _dl->_frmrInfo[2] |= W; // set the 'W' bit also

        // Transmit the FRMR
        _dl->XmitFrmr(_dl->_lastFrameRecd->GetPf(),errorCode);

        if ( errorCode == codeSuccessful ) {
            _dl->StartT1Timer(FALSE);
            CHANGE_STATE(dlFrameReject);
        }
        else
            return this;
    }
```

The HandleFrmrCondition() method is invoked for all the error conditions mentioned earlier. Finally, we get to see what happens when we receive
an invalid n(r) field in a I-frame, RR, RNR or REJ.

```
    dlStateMachine *
    dlInfoXfer::HandleIframe(int &errorCode)
    {
        // Check for ack
        // Transmit FRMR if invalid N(r)

        int nr = _dl->_lastFrameRecd->GetNr();
        int numAcked;
        if ( (numAcked = _dl->_win.ProcessAck(nr)) == -1 )
            return HandleFrmrCondition(Z,errorCode);

        // + all the rest of the code..
    }
```

Method HandleFrmrCondition() is also invoked when an invalid n(r) is
received in methods HandleRr(), HandleRnr() and HandleRej(). The
other methods which transmit a FRMR are:

```
dlStateMachine *
dlInfoXfer::HandleUndefined(int &errorCode)
{
    // Received an undefined control field.
    return HandleFrmrCondition(W,errorCode);
}

dlStateMachine *
dlInfoXfer::HandleIncorrectLength(int &errorCode)
{
    // Received info. field in a frame in which it is
    // not permitted.
    return HandleFrmrCondition(X,errorCode);
}

dlStateMachine *
dlInfoXfer::HandleIfrLengthExcess(int &errorCode)
{
    // Received I-frame with info. field which exceeds
    // Maximum limit.
    return HandleFrmrCondition(Y,errorCode);
}
```

Figure 12.5 State transitions for dlFrameReject state

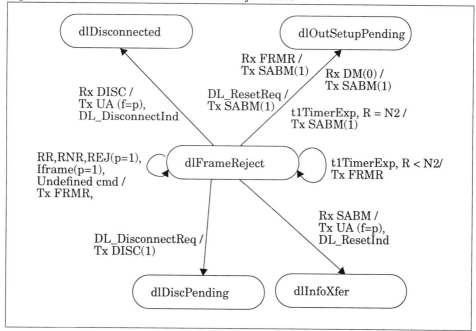

12.5 State dlFrameReject

The dlFrameReject state is entered after transmitting a FRMR from the dlIn-foXfer state. The dlFrameReject state is one in which the data-link is awaiting link reset because of irrecoverable error conditions. The remote DTE can initiate a link reset, or request for a link reset by transmitting a mode setting command (DM, F=0).

Figure 12.5 shows the state transitions that can occur in the dlFrameReject state. The class dlFrameReject inherits from class dlStateMachine and implements the state functionality.

```
/*
 * File : dlFrameReject.h
 */

class dlFrameReject : public dlStateMachine {

 public:
    dlFrameReject(dllayer *dl);
    virtual ~dlFrameReject() {}

    virtual dlStateMachine *DlResetReq(int &errorCode);
    virtual dlStateMachine *DlDisconnectReq(int &errorCode);

    virtual dlStateMachine *HandleSabm(int &errorCode);
    virtual dlStateMachine *HandleDisc(int &errorCode);
    virtual dlStateMachine *HandleDm(int &errorCode);
    virtual dlStateMachine *HandleT1Timer(int &errorCode);

    virtual dlStateMachine *HandleUndefined(int &errorCode);
    virtual dlStateMachine *
                HandleIncorrectLength(int &errorCode);
    virtual dlStateMachine *
                HandleIfrLengthExcess(int &errorCode);


    dlStateMachine *HandleIframe(int &errorCode);
    dlStateMachine *HandleRr(int &errorCode);
    dlStateMachine *HandleRnr(int &errorCode);
    dlStateMachine *HandleRej(int &errorCode);
    dlStateMachine *HandleFrmr(int &errorCode);

    virtual void PrintState();
 private:
    void HandleCmd(int &errorCode);
};
```

As usual, the constructor invokes the base class constructor.

```
dlFrameReject::dlFrameReject(dllayer *dl) :
dlStateMachine(dl)
{
}
```

The method `HandleSabm()` processes a SABM, and changes state to dlIn-foXfer. A DL_ResetInd is issued to the network layer with a reason code of `internalError`.

```
dlStateMachine *
dlFrameReject::HandleSabm(int &errorCode)
{
    _dl->XmitFrame(errorCode,FALSE,UA,
            _dl->_lastFrameRecd->GetPf());

    _dl->_nPlus1->Command(DL_ResetInd,errorCode,
            internalError);

    CHANGE_TO_INFOXFER(TRUE);
}
```

Method `HandleDisc()` processes a DISC, and changes state to dlDiscon-nected. This means a link reset was refused by the remote DTE.

```
dlStateMachine *
dlFrameReject::HandleDisc(int &errorCode)
{
    _dl->XmitFrame(errorCode,FALSE,UA,
        _dl->_lastFrameRecd->GetPf());

    _dl->_nPlus1->Command(DL_DisconnectInd,errorCode,
        internalError);

    CHANGE_STATE(dlDisconnected);
}
```

A DM(f=0) response from the remote DTE is a request to initiate a link reset. The `HandleDm()` method performs this task by transmitting a SABM and transitioning to dlOutSetupPending state (see Exercise 2).

```
dlStateMachine *
dlFrameReject::HandleDm(int &errorCode)
{
    // Ignore DM F=1, we should not even be getting this.
    if ( _dl->_lastFrameRecd->GetPf())
        return this;

    // If it is a mode setting command - start link reset
```

```
        _dl->XmitFrame(errorCode,TRUE,SABM,1);
        _dl->StartT1Timer(FALSE);
        _dl->_setupType = internalReset;// Note setup type is internal
        CHANGE_STATE(dlOutSetupPending);
}
```

Other commands in the form of I-frames, RRs, RNRs, and REJs with the P bit set to 1, result in a FRMR response being retransmitted. This is even done for command frames with errors. Note that for the invalid command frames (e.g., a command frame with an undefined control field) the original FRMR is retransmitted, not a new FRMR reporting the new error.

```
void
dlFrameReject::HandleCmd(int &errorCode)
{
    // Transmit FRMR only if p=1
    if ( _dl->_lastFrameRecd->IsCmd() == TRUE &&
        _dl->_lastFrameRecd->GetPf()) {
        _dl->XmitFrmr(1,errorCode);
    }
}

dlStateMachine *
dlFrameReject::HandleRr(int &errorCode)
{
    HandleCmd(errorCode);
    return this;
}

dlStateMachine *
dlFrameReject::HandleRnr(int &errorCode)
{
    HandleCmd(errorCode);
    return this;
}

dlStateMachine *
dlFrameReject::HandleRej(int &errorCode)
{
    HandleCmd(errorCode);
    return this;
}


dlStateMachine *
dlFrameReject::HandleIframe(int &errorCode)
{
    HandleCmd(errorCode);
    return this;
}
```

```
dlStateMachine *
dlFrameReject::HandleUndefined(int &errorCode)
{
    HandleCmd(errorCode);
    return this;
}

dlStateMachine *
dlFrameReject::HandleIncorrectLength(int &errorCode)
{
    HandleCmd(errorCode);
    return this;
}

dlStateMachine *
dlFrameReject::HandleIfrLengthExcess(int &errorCode)
{
    HandleCmd(errorCode);
    return this;
}
```

A DL_ResetReq and a DL_DisconnectReq from the network layer (while the data-link is in the dlFrameReject state) causes a transition to dlOutSetup-Pending state and dlDiscPending state, respectively.

```
dlStateMachine *
dlFrameReject::DlResetReq(int &errorCode)
{
    // now, go ahead and send a SABM

    _dl->XmitFrame(errorCode,TRUE,SABM,1);

    if ( errorCode == codeSuccessful ) {
        _dl->StartT1Timer(FALSE);
        _dl->_setupType = externalReset;
        CHANGE_STATE(dlOutSetupPending);
    }
    else
        return this;
}

dlStateMachine *
dlFrameReject::DlDisconnectReq(int &errorCode)
{
    // send a DISC

    _dl->XmitFrame(errorCode,TRUE,DISC,1);

    if ( errorCode == codeSuccessful ) {
        _dl->StartT1Timer(FALSE);
```

```
            CHANGE_STATE(dlDiscPending);
    }
    else
        return this;
}
```

The only event left to handle now is the expiration of the T1 timer. If the timer expires while in the dlFrameReject state it implies that the remote DTE has not responded to the FRMR. The original FRMR frame is retransmitted up to N2 times before the DTE resorts to a link reset itself.

```
dlStateMachine *
dlFrameReject::HandleT1Timer(int &errorCode)
{
    if ( _dl->_t1RetryCount < N2 ) {

        // Re-transmit a FRMR
        _dl->XmitFrmr(0,errorCode);

        if ( errorCode == codeSuccessful ) {
            // Re-start T1 timer.
            _dl->StartT1Timer(TRUE);
            return this;
        }

        else {
            // Failed to transmit FRMR
            _dl->_nPlus1->Command(DL_DisconnectInd,
                errorCode,noPeerResponse);
            CHANGE_STATE(dlDisconnected);
        }
    }
    else {

        // Retransmissions exceed N2, disconnect link
        _dl->XmitFrame(errorCode,TRUE,SABM,1);
        _dl->StartT1Timer(FALSE);
        _dl->_setupType = internalReset;
        CHANGE_STATE(dlOutSetupPending);
    }
}
```

12.6 Garbled Frames

Finally, there are some errors which are just ignored. These are errors connected with framing (they are detected when a frame object is formed from incoming data):

■ An error with the trailing and leading flags in a frame.

- A frame which contains less than 32 bits between the flags.

- A frame which has a wrong address field (other than address A or address B in our implementation).

- A frame with a frame check sequence (FCS) error.

All these frames result in a frame type of INVALID, and the `ProcessEvent()` method of the `dllayer` class ignores this event, thereby discarding these frames.

That concludes our implementation of the various states in the data-link layer.

12.7 Summary

12.7.1 Classes Developed

- `dlInfoXfer` - This class was augmented to handle error conditions arising out of out-of-sequence I-frames and REJ frames from the peer layer. Out-of-sequence I-frames result in a REJ frame being transmitted and a state change to the dlReject state. A REJ frame, which is received while in the dlInfoXfer state, causes retransmission of requested I-frames. A Go-back-N ARQ retransmission strategy is used to recover from I-frame sequence errors.

- `dlReject` - This class inherits from the `dlInfoXfer` class and redefines methods to provide functionality for the dlReject state of the data-link layer. This state is reached after detecting out-of-sequence I-frames. The reject condition is cleared, either after the I-frame with the correct n(s) is received or if the link is reset.

- dlFrameReject - This class inherits from the dlStateMachine class and redefines methods to provide functionality for the dlFrameReject state of the data-link layer. This state is reached when the data-link detects errors from which it cannot recover. These include receiving invalid n(r) values in a I-frame/RR/REJ/RNR, undefined control field in a frame, a frame with an information field that is not permitted, or an I-frame with the information field greater than the maximum allowed. A FRMR frame is transmitted by the data-link to indicate the error condition detected and as a request to initiate link-reset. Garbled frames are ignored and do not result in a FRMR being transmitted.

12.7.2 Source Files

- dlInfoXfer.h and dlInfoXfer.C

- dlReject.h and dlReject.C

- dlFrameReject.h and dlFrameReject.C

12.8 Exercises

1. The retransmission strategy employed in the ISO 7776 is a Go-back-N ARQ. What implementation changes would need to be made to incorporate selective repeat ARQ?

2. Identify the provider-initiated services implemented as part of the dlFrameReject class.

13

User Interface and
Conformance Testing

13.1 Introduction

In this last chapter we'll revisit the user interface and examine how it allows us to test out the data-link protocol that we have implemented in the last four chapters. We'll briefly touch upon the topic of conformance testing of protocols.

Finally, as an exercise to the reader, a rudimentary file transfer problem will be specified which can be implemented using the services of the data-link layer.

13.2 The User Interface

The user interface is implemented as part of the `nwlayer` class, which is both an `inputHandler` and a `layer`. It needs to be an `inputHandler` to process user input on STDIN. It needs to be a `layer` to handle data-link primitives invoked by the data-link layer on the network layer. These primitives have a direction of service-provider to service-user.

The code for the user interface (UI) is very simple, and mostly tedious. There is not much benefit in examining the code in detail in this chapter. Instead we'll just look at all the functionality provided by the UI. Chapter 8 introduced the `nwlayer` class, and showed how user input is processed. The menu-driven interface presented earlier is essentially expanded to provide additional functionality. Here's what the top-level menu looks like:

```
The following commands are available
Use the integer in brackets to invoke the given command

Set TRACE                (1)
Unset TRACE              (2)
Physical Layer commands (3)
Data link layer commands(4)
Network layer commands  (5)
Set system parameters   (6)
Exit                    (7)
Please type in (integer) command :
```

Let us examine all the various blocks briefly.

13.2.1 Tracing Module

The user interface allows us to interactively turn on/off the tracing in various modules. The level of tracing in each module can also be set to any desired value. We examined this implementation in Chapter 8.

13.2.2 Physical Layer Commands

The user-interface allows us to invoke primitives directly on the physical layer. The functioning of the physical layer can be tested out independently by invoking the following primitives:

- PH_ActivateReq

- PH_DeactivateReq

- PH_DataReq

Commands to block/unblock transmission and reception are also provided. This allows us to introduce error conditions into the system. Upon selecting "Physical Layer commands" from the main menu, the following sub-menu is displayed:

```
Activate Physical Layer     (1)
Deactivate Physical Layer   (2)
Send Data                   (3)
Block transmission          (4)
Block reception             (5)
```

```
            Unblock transmission        (6)
            Unblock reception           (7)

Type in command :
```

13.2.3 Data-link Layer Commands

The UI allows us to invoke the following primitives on the data-link layer:

■ DL_ConnectReq

■ DL_ConnectRes

■ DL_DataReq

■ DL_ResetReq

■ DL_ResetRes

■ DL_DisconnectReq

Invoking primitives on the local DTE means that frames are transmitted to the remote DTE via the local DTE. The user interface also provides mechanisms to transmit frames (both valid and invalid frames) to the remote DTE while bypassing the local DTE. This is done by accessing the physical layer directly. This feature is invaluable for testing, where various types of frames can be sent to the remote DTE without worrying about the local DTE.

Valid frames can be transmitted and the user can be queried for values for the n(r), n(s), p/f, address and information fields. Invalid frames can be created and transmitted by generating frames with erroneous values for:

■ Flags

■ Frame Check Sequence

■ Address byte

■ The number of bits in a frame between the leading and trailing flags

Further error situations can be created by block/unblocking transmission and reception in the data-link layer. Also, a receiver busy situation can be simulated by setting the receiverBusy flag to TRUE. The local DTE looks at this flag to determine whether to enter the receiver busy state or not. The following is a user session for sending an invalid SABM frame with a messed-up frame check sequence (starting with the sub-menu that is displayed upon selecting item 4 in the main menu):

```
    Send valid frame - bypass data link (0)
    Send invalid frame-bypass data link (1)
    Data Link Connect Req               (2)
    Data Link Connect Res               (3)
    Data Link Data Req                  (4)
```

```
                  Data Link Reset   Req                (5)
                  Data Link Reset   Res                (6)
                  Data Link Disconnect Req             (7)
                  Block transmission                   (8)
                  Block reception                      (9)
                  Unblock transmission                 (10)
                  Unblock reception                    (11)
                  Set Data Link to busy                (12)
                  Set Data Link to ready               (13)

                  Type in command : 1

                  Send valid frame - bypass data link (0)
                  Send invalid frame-bypass data link (1)
                  Data Link Connect Req                (2)
                  Data Link Connect Res                (3)
                  Data Link Data Req                   (4)
                  Data Link Reset   Req                (5)
                  Data Link Reset   Res                (6)
                  Data Link Disconnect Req             (7)
                  Block transmission                   (8)
                  Block reception                      (9)
                  Unblock transmission                 (10)
                  Unblock reception                    (11)
                  Set Data Link to busy                (12)
                  Set Data Link to ready               (13)
                  Type in command : 1

            Do you want any information field (y/n) :  n
                              IFRAME ( 0  )
                              RR     ( 1  )
                              RNR    ( 5  )
                              REJ    ( 9  )
                              DM     ( 15 )
                              SABM   ( 47 )
                              DISC   ( 67 )
                              UA     ( 99 )
                              FRMR   ( 135)
                  Unknown control field( 13 )

                          Select frame type : 47
                          Type in P/F bit :1

                  Mess up flags                        (1)
                  Mess up FCS                          (2)
                  Change address encoding              (3)
                  Have less than 32 bits between flags (4)
                  Toggle command / response frmames    (5)

                  Select type of error to be introduced: 2
```

```
Adding an extra byte..should mess it up!
```

13.2.4 Driver Layer Commands

The interaction with the driver layer from the user interface is minimal. Once again, transmission and reception can be blocked/unblocked. Also, the driver layer can be set up to either accept or deny connection and reset requests. This will allow us to further test the data-link layer functionality. The following sub-menu is displayed upon selecting item 5 from the main menu:

```
Block reception              (1)
Unblock reception            (2)
NW conn accept toggle        (3)

Type in command :
```

13.2.5 System Parameters

The user interface allows us to manipulate the values of the following system parameters:

- Timeout value for the T1 timer

- Value for maximum retry count variable N2

- The maximum length for an I-frame

- The maximum data packet size (which is exchanged between layers)

The following sub-menu is displayed upon selecting item 5 from the main menu:

```
Timer T1                    (1)
Retry count N2              (2)
Maximum I-frame length     (3)
Maximum data packet size(4)

Please select :
```

13.3 Executing the Software

The source code provided with this book can be compiled using the makefile that is provided. Ensure that the makefile has the correct path for the C++ compiler. The makefile creates an executable name "dl". The program "dl" takes three arguments:

- The name of the receive FIFO.

- The name of the transmit FIFO.

■ An integer flag whose value can be 0 or 1. This flag is used to select the command/response addresses for the data-link layer frames.

Here's how two processes will be started (note that the transmit FIFO for the first is the receive FIFO for the second, and vice-versa).

The first process:

```
$> dl xmit recv 0
```

The second process:

```
$> dl recv xmit 1
```

The integer flags should be 0 in one of the processes, and 1 in the other. This ensures that (as far as addressing is concerned) one process acts as a DTE, the other as a DCE.

Most unix systems have some kind of windowing environment, in which case each process can be run in a separate window. For systems running X windows, each process can be run in a separate xterm. Readers without the benefit of a windowing environment might have to resort to virtual terminals, so that the output of the two processes do not get mixed up.

Figure 13.1 Test bed setup

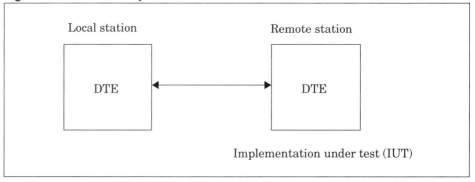

13.4 Conformance Testing

After a protocol has been implemented, it should be subjected to a suite of tests which verify that it conforms to the specified standards. ISO publishes documents which specify these test suites. The document which specifies the test suite for ISO 7776 is ISO/IEC 8882-2 - the "Data Link Layer Conformance Test Suite" [11].

Figure 13.1 shows the scenario specified by the document for testing. A remote station, a DTE, is said to be the implementation under test (IUT). A local station, also a DTE, is used to send (N)-protocol data units to the remote station in order to test out the IUT. The N-PDUs in this case are layer 2

PDUs. The test suites describe the behavior as observed mostly at the local station.

ISO 8882-2 organizes the test suites into the following categories:

- Disconnected phase - where the IUT has received a DISC and transmitted a UA or a DM.

- Link disconnection phase - where the IUT has transmitted a DISC.

- Link set-up phase - where the IUT has transmitted a SABM from the disconnected phase.

- Information transfer phase - where the IUT has received a SABM and transmitted a UA, or transmitted a SABM and received a UA while in the disconnected or information transfer phase.

- Frame reject condition - where the IUT has transmitted a FRMR from the information transfer phase.

- IUT busy condition - where the IUT has transmitted a RNR from the information transfer phase.

- Sent reject condition - where the IUT has transmitted a REJ from the information transfer phase.

- System parameters and error recovery - which tests out the setting of the system parameters T1 (retransmission timer) and N2 (maximum number of retry attempts by the IUT to transmit a frame).

Note that the above categories neatly tie in with the states that our data-link implementation can enter. The software provided with this book was tested out as per the test suites provided in ISO 8882-2. One caveat though - both the IUT and the tester are the same implementation in our case. Usually, when an implementation is being tested, the tester is an independent implementation. Our user interface is capable of transmitting all the different types of PDUs necessary to completely test out the implementation.

13.5 Summary

The user interface provides a menu-driven interface to interact with the physical layer, the data-link layer, and the driver layer, and to set system parameter values.

The user interface can be used to test out the data-link protocol implementation. Two processes, one acting as an implementation under test (IUT) and the other as a tester, can be used to verify the behavior of the protocol. The same user interface can also be used to learn about the functioning of the protocol.

13.5.1 Classes Developed

■ `nwlayer` - This class inherits from the `layer` class (to provide a layer interface for the driver layer) and from the `inputHandler` class (to read input on STDIN for the user interface). The driver layer part of the nwlayer class handles primitives DL_ConnectInd, DL_ConnectCnf, DL_ResetInd, DL_ResetCnf, DL_DataInd, and DL_DisconnectInd invoked by the data-link layer.

13.5.2 Source Files

■ nwlayer.h and nwlayer.C

13.6 Exercises

1. Implement a rudimentary file transfer protocol using the services of the data-link layer. The user interface should take in the following commands at any DTE:

   ```
   % put <localFile> <remoteFile>
   ```

   This command transfers the "localFile" from the directory where the local DTE was started to the "remoteFile" in the directory where the remote DTE was started.

   ```
   % get <remoteFile> <localFile>
   ```

   This command transfers the "remoteFile" from the directory where the remote DTE was started to the "localFile" in the directory where the local DTE was started. Ensure that data-link primitives are used to accomplish this task.

2. Obtain a copy of the "Data link layer conformance test suite"[11] and carry out the tests using the software provided.

3. Modify the code and the user interface to allow for modifications to the window size (modulus). Set the modulus to 128 and examine the functioning of the protocol.

Frame Check Sequence Calculations

A.1 Introduction

The frame check sequence (FCS) specified in the ISO 7776 is a 16-bit field which is appended to every frame that is being transmitted. The FCS is calculated based on the bits in the address byte, the control byte, and any information field that may be part of the frame. The leading and trailing flags are not part of the FCS calculation.

Bit strings can be treated as a method of representing polynomials with the coefficients taking values of 0 and 1 only. Thus, a 10-bit string 1000100111 can be said to represent a polynomial $x^9 + x^5 + x^2 + x^1 + x^0$. The bits in the frame ahead of the FCS field can be regarded as a binary polynomial $M(x)$.

ISO 7776 specifies a generator polynomial $G(x)$: $x^{16} + x^{12} + x^5 + x^1$. If k is the number of bits in the frame (representing $M(x)$), then the FCS is the ones complement of the remainder of the division by the generator polynomial $G(x)$ of the product of x^{16} and $M(x)$, i.e., the ones complement of the remainder of:

```
x16 M(x)  /  G(x)
```

If R(x) is the remainder, then the ones complement of R(x), which is the FCS, is appended to M(x). On the receiving end, the received message which is M(x) plus R(x) is divided by the generator polynomial G(x). If no bits have changed, i.e., no errors have occurred, the result of the division should be zero. A non-zero remainder indicates an error. Perez [12] mentions that the following type of errors can be detected by using the above method:

- All one- or two-bit errors

- All odd numbers of bit errors

- All burst errors less than or equal to the degree of the polynomial used

- Most burst errors greater than the degree of the polynomial used

Normally, the calculations are performed by hardware in a serial bit-wise manner. Typically, a 16-bit register at the transmitting end (which is preset to all ones) is modified by division by G(x) of the address, control and information fields. The ones complement of the content of this register is transmitted as the FCS.

Perez [12] also provides a solution for calculating the FCS using a byte-oriented algorithm. The solution provided is for the generator polynomial $x^{16} + x^{15} + x^2 + 1$. The following solution is based on the same analysis, but is developed for the generator polynomial specified by ISO 7776.

A.2 Byte-Oriented Algorithm

Figure A.1 shows a hardware shift register using flip-flops and exclusive-OR gates which implements the modulo-2 arithmetic needed to calculate the FCS. Each flip-flop represents one bit of the FCS register. The register is initialized to all ones to begin with. The input bit stream is the address, control, and information bits. Once all the input bits have been sent through the register, the contents of the register equal the FCS. These bits are appended to the input stream by serially outputting each bit. Software implementations, which try to emulate the hardware, tend to be slow.

A byte-oriented algorithm, which performs the calculations on each byte of input data, would be a much faster software solution. The algorithm should provide the same value as what would occur after eight shifts of the register.

Figure A.1 Shift register for calculating FCS

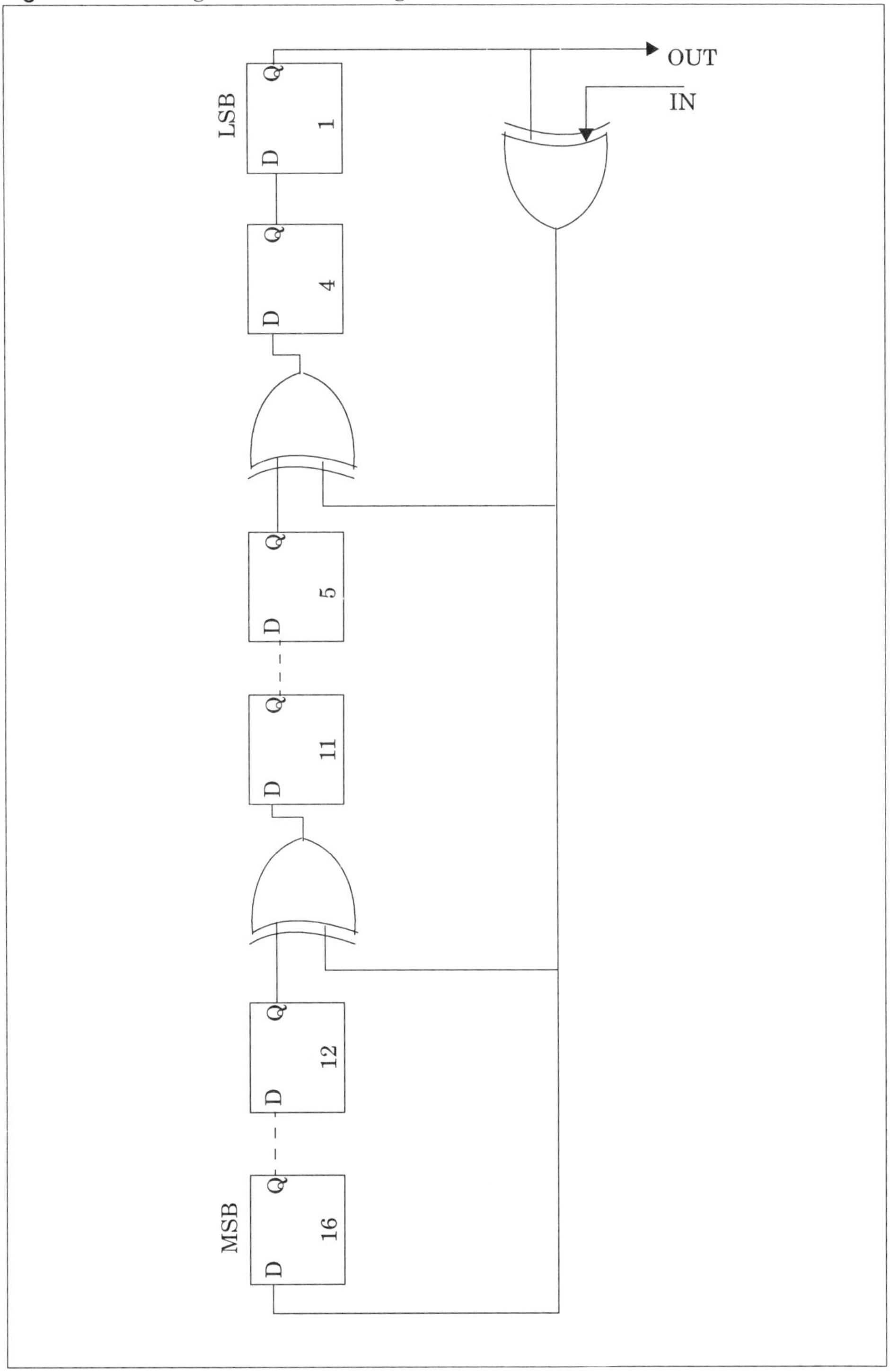

If C_i is the ith bit of the initial register, M_i is the ith bit of the current byte of input message $M(x)$, and R_i is the ith bit of the register, then the initial value of the register from MSB to LSB is:

C_{16}	C_{15}	C_{14}	C_{13}	C_{12}	C_{11}	C_{10}	C_9	C_8	C_7	C_6	C_5	C_4	C_3	C_2	C_1

The following is the content of the register after the first shift:

C_1	C_{16}	C_{15}	C_{14}	C_{13}	C_{12}	C_{11}	C_{10}	C_9	C_8	C_7	C_6	C_5	C_4	C_3	C_2
M_1					C_1						C_1				
					M_1						M_1				

Where the vertical columns represent entries that have to be exclusive-ORed to get the value for the ith bit of the register.

The following is the content of the register after the second shift:

C_2	C_1	C_{16}	C_{15}	C_{14}	C_{13}	C_{12}	C_{11}	C_{10}	C_9	C_8	C_7	C_6	C_5	C_4	C_3
M_2	M_1					C_2	C_1					C_2	C_1		
						M_2	M_1					M_2	M_1		

The following is the content of the register after the third shift:

C_3	C_2	C_1	C_{16}	C_{15}	C_{14}	C_{13}	C_{12}	C_{11}	C_{10}	C_9	C_8	C_7	C_6	C_5	C_4
M_3	M_2	M_1				C_3	C_2	C_1				C_3	C_2	C_1	
						M_3	M_2	M_1				M_3	M_2	M_1	

The following is the content of the register after the fourth shift:

C_4	C_3	C_2	C_1	C_{16}	C_{15}	C_{14}	C_{13}	C_{12}	C_{11}	C_{10}	C_9	C_8	C_7	C_6	C_5
M_4	M_3	M_2	M_1			C_4	C_3	C_2	C_1			C_4	C_3	C_2	C_1
						M_4	M_3	M_2	M_1			M_4	M_3	M_2	M_1

The following is the content of the register after the fifth shift:

C_5	C_4	C_3	C_2	C_1	C_{16}	C_{15}	C_{14}	C_{13}	C_{12}	C_{11}	C_{10}	C_9	C_8	C_7	C_6
C_1	M_4	M_3	M_2	M_1	C_5	C_4	C_3	C_2	C_1			C_5	C_4	C_3	C_2
M_5					C_1	M_4	M_3	M_2	M_1			C_1	M_4	M_3	M_2
M_1					M_5							M_5			
					M_1							M_1			

The following is the content of the register after the sixth shift:

C_6	C_5	C_4	C_3	C_2	C_6	C_{16}	C_{15}	C_{14}	C_{13}	C_{12}	C_{11}	C_{10}	C_9	C_8	C_7
C_2	C_1	M_4	M_3	M_2	C_2	C_5	C_4	C_3	C_2	C_1		C_6	C_5	C_4	C_3
M_6	M_5				C_1	C_1	M_4	M_3	M_2	M_1		C_2	C_1	M_4	M_3
M_2	M_1				M_6	M_5						M_6	M_5		
					M_2	M_1						M_2	M_1		
					M_1										

The following is the content of the register after the seventh shift:

C_7	C_6	C_5	C_4	C_3	C_7	C_6	C_{16}	C_{15}	C_{14}	C_{13}	C_{12}	C_{11}	C_{10}	C_9	C_8
C_3	C_2	C_1	M_4	M_3	C_3	C_2	C_5	C_4	C_3	C_2	C_1	C_7	C_6	C_5	C_4
M_7	M_6	M_5			C_2	C_1	C_1	M_4	M_3	M_2	M_1	C_3	C_2	C_1	M_4
M_3	M_2				M_7	M_6	M_5					M_7	M_6	M_5	
					M_3	M_2	M_1					M_3	M_2	M_1	
					M_2	M_1									

The following is the content of the register after the eighth shift:

C_8	C_7	C_6	C_5	C_4	C_8	C_7	C_6	C_{16}	C_{15}	C_{14}	C_{13}	C_{12}	C_{11}	C_{10}	C_9
C_4	C_3	C_2	C_1	M_4	C_4	C_3	C_2	C_5	C_4	C_3	C_2	C_8	C_7	C_6	C_5
M_8	M_7	M_6	M_5		C_3	C_2	C_1	C_1	M_4	M_3	M_2	C_4	C_3	C_2	C_1
M_4	M_3	M_2	M_1		M_8	M_7	M_6	M_5				C_1	M_7	M_6	M_5
					M_4	M_3	M_2	M_1				M_8	M_3	M_2	M_1
					M_3	M_2	M_1					M_4			
												M_1			

The above columns show the state of the register after eight shifts. If Xi is defined as Ci (ex-or) Mi, then the above register will look like:

X_8	X_7	X_6	X_5	X_4	X_8	X_7	X_6	C_{16}	C_{15}	C_{14}	C_{13}	C_{12}	C_{11}	C_{10}	C_9
X_4	X_3	X_2	X_1		X_4	X_3	X_2	X_5	X_4	X_3	X_2	X_8	X_7	X_6	X_5
				X_3	X_2	X_1	X_1					X_4	X_3	X_2	X_1
												X_1			

The above register value can be obtained by first shifting the high-order byte into the low-order byte of the register, and then exclusive-OR a given 16-bit word with the register. Then the above register will look like:

0	0	0	0	0	0	0	0	C_{16}	C_{15}	C_{14}	C_{13}	C_{12}	C_{11}	C_{10}	C_9
X_8	X_7	X_6	X_5	X_4	X_8	X_7	X_6	X_5	X_4	X_3	X_2	X_8	X_7	X_6	X_5
X_4	X_3	X_2	X_1		X_4	X_3	X_2	X_1				X_4	X_3	X_2	X_1
					X_3	X_2	X_1	X_1				X_1			

Perez [12] identifies the following algorithm:

1. Exclusive-OR the input byte with the low-order byte of the register to get Xi's.

2. Shift the register eight bits to the right.

3. Calculate a value from the Xi's which will give the 16-bit value defined by everything below the first row in the above table.

4. Exclusive-OR the register with the calculated value.

5. Repeat steps 1 to 4 for all message bytes.

Using the above algorithm and shift register scenario depicted above, the following piece of code can be written to calculate the frame check sequence.

```
/*
 * Function : CalculateCksum()
 *
 * Description : Given a initial CRC value, a array
 * of unsigned char values (as data), and the length
 * of the data, this function returns a frame
 * check sequence for the data.
 */
```

```
unsigned short
CalculateCksum(unsigned short crc,
        const unsigned char *s, int n)
{
   unsigned int xi;

   while ( n-- ) {
      int i = (crc ^ *s++) & 0xff;

      int x4321 = (i & 0x0f);
      int x8765 = (i & 0xf0) >> 4;
      int xx = x4321 ^ x8765;
      xi =  ( xx << 12) +
            ((x4321 << 8) ^ (xx << 7)) +
            ((x4321 << 3) ^ xx);
      crc = xi ^ (crc >> 8 );
   }
   return crc;
}
```

B

FSM Conventions

The following are the conventions followed in this book for depicting finite state machine transition diagrams (refer to the example in Figure B.1).

- Each transition arrow depicts a transition from one state to another.

- Each transition arrow has a legend < Event / Action > associated with it. The Event, obviously, is the event that has occurred, and the Action denotes the action being taken before the state is changed.

- The Event can be a composite of many conditions.

- The Action can be decomposed into many actions.

- A received frame is identified as Rx <frame>.

- A transmitted frame is identified as Tx <frame>.

- The P/F bit is shown in parentheses. For example, SABM(1) means a SABM frame with P bit = 1, a UA(0) means a UA frame with F bit = 0.

- A frame with the P bit shown is implicitly a command frame, a frame with the F bit is implicitly a response frame. For example, RR(p=1) implies a RR command frame, and a RNR(f=0) implies a RNR response frame.

- The direction of the primitives is not shown. It's implied by the nature of the primitive. For example, a DL_ConnectInd primitive implies that it is being invoked on the network layer.

- The diagrams show only those events for which actions are required (even if there are no state transitions). Events which do not result in actions, and do not cause state transitions (e.g., "Invalid frame") are not shown in the transition diagrams, in order to keep the diagrams uncluttered. These will be obvious from the source code and the text.

- R < N2 means retransmissions less than N2 times.

- R = N2 means retransmissions equal N2.

Figure B.1 Example of a transition diagram for dlDiscPending state

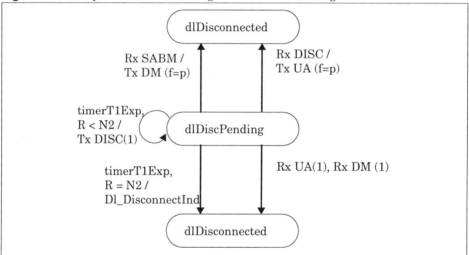

C

System Constants

This appendix lists the header files which contain constant definitions.

types.h

```c
/*
 * File : types.h
 *
 * Description : This file contains some constants, enums and
 * extern variable declarations
 */

#ifndef _types_h_
#define _types_h_

#define STDIN_FILENO 0

enum LinkStatus {DOWN, UP};
enum Boolean {FALSE = 0, TRUE};

#define MAXLINE 81
```

```
            // Value for timer T1 - this can be set
            // from the UI. Default value in file
            // nwlayer.C set to 10
            extern int T1;

            // Value for number of retransmissions - this
            // can be set from the UI. Default value in
            // file nwlayer.C set to 10

            extern int N2;

            const int MODULO = 8;    // Modulo of sliding window
            const int K = 7;         // Max. number of outstanding I-frames

            // Values for reason code in DL_ResetInd, DL_DisconnectInd
            // primitives

            const int peerReset        =      0;
            const int internalError    =      1;
            const int peerDisconnect   =      2;
            const int noPeerResponse   =      3;

            // Maximum I-frame length - can be set from the UI
            // default set in file nwlayer.C to 200.

            extern int MaxIframeLength;

            // Maximum packet size - can be set from the UI
            // default set in file nwlayer.C to 200.

            extern int MaxPacketSize;

            const char addressA = 0x03; // DTE to DCE response address
            const char addressB = 0x01; // DTE to DCE command address

            // FRMR conditions

            enum FrmrConditionType { W=1, X = 2, Y = 4, Z = 8 };

            #endif
```

errorCodes.h

```
            /*
             * File : errorCodes.h
             *
             * Description : Contains error code return values.
             */
```

```
#ifndef _errorCodes_h_
#define _errorCodes_h_

const int codeSuccessful       = 0;    // succesful
const int codeGeneralFailure   = 1;    // any general failure
const int codeNotImplemented   = 2;    // not implemented
const int codeRemoteBusy       = 3;    // remote station busy

#endif
```

phEvents.h

```
/*
 * File : phEvents.h
 *
 * Description : This file contains constant definitions
 *   for physical layer primitives, and internal events.
 */

#ifndef _phEvents_h_
#define _phEvents_h_

/*
 * Physical layer primitives
 */

const int PH_ActivateReq       = 100;
const int PH_ActivateInd       = 101;
const int PH_DeactivateReq     = 102;
const int PH_DeactivateInd     = 103;
const int PH_DataReq           = 104;
const int PH_DataInd           = 105;

/*
 * Events caused by data on the FIFO - internal to
 * the physical layer.
 */

const int PH_Activate          = 106;
const int PH_Data              = 107;
const int PH_Deactivate        = 108;

const int PH_Unknown           = 109;
#endif
```

dlEvents.h

```
/*
 * File : dlEvents.h
```

```
 *
 * Description : This file contains constants for primitives
 * and other data-link events.
 */
#ifndef _dlEvents_h_
#define _dlEvents_h_

const int DL_ConnectReq      = 200;
const int DL_ConnectInd      = 201;
const int DL_ConnectRes      = 202;
const int DL_ConnectCnf      = 203;

const int DL_DataReq         = 204;
const int DL_DataInd         = 205;

const int DL_ResetReq        = 206;
const int DL_ResetInd        = 207;
const int DL_ResetRes        = 208;
const int DL_ResetCnf        = 209;

const int DL_DisconnectReq   = 210;
const int DL_DisconnectInd   = 211;

const int t1TimerExp         = 212;
const int rejTimerExp        = 213;

#endif
```

D

LAPD and Frame Relay

D.1 LAPD

In this appendix we'll examine briefly the evolution of LAPD and frame relay technologies. This book has examined the LAPB protocol in detail. The protocol was developed two decades ago as the data-link layer of the X.25 standard. The next protocol to evolve out of the LAPB standard was LAPD (Link Access Procedures on the D-channel). LAPD is used as the data-link protocol in ISDN.

Figure D.1 Example X.25 network

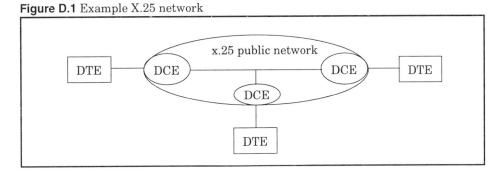

LAPB is a point-to-point protocol used for communications between DTEs and DCEs in a X.25 network. Figure D.1 shows an example of the topology. The point-to-point restriction in LAPB is considered a limitation.

LAPD allows for the following configurations (Figure D.2):

- Point-to-point communication between a DTE and a DCE.

- Multiple DTEs communicating with a single DCE in a star configuration. Here, each DTE has a separate physical connection to the DCE.

- Multiple DTEs communicating with a single DCE in a multipoint configuration, where the DTEs share the same physical link to the DCE.

Figure D.2 Example DTE-DCE configurations in ISDN

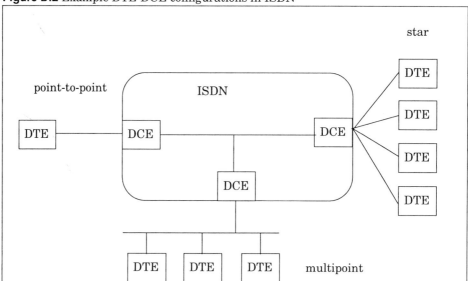

The D-channel in ISDN refers to the separate channel used for signalling to set-up connections so that data can be transferred over a B-channel. For our discussion, we can put aside the distinctions between the D-channel and the B-channel.

LAPB exclusively services one service-user, the X.25 network layer. LAPD allows for different entities to use the services provided by the data-link layer, e.g., X.25 layer 3, layer 2 management procedures, or call control procedures. See ITU Recommendation Q.921 [16] for details.

The LAPD protocol is almost identical to the LAPB protocol except for the provisions it makes to accommodate the various DTE-DCE configurations and multiple service users. The main difference is in the way the address field is encoded. In the LAPB implementation in this book, the address could be one of address A or address B and it was one octet long. The LAPD address consists of the following (see Figure D.3):

- Service access point identifier (SAPI) - This identifies the service user.

- Terminal endpoint identifier (TEI) - This identifies the DTE.

- C/R - A command/response bit to identify whether the frame is a command or response.

- A address field extension bit (EA). In the first octet EA is set to 0, in the second octet it is set to 1. The address field can be extended further by setting the EA bit in the second octet to 0. The EA bit is always set to 1 in the final octet of the address field.

Figure D.3 LAPD address field format

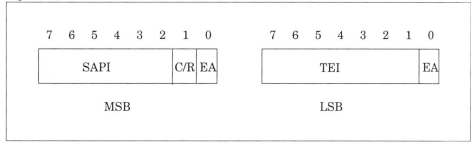

LAPD has a similar complement of control frames as LAPB, except for one addition - the XID frame, which is used for exchanging identification information during connection management.

The similar nature of LAPD and LAPB is emphasized by the fact that LAPD allows for a LAPB connection within the D-channel.

D.2 Frame Relay

Both LAPB and LAPD provide elaborate error detection and recovery mechanisms along with flow control procedures. These were necessary because the transmission media two decades ago were not reliable enough, and robust protocols at the link-level were designed to work with unreliable physical channels. The current transmission media technologies are far superior (specially optical media), and the need for error detection/recovery and flow control mechanisms at the link level have become a needless overhead. (This is not to say that the higher layers do not implement these procedures. No link is completly fail-safe, and hence, both error detection/recovery and flow control are necessary at some stage in the protocol hierarchy.) The next protocol to evolve out of this scenario has been the frame relay protocol.

D.2.1 Frame Relay vs. X.25

It is worthwhile to examine frame relay by contrasting it with X.25 networks. Chapter 4 examined the architecture of an DTE-DCE interface in an X.25 network. The interface requires the first three layers in the protocol stack - the network layer, the data-link layer and the physical layer. The frame relay, in comparison, dispenses with most of the network layer functionality and provides a data-link layer which is significantly lighter weight than LAPB. Figure D.4 shows a comparison of the protocol stacks.

Figure D.4 Frame relay and X.25 protocol stack

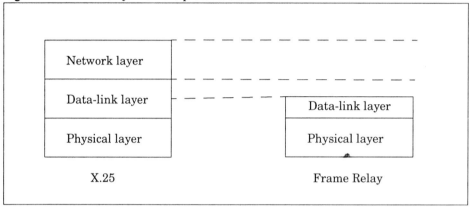

Figure D.5 shows an example of how DTEs communicate using a frame relay network. A connection to the frame relay network is known as a permanent virtual circuit (PVC) and is identified by a data-link connection identifier (DLCI). This DLCI is preset for a given connection. The DLCI is used for addressing and the frame relay network uses it to route data-link frames through the network. This routing is much simpler than the routing necessary in X.25.

Figure D.5 Example frame relay network

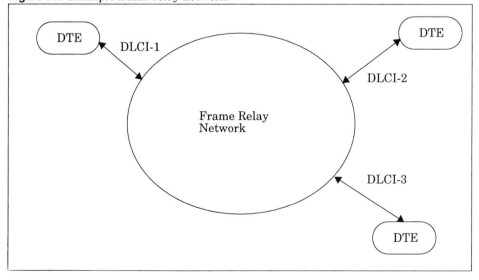

D.2.2 Frame Relay Frame Encoding

The frame format used for sending messages using a frame relay network will further clarify the simplicity of frame relay networks. Figure D.6 shows the format of a frame relay frame.

Figure D.6 Frame relay frame encoding

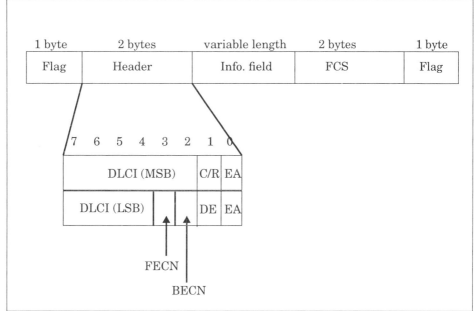

- Flags - The flags used to delimit the frame are identical to the ones used for LAPB.

- Information field - This is a variable length field which contains user data.

- FCS - The frame check sequence, similar to LAPB.

- Header - Which consists of the DLCI, C/R, FECN, BECN, DE and EA bits.

- DLCI - The data-link connection identifier.

- C/R - A command/response bit. The frame relay network ignores this bit. It is used solely for user-defined purposes.

- FECN, BECN - These are the forward explicit congestion notification and the backward explicit congestion notification bits, respectively. These bits are used by the frame relay network for congestion avoidance within the network. A discussion of this feature is beyond the scope of this book. See Black [17] for details.

- DE - The discard eligibility bit. This bit provides a simple priority scheme for the frame relay network to discard frames during congestion. During congestion, the network will discard frames with a DE bit set to 1 before it discards frames with a DE bit set to 0. The DE bit is set by the DTE using the frame relay service.

The frame-relay service and the LAPB data-link layer have the following features in common:

- Framing (using flags to delimit frame boundaries)

- Bit transparency (using bit stuffing and bit stripping to avoid flags from occurring in the data stream)

- Error detection using CRC

The following features are prominently absent in frame relay:

- Error recovery procedures using Go-Back-N ARQ.

- Flow control.

- Connection management. Frame relay uses permanent virtual circuits, i.e., no connection needs to be set up before transmitting service-user data.

A direct consequence of the absence of the above-mentioned features is that the frame relay protocol is extremely simple, and does not need all the control frames that LAPB uses.

References

[1] Gerard J. Holzmann [1991], *Design and Validation of Computer Protocols*, Prentice-Hall Software Series, Englewood Cliffs, NJ

[2] International Standard, ISO 7498 [1984], *Information Processing Systems - Open Systems Interconnection - Basic Reference Model*

[3] A. Tanenbaum, [1988], *Computer Networks,* 2nd ed., Prentice-Hall, Englewood Cliffs, NJ

[4] *C++ Tutorial*, Microsoft C/C++, Version 7.0, Microsoft Corporation

[5] International Standard, ISO 7776 [1986], *Information Processing Systems - Data Communications - High-level Data Link Control Procedures - Description of the X.25 LAPB-compatible DTE Data Link Procedures*

[6] Jonathan Shapiro [1991], *A C++ Toolkit*, Prentice-Hall Series in Innovative Technology, Englewood Cliffs, NJ

[7] Keith G. Knightson, Terry Knowles and John Larmouth [1988], *Standards for Open Systems Interconnection*, McGraw-Hill Publishing Company, New York, NY

[8] Grady Booch [1991], *Object-Oriented Design with Applications*, The Benjamin/Cummins Publishing Company, Inc.

[9] James Rumbaugh, Michael Blaha, William Premerlani, Frederick Eddy and William Lorensen, *Object-Oriented Modeling and Design,* Prentice-Hall, Englewood Cliffs, NJ

[10] W. Richard Stevens, [1992], *Advance Programming in the Unix Environment,* Addison-Wesley Professional Computing Series

[11] International Standard, ISO/IEC 8882-2 [1992], *Data Link Layer Conformance Test Suite*

[12] Aram Perez, Wismer & Becker, "Byte-wise CRC Calcuations", *IEEE Micro,* June 1983

[13] Internation Standard, ISO 7809-1984 (E), *Information Processing Systems - Data communication - High-level Data Link Control Procedures - Consolidation of Classes of Procedures*

[14] Ted Faison, "Object-Oriented State Machines", *Software Development,* Sept. 1993

[15] Sean Gavin, Internet acquaintance

[16] International Telecommunication Union, Recommendation Q.921, *ISDN User-Network Interface - Data Link Layer Specification*

[17] Uyless Black [1994], *Data-Link Protocols*, Prentice-Hall Inc., Englewood Cliffs, NJ

Index